Staff

Administration

K. J. Hilton, Ll.B.

Afforestation

N. S. Casson, from 1 April 1962 to 14 September 1963
B. R. Salter, B.A. (Forestry), from 1 Aug. 1963 to 11 Sept. 1965
W. B. Walker, B.Sc. (Forestry), from 23 Aug. 1965

Biology

Mrs Ruth L. Gadgil, B.Sc., Ph.D.
P. D. Gadgil, M.Sc., Ph.D.
*G. T. Goodman, M.Sc.

Economics

*R. O. Roberts, M.A.
Mrs Susanne H. Spence, B.Sc. (Econ.)

Engineering

*H. E. Evans, B.Sc., Ph.D., F.G.S.
F. E. Weare, D.I.C.

Geography

*E. M. Bridges, M.Sc.
D. C. Ledger, M.A.
*D. H. Maling, B.A., Ph.D., F.R.G.S.
*J. Oliver, B.A., F.R.Met.S.

Geology

W. F. G. Cardy, M.A.

Sociology

Mrs D. Yeoman, B.A.
*Mrs Margaret Stacey, B.Sc. (Econ.)

* Teaching Staff of University College, Swansea.

Staff

The following contributed to the study reports:

Geology—gravity survey

D. E. T. Bidgood, B.A., Ph.D., Department of Geology, University College of South Wales and Monmouthshire

Soil mechanics and foundation engineering

H. G. Clapham, M.Sc., A.M.I.C.E., M.I.H.E., Ground Engineering Ltd.

Investigation into the feasibility of creating an artificial lake

R. E. Davies, B.Sc., University College, Swansea

The hardcore industry

G. Holt, B.Sc. (Econ.), University College, Swansea

Large-scale grass trials

L. J. Hooper, B.Sc., R. Garrett Jones, M.A., National Agricultural Advisory Service

Study of respiratory symptoms

Mrs Margery McDermott, B.Sc., A.R.C.S., Pneumoconiosis Research Unit (M.R.C.)

Study reports

Sets of the twelve reports upon which this book is based have been deposited as follows:

University College of Swansea Library (2 sets)
National Library of Wales, Aberystwyth (1 set)
The British Museum (1 set)
The Guildhall, Swansea (1 set)

1 The Human Ecology of the Lower Swansea Valley.   Margaret Stacey, B.Sc. (Econ.)

2 Report on Transportation and Physical Planning in the Lower Swansea Valley.   R. D. Worrall, B.Sc., M.S., Ph.D.

3 Report on the Hydrology of the Lower Swansea Valley.   D. C. Ledger, M.A.

4 Report on the Geology of the Lower Swansea Valley.   W. F. G. Cardy, M.A.

5 The Soil Mechanics and Foundation Engineering Survey of the Lower Swansea Valley Project Area.   H. G. Clapham, M.Sc., A.M.I.C.E., M.I.H.E., H. E. Evans, B.Sc., Ph.D., F.G.S. and F. E. Weare, D.I.C.

6 The Prospects for Industrial Use of the Lower Swansea Valley—A Study of Land Use in a Regional Context.   Susanne H. Spence, B.Sc. (Econ.)

7 Lower Swansea Valley: Housing Report.   Margaret Stacey, B.Sc. (Econ.)

8 Lower Swansea Valley: Open Space Report.   Margaret Stacey, B.Sc. (Econ.)

9 Plant Ecology of the Lower Swansea Valley:

   (a) Vegetation Trials.   Ruth L. Gadgil, B.Sc., Ph.D.
   (b) Large-scale Grass Trials.   L. J. Hooper, B.Sc. and R. Garrett Jones, M.A.
   (c) Soils.   E. M. Bridges, M.Sc.

10 Soil Biology of the Lower Swansea Valley.   P. D. Gadgil, M.Sc., Ph.D.

11 Afforestation of the Lower Swansea Valley.   B. R. Salter, B.A. (Forestry)

General acknowledgements

The Project is greatly indebted to its principal sponsors the Nuffield Foundation, the Natural Environment Research Council (*ex.* the Department of Scientific and Industrial Research), the Swansea County Borough Council and the Welsh Office (previously the Welsh Office of the Ministry of Housing and Local Government), for their financial and moral support and to the Council of the University College of Swansea for providing office and laboratory accommodation, equipment and technical services.

The help given by the following people is also acknowledged:—

The Editor and Staff of the *South Wales Evening Post*; the Chief Constable of Swansea and his staff; Carl Stockton, A.R.P.S., for photography and help with exhibitions; D. E. Price for photographic and technical assistance; Hugh Daniel, G. B. Lewis, B.Sc., and Leo Nantel for drawings; John Noël, A.R.I.B.A., for help with exhibitions and models; Peter Howell, A.R.I.B.A., for drawings and Owen Davies for records of air pollution.

Finally, we sincerely thank the Secretarial Staff of the Director's Office and especially Mrs Judi Cross for the contribution they have made to the work of the Project, and to this Report.

Editor's Note

Material included in this report is based upon information available in the Autumn of 1966.

How the Project came about and what it was intended to achieve

'It came to pass in days of yore
The Devil chanced upon Landore
Quoth he, by all this fume and stink,
I can't be far from home, I think.'

These lines were the winning entry in a 'railway carriage eisteddfod' which was held between Newport and West Wales in the year 1897. The competitors were Welshmen returning from an Eisteddfod at Newport, full of the 'hwyl' of the occasion, and a solitary Englishman who joined their carriage at Cardiff. It is not recorded whether the winner was English or Welsh or what other entries were considered, but the competition we know was held in English; a nice touch of Welsh courtesy. What is interesting about the occasion is that the subject matter of the winning verse even then impressed itself on railway travellers passing through Swansea, as it has continued to do ever since.

Nearly a century later the visual image of Landore stirred the imagination of another railway traveller. Robin Huws Jones was then the Director of courses in Social Administration at the University College of Swansea. His duties obliged him to travel often, and over a period of years the grim desolation of the land on each side of the railway approach to Swansea prompted him to make inquiries about its problems and their solution. These convinced him that a new and independent initiative was needed if the area was to be reclaimed and a century-old eyesore, so much in contrast to the natural beauty of the west side of Swansea, was to be finally removed. He suggested that the University College, in partnership with the Ministry of Housing and Local Government, the Swansea Borough Council and other interests, should carry out a comprehensive survey of the area as a first step towards its reclamation.

This book then is about the Lower Swansea Valley, a once beautiful river valley on the east of the County Borough of Swansea transformed by two hundred years of use by industry into a barren wilderness three and a half miles long and a mile wide: a giant rubbish dump of tips on either side of the river which had become an industrial sewer. (Plate 2)

An inquiry can be a way of breaking out of a static situation: it has the merit of being impartial and uncontroversial, at least in its intention. There was much in the Swansea Valley situation that was static simply because it was unknown; the initiative was therefore welcomed. For those concerned with its beginnings, there was a sense of adventure. They felt they were embarking on an historic rescue operation—for the image of Swansea was involved—and a pioneering task of reconstruction out of desolation. The suggestion that the survey should be carried out by a team based on the University College was also favoured. The College was fortunate at this time in having John Parry as its Principal. He immediately appreciated the importance of the study not only to Swansea but also to the College. Apart from associating the College with the solution of a long-standing local problem, it provided a unique opportunity for a large interdisciplinary study. It was the kind of exercise in which the College with its wide range of specialisms could take part but for which there were few precedents.

The College is situated on the favoured western side of the town in a natural setting of great beauty on a site provided by the Corporation which was once the family estate of the Vivians. It was perhaps fitting that an inquiry into derelict industrial land should originate in an institution which had grown around the home of one of the Valley's greatest industrialists. (Plates 3 and 4)

Under the leadership of the Principal, the heads of the College departments concerned gave their support and were joined by representatives of the Borough Council, the Welsh Office and Industry. This Working Group, which was informal at this stage, began in 1960 the difficult task of finding the money needed to meet the cost of the sort of detailed inquiry that it had in mind. The College at the time was itself raising funds for its own development by a large public appeal. Its Council nevertheless agreed to provide the office, laboratory and technical facilities required which was a substantial contribution in kind. A generous grant was made by the then Department of Scientific and Industrial Research to the Department of Botany for work on the revegetation of industrial waste and the Welsh Office of the Ministry of Housing and Local Government and Swansea Borough Council made separate contributions.

In this way nearly half of the total of £48,750 which the group had estimated would be required was assured, and this led the Trustees of the Nuffield Foundation to agree to contribute an initial sum of £22,500. The generosity of the Trust and of the other donors has been acknowledged elsewhere in this Report; without their help a start could not have been made. The continuing interest of the Trustees of the Nuffield Foundation and the support and encouragement of their Director have been specially sustaining. The most lasting tribute to them all will not be in this book but in the future transformation of the Lower Swansea Valley and the example that the whole Project—the idea, the method and the action—will provide for other areas similarly blighted in Britain and elsewhere.

With its finance assured, the informal Working Group became a Committee, sub-committees were set up and by August 1961 Kenneth Hilton was appointed the executive Director of what became known as the Lower Swansea Valley Project.

The Project's terms of reference were 'to establish the factors which inhibit the social and economic use of land in the Lower Swansea Valley and to suggest ways in which the area should be used in the future.'

These were derived from the original application to the donors from the Working Group which is included as a memorandum at the end of this chapter because it forms a significant part of the record of this unusual operation. It provides, as will be seen, an outline of the scope of the study and the reasons for it.

Briefly, the Project was to be an investigation into the physical, social and economic situation in the Lower Swansea Valley, to understand the reasons which had inhibited its development in the past and to provide the information and analysis necessary for its future development. The area to be studied comprised an industrial valley floor, where the physical problems of redevelopment—flooding, levels, roads etc.—were predominant, and

How the Project came
about and what it was
intended to achieve

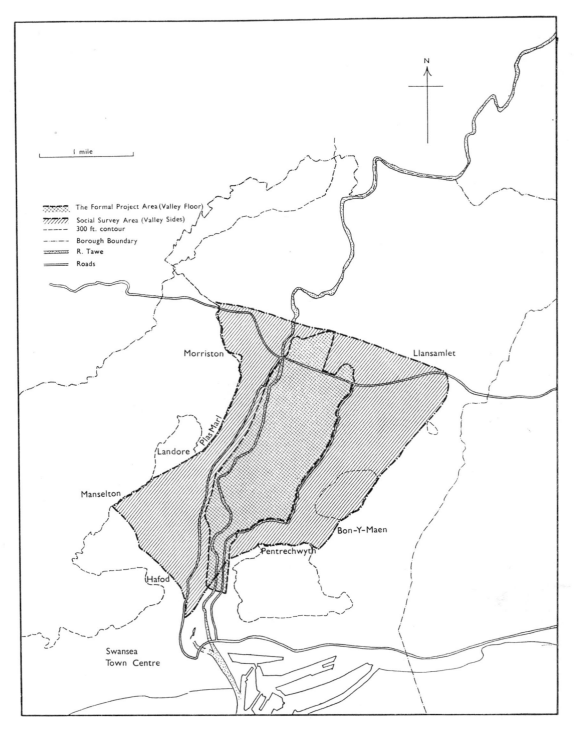

Figure 1.1 The boundaries of the Survey Area

the largely residential valley sides where the human problems were paramount. These two
areas are illustrated in Figure 1.1. Because the future use of these areas is closely affected by
the functions and needs of the population of the County Borough of Swansea, within whose
administrative area it lies, it was also necessary to consider the implications of this. Finally
the valley had to be considered as part of an even wider subregion extending from Port
Talbot in the east to Kidwelly in the west, which is illustrated by Figure 1.2 and discussed
in Chapter 9. There were therefore four areas in descending order of size: western South

Wales, Swansea County Borough, the valley sides, and finally the valley floor, all of which had to be considered against a background of national policies and legislation.

The studies themselves may be divided into two groups, those which deal with the physical problems of the valley floor such as contour mapping, geology, soil mechanics, hydrology and biology; and the socio-economic studies of the residential and industrial populations, their employment, housing and recreation. A complete guide to all the studies undertaken by the Project is provided on page xiii.

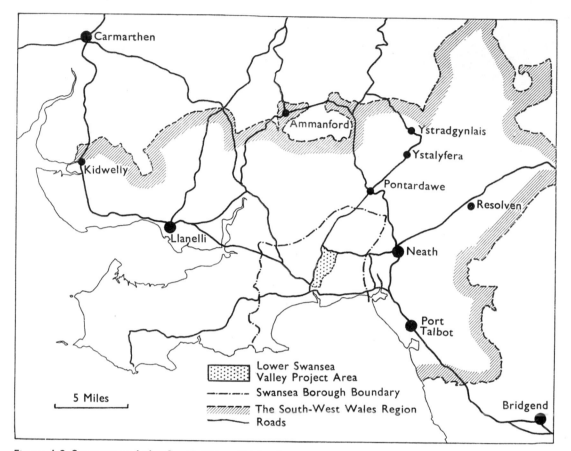

Figure 1.2 Swansea and the South-West Wales Region

The research teams were all specially appointed to carry out a particular part of the programme and worked as staff members of the appropriate College Department. Important sections of the work were also carried out by teaching staff of the College whose names appear on page xi. Altogether six College Departments were concerned with the study. The time given by the Heads of Departments in supervising research, editing reports and in taking part in the work of its Committees was an important contribution.

The administration of the Project and its relations with the public devolved on the Director and on the Committees and Sub-Committees whose composition is given on page ix. The chief executive organ throughout has been the Steering Committee in which the three main interests, the College, the Welsh Office and the Borough Council, were represented. This Committee was also fortunate in having R. B. Southall, a Director and General Manager of B P Refinery (Llandarcy) Ltd, as its Vice-Chairman for three years. It was in his office that the early stages of the Project were planned, and his death in December 1965 deprived the Committee of his wisdom and invaluable industrial experience at a critical time. It is notable that the sectional interests of the Committee's members have always been subordinated to the task in hand—the ultimate reclamation of the Lower Swansea Valley.

This has been the practical aim of the research efforts which has been strengthened by the participation of officials from the Welsh Office, and the local authority. The land use proposals which are discussed in Chapter 11 were first worked out by the research team, particularly Dr Worrall, and later developed in association with the Borough Engineer and Planning Officer and his staff.

The outline plan which is based on the land use proposals envisages the valley not only as a place for industry as it has been in the past but, especially in its southern half towards the town centre, as an area in which housing, a new comprehensive school and over 120 acres of new amenity and recreational space can be provided. The river Tawe has a special function in the plan. The proposals for maintaining a tidal river at what is virtually a perpetual state of high tide is imaginative and we believe practical.

It was appreciated by the original working group that a university research study could not on its own build up the momentum that was required to carry ideas forward to practical action; this was made clear from the first application for financial help. People everywhere, people in Swansea, Council members and officials; people outside Swansea, Members of Parliament, the Secretary of State for Wales, and our associates in the Welsh Office, all had to believe that the redevelopment of the valley was practicable and necessary. Therefore during the past four years a special effort has been made through local societies and schools, in conferences meeting in the neighbourhood, by means of exhibitions and through the press and television, to make contact with the public at large, to draw attention to problems which are national as well as local and to the Project as an experimental method. We have in consequence received inquiries and visitors from all over Britain and from Czechoslovakia, Denmark, West Germany, the United States and Canada as well as from Asia. These have encouraged us to think that the problems of derelict industrial land are also international.

The cooperation which we have obtained from the private owners of land in the valley has been an outstanding feature of the whole scheme so far. The Project in fact has been a cooperative enterprise through all its stages: interdepartmental cooperation in the College; cooperation between College staff and Council members and officials; links through the surveys with the people who live and work in the valley; links with the schools through their work for the Project; links with the Territorial Army in the clearance of derelict buildings; links with the Forestry Commission in the creation of new woodlands. A considerable fund of goodwill has been built up as a result of these links during the study period and we hope that the inevitable time lag between planning and development will not be so long that this will wither away. The phase of inquiry is over, what is now required is action.

The report may be divided into three parts—Chapters 1–3 deal with the industrial history of the area, describing the attempts made to deal with it in the past and leading to the Project's inception. Chapters 4–10 describe the research undertaken by the Project and have been written by the individual authors concerned with the work. Chapters 11–13 form a concluding section in which proposals for the future development of the area are discussed. For general convenience, a comprehensive summary of the Report's main conclusions and recommendations is included at the end of the book with an Appendix on Climate and Air Pollution which has a general relevance to all parts of the study.

For ease of reference the whole Project area has been divided into plots which correspond broadly with the pattern of ownership which existed in 1961. These plots are shown on the base plan at the end of the book.

Memorandum
Swansea Valley Development Project

Prepared by R. Huws Jones, 1961

The area

1 The Lower Swansea Valley, as defined and mapped in Note 1, is notorious for its blighted appearance. This once economically active area has in large part become derelict and is now covered with ruins and mounds of industrial debris; there are acres of noxious land that bear no vegetation at all; over the rest the vegetation is so poor that it accentuates the bleakness of the scene. This blighted area lies at Swansea's front door for it adjoins the principal railway station and is only a few minutes by road from the High Street and the docks. The town suffers accordingly in reputation, in morale and in its economy.

2 The desolation is not complete, for the area (which covers some 800 acres) is still the centre of older heavy industries employing several thousand workers; thousands of others live on the borders. Economic life is sluggish but not absent, suggesting that recovery is not impossible.

3 Any remedy for the present desolation must seek to ascertain what 'economic inhibitors' led to the area falling into disuse and now prevent any spontaneous return of life. This is one essential and unifying element in the necessary research. It is also one of the many aspects of the research which are likely to be useful to other regions.

4 Enough is known to make it clear that some of the 'inhibitors' are physical; atmospheric pollution, now largely removed; destruction or erosion of soil; chemical pollution; the existence of ruins, refuse heaps, hollows and concealed cavities; dissection by railways, a canal and the river. Other inhibitors might be described as social: dirt and corrosion due to past atmospheric pollution, which breed spiritual depression and make the area repellent; the existence of obsolete or under-occupied works, suggesting economic depression; the neighbourhood of dirty down-at-heel streets, obviously the unattractive stagnant end of the town.

The purpose of an enquiry

5 Any enquiry must begin by examining the various obstacles and studying how to remove them. The first steps must be to secure the confidence of the occupiers and owners and learn whether any of them have plans for withdrawal from or development of their sites. There may, for instance, be plans for making economic use of the waste materials on the land. In so far as this study reveals that much of the area has no early prospect of economic use it will be necessary to examine the reasons for this. Some will be obvious, such as the existence of obstructive ruins; others will require elaborate study, for instance, to ascertain how far chemical pollution of the soil, or concealed craters in the tips, are peculiar difficulties in this area.

6   Throughout these investigations it will be necessary to take a very broad view of the possible economic uses of the area. In certain parts it may prove feasible to create good industrial sites; in others public buildings, perhaps an airstrip or a helicopter landing ground, may be appropriate. Housing, open spaces for parks and playing fields, and a riverside drive should also be considered, and this emphasizes the importance of discovering how vegetation can be improved. The main aim should be to bring the area back into the natural stream of social and economic use, modified from time to time in accordance with changes in demand.

Immediate action

7   All this means that a watchful eye should be kept throughout for opportunities of immediate practical action. There is no doubt that the area suffers from a vicious circle; because it is derelict it is unattractive and new developments shun it, thus emphasizing its dereliction; there is a strong case for deliberately trying to break this circle.

8   The very fact that a survey of this kind is under way should assist immediate practical measures. What is envisaged is that the administration set up to conduct the survey should encourage efforts by all sorts of other agencies. Industrialists and landowners for instance might be willing to level some of the worst areas and demolish ruined buildings even if they had no immediate use for the land if it could be shown that other bodies were cooperating. The local authority might press on with certain improvements, the Forestry Commission might assist with planting belts of trees at certain points, etc. Such improvements would make an important contribution to amenity and this in turn would encourage economic use. What is needed is not just a brief push but a steady campaign which would improve matters over a period of years.

Long-term action

9   The process of study and the preparation of plans for action thus offer exceptional—perhaps unique—opportunities for cooperation between several academic disciplines, and also for cooperation between the college, central government, local authority, industrialists, and ordinary citizens.

10   In these circumstances it is impossible in advance to say what action will certainly follow on research. On the other hand the whole object of the research will be to show how to remove the hindrances to action which have been encountered in the past and to present proposals in a report that will inform and enliven public opinion, and provide an impetus to cooperative effort. Feeling about the area is already so strong that once a breach has been made in an apparently formidable problem there should be no difficulty in getting action moving, especially as the interests of essential partners are already manifestly engaged.

The administration of the Project

11   The College proposes to set up a committee under the chairmanship of the Principal. It will consist of representatives of all the Departments of the College that are likely to be

involved, the Welsh Office of the Ministry of Housing and Local Government, the County Borough of Swansea, local industrialists, etc. There will be a small Steering Committee and an academic Working Group concerned with the coordination of the various enquiries. Details are given in Note 2.

12   It will be necessary to appoint a Project Director with the experience and status required to administer a complicated enquiry, to serve the various special studies and also able, under the direction and with the support of the Steering Committee, to promote immediate action (involving negotiations with occupiers and others) on the lines indicated in paragraph 8. The Director should of course be able to carry out much of the drafting of the final Report and to promote the good public relations needed to ensure urgent consideration of the recommendations when they are published. It will be helpful if the Director has qualifications which enable him to contribute to one of the special enquiries—as for instance if he were a geographer, a historian or lawyer. The Director will require clerical assistance.

13   It is assumed that the Project, from the appointment of the Director to the publication and discussion of the final Report and recommendations, will take about four years.

Special enquiries

A   Geography

14   A detailed contour survey of the area on a large scale is a prerequisite for subsequent work. This could be completed within six months by one full-time person working under the direction of the Geography Department; an assistant would be necessary for levelling but this assistance could probably be supplied from the Department's own resources.

15   An investigation into the hydrology of the area and its liability to flooding would also be desirable. It would be sensible to combine this enquiry with the geographical survey and ask the same person to undertake both, thus offering an appointment for one academic session.

16   An aerial survey might prove very helpful in the early stages; certain material may be available from Government aerial surveys but some supplementary photography may be necessary.

17   The supply, enlargement and duplication of maps, map extracts, etc., which would be required as the work progresses, could be undertaken through the normal channels in the Department of Geography.

18   Towards the conclusion of the enquiry there might be a need for cartographic and drafting assistance for maps to accompany the report. Some allowance should be made for part-time assistance for this work.

B   Economic history and economics

19   An economic historian should be appointed to enquire into the history of the area, the reasons why so many firms closed down or moved away, why the abandoned sites were not reoccupied—and why a few firms have remained or even moved into the area. This study should also examine the reasons why industrial life has not returned 'spontaneously' as apparently has happened in some other derelict districts, including parts of the Midlands.

20 A member of the staff of the Economics Department is acquainted with the historical sources on this area and with the local history of the industries themselves; he is prepared to direct the work of a research scholar who it is expected could use the material also in preparation for a higher degree.

21 The economic work in connection with this project would fall into two parts—the collection of information and the evaluation of the various alternative courses of action that might be physically practicable.

22 In order to assess the probable value, in various uses, of land that might be rehabilitated it would be necessary to know the present size and age composition of the population of Swansea and its environs (within reasonable travelling distance of the area to be studied) and to make statistical estimates of the likely future population. This would clearly have a bearing on the number of industrial jobs that will be needed and on the demand for land for housing, social services, recreation, etc. A study would also be necessary of the present industrial structure of the Swansea district to throw light upon the industries that are likely to expand and the type of new firms which might be expected to come here. Some of this information will have been collected already by government departments and local authorities. In so far as this is so, a research worker would need only to assimilate this information and focus it on this particular project; it seems likely, however, that some additional information would have to be collected in the field, though it would be important to check with departments and local authorities before doing this.

23 The second and more difficult job for the economist would come when engineers, geologists, biologists, etc., had nearly completed their work. It may be assumed that this work would show that several courses of action are possible. For example, one programme might result in a large area of land suitable for afforestation, but only small areas for factory sites or housing while another and more costly programme might give a considerably larger area for these last two uses. It would then be necessary to estimate the value of land in each alternative use (in the light of present value and of any changes in population, industrial structure, etc., that can be foreseen) and so to give an indication of which course of action offers the prospect of the best value for money.

24 General advice and direction for this work could be given by members of the Economics Department, but a fairly senior full-time research worker would also be needed probably for two years.

C *Geology*

25 It is difficult to give an accurate estimate of the time required for the preparation of a geological map of the area without further study of the topography and outcrops, but it seems probable that a relatively junior graduate, working under the direction of the Department, could complete the work required within one academic year. There would be virtually no expenditure involved for apparatus or material though some allowance should be made for transport.

26 The Department of Geology would be glad to provide laboratory facilities for the soil analyses which would be undertaken by a soil chemist working mainly with the Department of Botany. No additional apparatus would be necessary for this work; the cost of expendable materials would amount to about £300.

D Civil engineering

27   The Department of Civil Engineering has a traditional interest in Soil Mechanics and a senior member of staff is a specialist in the field of foundation engineering. It seems clear that foundation problems are likely to be among the most critical and difficult in the enquiry.

28   At the outset, the Department would approach all the firms and organizations that have been active in the area in the hope of obtaining the results of any site investigations already undertaken. However, at best these enquiries would have to be supplemented by further site investigations which would use as a basis the existing Geological Survey supplemented by material obtained for the purpose by the Department of Geology.

29   The extent of the area (approximately two square miles), the natural configuration of the valley and the peculiar difficulties presented by the accumulation of metallic and other industrial waste over a century and a half, suggest that a reasonably thorough site investigation is essential to enable the potentialities of the district to be assessed accurately enough for a development plan to be prepared. A preliminary consideration of the district suggests that about twenty areas (determined finally after the results of a few early boreholes are available) should be selected with, say, five boreholes drilled in each area, giving about a hundred in all. The depth of the bores is very problematic; to be of value each hole should be taken down to some clearly defined geological stratum, whose depth could be foreseen only after some knowledge of the site conditions had been obtained. An average depth of 40 ft seems a reasonable assumption, yielding a total of about 500 soil samples for testing.

30   The work of drilling, soil sampling and reporting would have to be undertaken by a specialist firm working under the direction of the Department. On the assumptions set out above, the total cost would be £12,500.

31   More detailed information concerning specific areas would have to be obtained if for instance it was proposed to erect a particularly large factory building or other heavy structure on any given location. No attempt is made to estimate for this, as subsequent investigations would be the responsibility of organizations interested in using the sites.

E Botany

32   It is essential that there should be a preliminary study of the biological aspects of the area between say the early spring and the late summer of this year. This survey would provide information about the soil and drainage conditions, about plants now growing in the area, the possibilities of a general improvement of the plant cover, etc.

33   In the light of information of this kind it would be possible to assess the magnitude of the botanical problems involved and the feasibility of their solution, and on this basis realistic proposals could be made for the research programme proper. During the preliminary period the Head of the Department and one other member of the staff should visit other parts of the British Isles where somewhat similar problems exist; certain botanists with experience in this field should also be invited to Swansea for consultation. Undergraduates could be employed during their vacation to help with the mapping of the existing plant cover and to do certain preliminary tests on soil samples. Certain expendable materials would be required for the preliminary biological tests on the soil. The sum of £300 would cover the cost of this initial work.

34 For a full two-year research programme, including a programme of experimental planting, it would be necessary to employ two senior people, one of whom would be a plant ecologist, the other a soil chemist with a bias towards the study of soil as a medium for plant growth. A gardener would be required to assist the ecologist and a technical assistant for the soil chemist. In addition, special equipment, chemical and other materials, transport and plants would be necessary. Some of the experiments established during the two-year period could yield only preliminary data within that time; it would therefore be desirable to retain the services of the ecologist and gardener for a third year and allowance is made for this in the estimates.

35 The Department is particularly well equipped to undertake the general direction of work of this kind as the Head of the Department is a plant physiologist and the staff includes a very experienced plant ecologist; the special equipment needed by the soil chemist would be available in the Department of Geology. In addition, further expert assistance could probably be obtained from the Forestry Commission in Wales, the Welsh Plant Breeding Station, the Agricultural Research Council and from laboratories like the Water Pollution Research Laboratory of the D.S.I.R.

F   *Legal*

36 There are indications of some obscurity about the legal ownership of parts of the area although it is not thought that purely legal problems will present major difficulties. The suggestion, therefore, is that a firm of lawyers with local knowledge and with special experience in ascertaining the legal ownership of complicated areas of land should be asked to assist with difficulties as they arise. General advice and oversight could be obtained through the Board of Legal Studies, The University of Wales.

G   *Landscape planning*

37 A firm of landscape architects should be consulted about such questions as terracing, the siting of belts of trees, and the final layout of the area. The amount of work involved will not be clear until the findings of the other enquiries are available and the estimated consultants' fee (based upon discussion with an independent body with experience in these matters) must at this stage be speculative.

H   *Social science*

38 There should first be a short preliminary study of the 'human ecology' of the area: the houses and huts and their inhabitants; the people who work there, where they live, their occupational grades, labour turnover, morbidity, etc.; any special antisocial elements such as are often associated with derelict areas; the use of sites as official and unofficial sports grounds, 'junk playgrounds', etc. A good deal of the information will be in the possession of various departments of the Corporation, local firms, etc. Other information will have to be gathered by direct methods. Given an investigator with experience in urban sociology, this inquiry should take about six months full time.

39 A second and more detailed study is likely to be necessary when the uses to which the area can be put are better understood; this should take from one to two years according to the importance attached to housing in the proposals that emerge.

How the Project came
about and what it was
intended to achieve

Finance

40 Financial estimates are presented in Note 3. The unusually complex nature of the problem, the dependence of major parts of the study on the results obtained in other parts and the fact that, to our knowledge, no similar enquiry is available to provide guidance, make it inevitable that most of the estimates should be approximate and contingent at this stage.

41 No allowance is made in the estimates for the publication of the Report.

Note 1 Preliminary definition of the area

The area to be considered is roughly triangular in shape. The base of the triangle is formed by the road from Llansamlet to the new Wychtree bridge at Morriston; the apex is immediately east of the High Street goods station.

On the west the old Swansea canal provides a fairly distinct boundary between the derelict area and the present built-up area from Morriston to Hafod.

On the east the boundary is somewhat less precise. The line runs south from Llansamlet to the Colliers Arms, thence along the Jersey road via Winchwen and Cwm to Pentrechwyth; then along the Pentrechwyth-Pentreguinea roads as far south as Maesteg Street, Foxhole.

The district thus defined does not include four contiguous areas that are similar in character and should be taken into account:

(*a*) to the west, the slag tip in the Pentre area, bounded on the north, east and west by the Swansea loop railway line.

(*b*) to the north, the area by the Wychtree bridge, the site of the Worcester & Forest Steel Works.

(*c*) to the north-east, the area between St Samlet's Church and the main road, including the site of the Aber tinplate works.

(*d*) to the south-east, the area known as White Rock tips.

Within the region indicated, there are substantial blocks which do not require attention, such as the works of the National Smelting Corporation and the playing fields of Richard Thomas and Baldwins and I.C.I. The future of certain other works, for instance the Dyffryn Steelworks, is uncertain.

Note 2 Administration

Main Committee

Chairman   The Principal, Dr J. H. Parry, C.M.G., M.B.E.
Vice-Chairman   R. B. Southall, C.B.E., J.P.
Director

Administration

Academic Members

Professor W. G. V. Balchin	Geography
Professor C. H. Hassall	Chemistry
R. Huws Jones	Social Science
Professor F. Llewellyn-Jones	Physics
Professor E. Victor Morgan	Economics
Professor B. G. Neal (or successor)	Civil Engineering
Professor Hugh O'Neill	Metallurgy
Professor F. H. T. Rhodes	Geology
Professor H. E. Street	Botany
Professor Glanmor Williams	History
The Registrar	

Swansea Corporation

Councillor Percy Morris, Leader of the County Borough Council
Iorwerth J. Watkins, the Town Clerk

Welsh Office, the Ministry of Housing and Local Government

F. Blaise Gillie, C.B., Welsh Secretary

Industry, etc.

Capt. H. Leighton Davies, C.B.E., J.P., Chairman, Welsh Board for Industry
G. Froom Tyler, Editor of the *South Wales Evening Post*
A local member of the Institution of Civil Engineers

Steering Committee

The Principal	The Town Clerk
R. B. Southall	Professor H. O'Neill
F. Blaise Gillie	R. Huws Jones
The Director	

Academic Working Group *for the coordination of enquiries*

The Principal	Professor Neal
Professor Balchin	Professor O'Neill
Professor Hassall	Professor Rhodes
R. Huws Jones	Professor Street
Professor Morgan	The Registrar
The Director	

(The Committee to have power to co-opt.)

Note 3　Financial Estimates

	£
1　*Administration*	
Director—salary, increments, F.S.S.U., etc., for 4 years	10,000
Clerical assistance, travelling, etc.	3,200
2　*Geographical surveys*	
i Research assistant for contour survey and hydrological investigation for 1 year, salary, F.S.S.U., etc.	850
Transport	100
ii Cartographical assistance and aerial survey	400
3　*Economic history and economics*	
i Research Scholarship for 2 years	1,000
ii Senior Research Economist for 2 years, salary with F.S.S.U., etc.	3,200
4　*Geology*	
i Research assistant for 1 year, salary with F.S.S.U., etc.	800
Travelling expenses	100
ii Expendable laboratory material for soil chemistry	300
5　*Civil engineering*	
Preliminary sampling, drilling approx. 100 boreholes to average depth of 40 ft, analysing about 500 soil samples, and preparation of report, to be undertaken by a specialist firm under the direction of the Department of Civil Engineering	12,500
6　*Botany*	
i Expenses of preliminary Survey	300
ii Senior Soil Chemist, salary, F.S.S.U., etc., for 2 years	2,200
Technical Assistant for 2 years	1,000
iii Senior Plant Ecologist, salary, increments, F.S.S.U., etc., for 3 years	3,500
Gardener for 3 years	1,800
iv Special services (including bulldozing, ploughing and fencing), transport, equipment, chemicals, plants, etc.	4,000
7　*Legal enquiries*	
Ascertaining legal ownership of land by a law firm in cases of difficulty	400
8　*Landscape planning*	
Consultants' fee to a firm of Landscape Architects	500
9　*Social science*	
Research worker: for preliminary survey (6 months)	500
expenses	100
Research worker: for full study (about 18 months)	1,800
expenses	200
	———
Total	£48,750

Note: No allowance is made for the cost of publication.

2 An outline of the industrial history of the Lower Swansea Valley

The conditions which made the Tawe valley attractive to certain industries were laid down some 270 million years ago when, as a result of the vagaries of climate and topography, the great swamps of Carboniferous times formed the South Wales Coalfield. Subsequent earth movements and glaciations brought its outcrop close to the sea. But for all of this, it is highly probable that Swansea would have remained the sea-side holiday town that its burgesses once considered to be its destiny; another Llandudno or Rhyl perhaps.

Coal *

The South Wales Coalfield is roughly oval in shape, and in section looks much like a sliced onion (Figures 2.1 and 2.2); the coal seams and intervening strata lying in layers with outcrops in the north and in the south near the coast. Exposure of the seams was helped by the river valleys which cut into the coalfield, and in the valley of the Tawe the earliest workings were tunnels or adits which followed the seams into the hillsides, at Kilvey Hill and again above Morriston. From the fourteenth century onwards these hillsides, east and west of the Tawe, were continuously exploited, and an export trade in coal developed out of Swansea to Devon and Cornwall, to the Channel Islands and to Ireland.

In Great Britain during the sixteenth and seventeenth centuries there was a virtual revolution in the production and use of coal. Output increased over ten times and shipments from Swansea and Neath by nearly twice as much again, as shown by the following figures:

Estimated production of coal (tons)

	1551–60	1681–90
Swansea and Neath (shipments)	2,400	40,000
Wales	20,000	200,000
Great Britain	210,000	2,982,000

Source: J. U. Nef, 1932

There were several reasons for this: increase in population, the development of industry and a growing national shortage of timber. At least 200,000 trees a year were felled by smelters in the seventeenth century, the ironmasters of Sussex turned westward to the Forest of Dean and to Wales as the forests in the south-east were consumed and replaced by grazing grounds for sheep. Even as far west as Pembrokeshire a Welshman lamented in 1603 that 'This countrie groneth with the generalle complainte of other countries of the decreasing of wood'.

* This section is based on sources listed in the Bibliography, p. 37, nos. 10, 11, 16, 19, 25, 31.

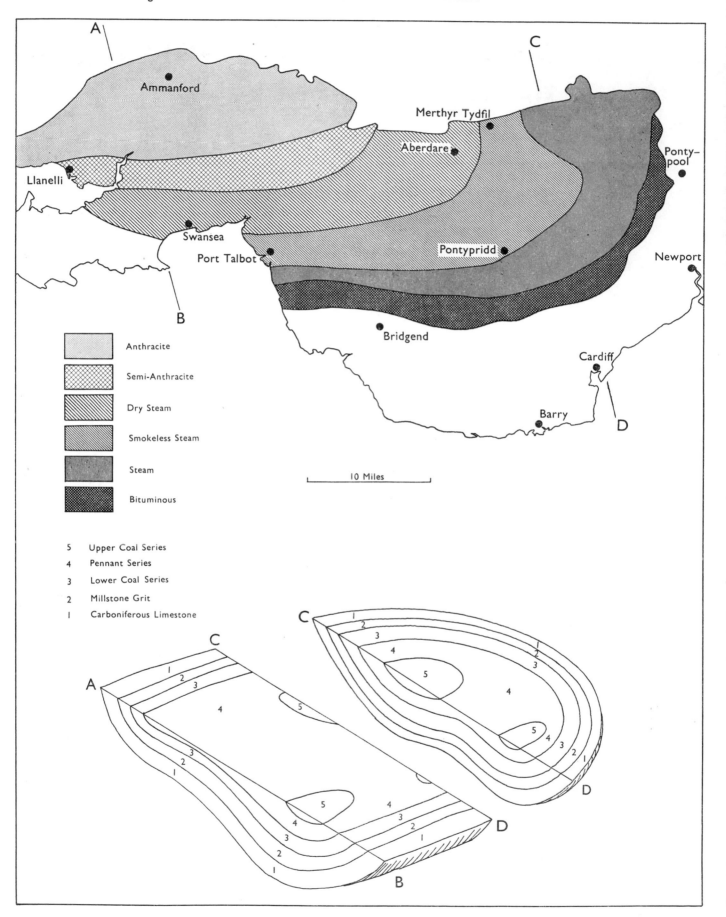

Figures 2.1 and 2.2 Cross-section of the South Wales coalfield

Anthracite

Semi-Anthracite

Dry Steam

Smokeless Steam

Steam

Bituminous

10 Miles

5 Upper Coal Series

4 Pennant Series

3 Lower Coal Series

2 Millstone Grit

1 Carboniferous Limestone

As a result of this acute shortage there was an incentive to explore the use of coal in the many industrial processes where the use of wood or charcoal had been traditional. The change was made first in brewing, salt boiling, malting and glassmaking. By 1700 coal had also replaced wood in brass making and in the smelting of lead and copper. This was assisted in the 1680s by the adaptation of the reverberatory furnace which enabled ore to be smelted by the indirect heat of a coal-burning hearth. In 1709 Abraham Darby produced pig iron at Coalbrookdale, using coke in place of charcoal in a blast furnace. All these developments led to an ever-increasing exploitation of the coalfields and especially of seams near the sea at a time when the pack-horse and the wagon were the only means of transport inland.

In 1707 Swansea's 297 houses were clustered around its Norman castle which overlooked the river ferry and the way westward to Gower. Apart from its straw hats the town was known for its coal; to find a hundred sailing vessels in the bay waiting for coal was not uncommon. Swansea's advantage lay not only in having a coalfield on its borders but also in having the seams less than three miles from the sea, for it was cheaper to transport coal 300 miles by sea than to carry it twenty miles overland by pack-horse and wagon. In 1707 coal from workings on the east side of the river, from Great Pit and Little Pit, from Middle Pit and Keven Pit was being shipped at White Rock quay. On the west side the coal banks owned by the burgesses handled the production of pits at Cwmbach and Penvilia.

Few records of these early workings survive and many of their locations can no longer be traced. Mining was greatly intensified with the setting up from 1717 onwards of smelting works in the valley; and until 1798, when the Swansea Canal made it easier to bring coal down from inland pits, many new shafts were sunk, particularly around Llansamlet. Here in 1750, Chauncey Townsend, an Alderman of the City of London, secured an interest in Church Pit from the Morgan family of Gwernllwynchwyth. This was developed by his son-in-law John Smith into a complex of pits, some of which, such as George and Emily, were named after members of the Smith family. The locations of the pits which were sunk in this area which are known are shown on Figure 4.1. After 1775 the development of the steam engine for pumping and ventilation meant that deeper shafts, such as the Marsh Pit, could be sunk on the valley floor to reach the seams that outcropped on the sides.

In this historical account of the coal industry we have been concerned with coal mined in the Lower Valley itself. As industry developed on the valley floor, its demands exceeded the supply available from local pits, which were troubled by problems of drainage. The Callands Pit acted as a sump which drained pits on both sides of the river, and had to be continually pumped. Improved communications, particularly the coming of the railway after 1850, accelerated their closure so that by 1931 there was no pit working in the Project area (defined in Chapter 1). In time the port of Swansea came to serve a hinterland that produced large quantities of steam coal and anthracite. Out of a total of 1,999,687 tons of anthracite exported from South Wales in 1907, Swansea alone shipped 1,761,687 tons; little of this was mined in the Lower Valley. Swansea became the great entrepôt for the western part of the coalfield and the valley merely accommodated the tracks and acres of sidings that fed the port.

Copper*

It was largely cheap and accessible coal that attracted a Bristol doctor, John Lane, to establish Swansea's first copper smelting works at Landore in 1717, and induced others to follow him. (See Tables 2.1, 2.2 and 2.3 for a chronological account of the metal works of the Swansea area.) The history of coal mining in the valley is intimately linked with its smelting industries. In the nineteenth century it required eighteen tons of coal to smelt thirteen tons of copper ore to produce one ton of copper by the Welsh process, so that it was profitable to bring the ore from Cornwall to the coal in South Wales and to carry coal back again to fire the furnaces which drove the steam pumping engines developed by Boulton and Watt and other engineers. It was also natural that the copper smelters should try to secure their supplies by developing their own mines. Robert Morris, who with his partner Thomas Lockwood took over Lane's Works in 1727, tells of his early difficulties with rapacious landowners. When he eventually worked his own pit at Treboeth he notes with relief that 'the well being of the Copper Works is in a great measure owing to this Colliery; for now it is out of Mr Popkin's power by any tricks or shifts to distress us' (Morris MSS.).

Swansea coal was cheap. Robert Morris in 1727 claimed that the coal at Landore was a third of the price of coal at Holywell, Flintshire and in 1812 Pascoe Grenfell, of the partnership which operated the Upper Bank Works, preferred Swansea to St Helens because coal was so much cheaper there. Certainly the distances between the early pits on the hillsides and the smelting works on the river were short and the latter could be served by wagon roads and later by tramways. Since the price of coal is supposed to have doubled every two miles it was transported from the mines, it is not surprising that Swansea coal was relatively cheap.

The factors which contributed greatly to the expansion of a smelting industry in the Swansea Valley may be briefly summarized. Ample supplies of cheap, semi-anthracite steam coal suitable for use in reverberatory smelting furnaces; coal that burned with a bright flame and little smoke and which did not clog the grates; coal that could be mined close to a port which itself was only a short sea journey away from supplies of ore in Devon and Cornwall; a port that was served by a river navigable for two and a half miles from its mouth providing industrial sites along its banks and capable, through the construction of weirs, of supplying both water and power; finally, it was a location that was midway between its raw material and its main market—the industrial Midlands. In time other factors, notably the presence of suitable refractory fireclays for furnace linings and retorts, skilled labour and the local acceptance of heavy air pollution, considerably strengthened the suitability of the valley for the smelting of metals.

The growth of the copper industry in the Swansea Valley was spectacular. It started with Lane's small works in 1717, whose buildings cost their owner £3,000 and employed fewer than forty men. By 1823 there were eight other works, which together with the collieries and the shipping which were dependent on them supported a population of from eight to ten thousand. Out of this industry there developed a complex of non-ferrous smelting works which produced gold, silver, lead, tin, brass, yellow metal, nickel, cobalt and zinc. Of these, copper and zinc were the most important for Swansea and Great Britain.

Although copper was first smelted at Neath in 1584, it was in the Swansea Valley that the

---

* Sources: Bibliography nos. 1, 4, 7, 10, 15, 16, 18, 20, 21, 26, 27, 28, 30, 32, and unpublished material by R. O. Roberts, University College of Swansea.

greatest development took place, particularly in smelting techniques. The 'Welsh process', as it came to be called, consisted of a series of roastings or calcinations in reverberatory furnaces to remove the sulphur from the ores, followed by treatment in melting furnaces in the course of which the metal was gradually separated from the iron, silica and other base residues, which were eventually discarded in huge tips of slag and furnace ash. The last of six operations was refining, in a refinery furnace, and the production of metal as cake, billet, strip or granulated for brass making. (For accounts of the Welsh process see Sources 1 and 21.)

In all thirteen copper smelting works were established in the Lower Swansea Valley between 1717 and 1850 and their locations are shown in Figure 2.3. It will be noticed that they were all sited with the river on one side of them and a canal or a railway on the other. Up the river came the ore, and down the canals and the railways the coal. From the names of those associated with the direction of the thirteen works of this industry (see Table 2.1) it will be noticed that in this field of endeavour, and in contrast to the tinplate industry later, it was the English who were the entrepreneurs. Robert Morris came from Shropshire, the Percivals from Bristol, the Vivians from Cornwall. It was an industry in which substantial capital was required and this was put up by trading families in Bristol, Birmingham and London who had the courage to risk an investment in copper on the Swansea river. Similarly with the managerial and technical staff. Of eighty-four agents, managers and under-managers traced between 1800 and 1920, only twenty-five appear to have been Welshmen.

Compared with the iron, and with the later steel and tinplate industries, the number engaged in the smelting of non-ferrous metals was small. In the eighteenth century fifty was an average number for a copper works. At the Hafod Works about 330 men were employed at the peak of its operations in 1879. According to the Census of 1851, the five works then operating in the valley employed 1,214 men, an average of just over 200 men per works. Twenty-five years later the Landore Siemens Steel Works alone employed over 2,000.

Although small in size, the contribution made by the industry in South Wales, and by that part of it that was located in the Swansea Valley, was significant. The region from Neath to Llanelli, in the century up to 1880, had 90 per cent of Britain's copper smelting capacity, and in 1880 Swansea itself smelted more than two-thirds of the copper ores imported into Great Britain, and refined half of the imported regulus and precipitates. Yet copper was smelted in the valley for the last time between 1920 and 1921, by which time only one works was still operating. What had caused this transformation?

The reasons, as might be suspected, are complex. First the decline in the production of local ores. Copper ore was mined in Devon and Cornwall in the seventeenth century, and was even smelted at Hayle and Redruth. As the demand for the metal increased for brewing and distilling, for dyeing, for cannon, for household and kitchen utensils, for sheathing sailing ships, so output increased, mines went deeper, pumping machinery enabled richer veins to be exploited as with coal mining. Up to 1840 the United Kingdom was the largest producer of copper ore in the world: by 1900 it was, next to Sweden, the smallest. Some indication of this rise and fall is given in the following table:

Output of copper ore in Cornwall and Devon (tons)

Beginning: 1725–30	Peak: 1855–60	End: 1890–95
6,000	191,130	3,730

Source: D. B. Barton, 1961

An outline of the
industrial history of
the Lower Swansea
Valley

In time as the richer veins were worked out, it was found economical to transport ore
across the Atlantic from new fields in South America. The first cargo of foreign ore entered
Swansea in 1827. Later, to save freight costs again, the ore was partly refined at source with

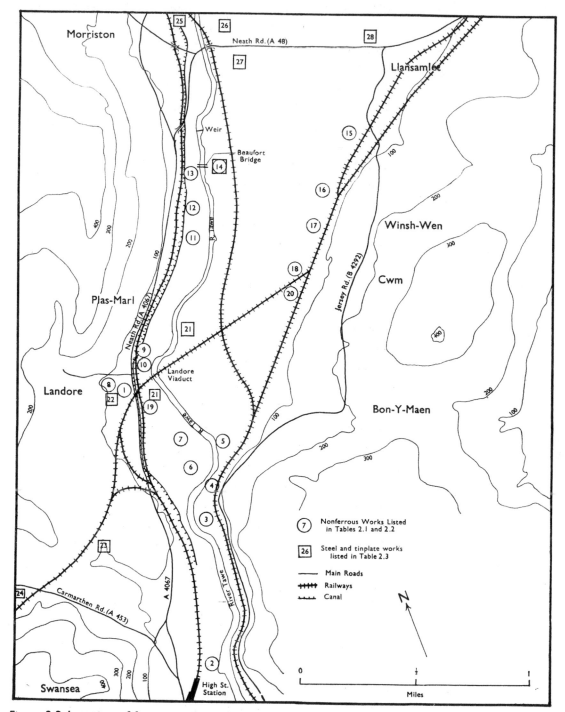

Figure 2.3 Location of ferrous and non-ferrous works in the Lower Swansea Valley

South Wales coal carried as a return cargo in the ore clippers from Swansea. These trends
developed after 1850 and reached their peak around 1890 when, with the help of Welsh
smelting skills, the ore-producing countries began to export refined copper instead of
blister bar and cake.

Table 2.1 A chronology of the copper, silver and lead smelting works in the Lower Swansea Valley

by R. O. Roberts

Site no. on Fig. 2.3	Name of works and metals smelted		Names and dates of firms operating the works
1	Landore or Llangyfelach		
	Works	(a) Dr John Lane	1717–26
	(copper, lead,	(b) Robert Morris	1726–27
	silver)	(c) Morris Lockwood & Co.	1726–48
2	Cambrian Works		
	(copper)	(a) James Griffiths & Co.	1720–c.1730
		(b) Richard Phillips	1730–35
		(c) Robert Morris	1735–45
3	White Rock		
	(copper)	(a) White Rock Copper Co. alias John Hoblyn & Partners	1737–?
		(b) Joseph Percival & Co.	1744–64
		(c) John Freeman Copper Co.	1764–1870/1
	(silver and lead)	(d) Williams, Foster & Co. and Vivian & Sons	c.1871–74
	(silver and lead)	(e) Vivian & Sons	1874?–1924
		(f) British Copper Manufacturers Ltd	1924–28
4	Middle Bank or Plas Canol		
	(lead)	(a) Chauncey Townsend & Co.	1755–64
	(copper)	(b) John Rotton & Co.	1765–9
	(copper)	(c) George Pengree & Co.	1769–85?
	(copper)	(d) The Stanley Co.	1787–c.1804
	(copper)	(e) (Owen) Williams and Grenfell	c.1804–c.1825/6
	(copper)	(f) Pascoe Grenfell & Sons	1828–90
	(copper)	(g) Pascoe Grenfell & Sons Ltd	1890–3
	(copper)	(h) Williams Foster & Co. and Pascoe Grenfell & Co. Ltd	1893–1924
5	Upper Bank or Plas Uchaf		
	(lead and spelter)	(a) Chauncey Townsend and John Smith	c.1757–?
	(copper and lead)	(b) Joseph Rotton & Co.	1777–?
	(copper)	(c) Parys Mine Co.	1782–1804
	(copper)	(d) Williams & Grenfell	1804–c.1825/6
	(copper)	(e) Owen Williams	1828–33?
	(yellow metal)	(f) Muntz Patent Metal Co.	1838–42
	(copper and spelter)	(g) Pascoe Grenfell & Sons Ltd	?1850–90
	(copper)	(h) Pascoe Grenfell & Sons Ltd	1890–92
	(copper and spelter)	(i) Williams Foster & Co. and Pascoe Grenfell & Co. Ltd	1892–1924
		(j) British Copper Manufacturers Ltd	1924–8
6	Hafod		
	(copper, silver, gold)	Vivian & Sons	1810–1924
7	Morfa		
	(copper)	(a) Williams Foster & Co.	1835–80
	(copper)	(b) H. R. Merton & Co.	1880
	(copper)	(c) Williams Foster & Co.	1880–93
	(copper)	(d) Williams Foster & Co. and Pascoe Grenfell & Sons Ltd	1893–1924
8	Nant-rhyd-y-Vilias		
	(copper and iron by re-smelting slags)	Messrs Bevan	1814– before 1817

An outline of the
industrial history of
the Lower Swansea
Valley

Table 2.1   *cont.*

Site no. on Fig. 2.3	Name of works and metals smelted	Names and dates of firms operating the works	
9	Landore		
	(copper)	(a) Morris, Lockwood & Co.	1793–?
		(b) The British Co.	1807/8–c.1823
		(c) Daniell, Nevill & Co.	1823–7
		(d) Henry Bath & R. J. Nevill	1827–37
		(e) Williams Foster & Co. alias The British and Foreign Copper Co.	1840–76
10	Little Landore		
	(copper)	(a) Landore Arsenic & Copper Co.	1863–?
		(b) Thomas Elford, Williams & Co. alias Landore Copper Co.	1880–92
		(c) Landore Copper Co. Ltd	1892–96
11	Rose		
	(copper)	(a) Fenton (alias Chacewater) & Co.	1780/1–97
		(b) Rose Copper Co.	1797–c.1820
		(c) Grenfell, Williams & Fox	1823–9
		(d) Williams Foster & Co.	1829–50–?1878
12	Birmingham or Ynys		
	(copper)	(a) The Birmingham Mining & Copper Co.	1793–1833
13	Forest or Fforest		
	(copper)	(a) Morris, Lockwood & Co.	1746–c.1793
	(copper)	(b) Harford & Co. alias Bristol Brass Wire Co.	1793–1808
	(crushing slags)	(c) N. Troughton	c.1820
	(copper)	(d) Usborne Benson & Co. alias Benson Logan & Co.	1833–41
	(copper)	(e) Governor & Co. of Copper Miners in England	1841–8
		(f) The Bank of England	1848–51
	(copper?)	(g) Messrs J. H. Vivian and Michael Williams	1851–?
19	Landore		
	(silver)	L. H. Dillwyn & Co.	1853–5
20	Llansamlet		
	(copper and arsenic)	Jennings & Co.	c.1866–7
		T. P. Richards & Co.	c.1867–82
		Llansamlet Smelting Co. Ltd	1882–1905
	Other non-smelting works		
14	Forest (Battery) works		
	(copper rolling)	(a) Morris, Lockwood & Co.	?1746–c.1793
	(copper rolling)	(b) The London Co. (Morgan & Ward, Whitechapel)	1805–8

There does not seem to be any record of attempts in Britain to apply the more econo-mical Bessemer process to the refining of copper. In 1866 Rath obtained a U.S. patent and in 1880 Manhès in France made a technical and commercial success of the copper converter. It is significant that the horizontal copper converter based on Manhès Patents is now standard in America and Rhodesia. Adherence to the Welsh process put the Swansea smelters at a disadvantage in competition with foreign smelters using the Bessemer process.

The South Wales smelters had occupied an intermediate position, economically as well as physically, between the Cornish miners and the Birmingham manufacturers. It was in their interest to buy ore cheap and to sell copper dear, and there is little doubt that at times both at Bristol and at Swansea, combinations of smelters were formed which tended to exercise a monopolistic influence on trading arrangements. Both miners and manufacturers fought to protect themselves, the miners by the formation in 1785 of the Cornish Metal Company, in which smelters and miners joined forces; the manufacturers by constant agitation inside and outside Parliament to reduce the duties on imported foreign copper, and by smelting copper themselves.

It has been suggested that the oligarchy of the smelters contributed to their eventual failure, but more powerful forces were beginning to operate by the turn of the century. The world production of copper climbed from around 9,100 tons in 1810 to over 354,700 tons in 1898, stimulated by the development of electricity and its uses in many fields. Over 11,000 miles of submarine cable, for example, were laid by 1861. Britain could never have competed in scale and economy to meet this demand, located as she was off the main ore fields of the world. In 1890 just over 5,200 tons of manufactured copper were imported into the United Kingdom; ten years later this had risen to just under 350,000 tons. The flood-gates had opened, the halcyon days of copper smelting in Swansea were over.

After 1900 a series of amalgamations gradually brought all the industry in the valley under the control of two firms, Vivian and Sons Ltd and Messrs Williams Foster and Co Ltd. In 1924 both firms were acquired by British Copper Manufacturers Ltd, and this Company by I.C.I. Ltd in 1928. The same trend—the concentration of an industry consisting of a number of small units into a few large ones—was soon to be followed in the steel and tin-plate industries. Unfortunately there did not develop in the Swansea district that richly assorted and adaptable user industry that was the strength of the Midlands. Buttons and buckles, needles and pins were not fashioned in the railway arches of Landore, and when the smelters closed, their sites in the Valley remained unfilled. Today, Yorkshire Imperial Metals Ltd, a joint company of Yorkshire Metals and I.C.I., occupies the site of the Hafod and Morfa Copper Works and still carries out some refining of copper—the only remaining link with the past.

Zinc*

Fortunately for Swansea, its smelting skills were adaptable and its industrial location suitable for the smelting of other metals. By the time that copper was beginning to decline in the 1860s many of the smelters had developed interests in zinc, lead and silver which enabled them to prolong the lives of their works. Spelter or zinc was not produced in Britain in its metallic form until about 1738 when William Champion, a Bristol copper smelter, is reputed to have succeeded using a process which he is said to have brought with him from

* Sources: Bibliography nos. 14, 29 and unpublished notes on the history of zinc smelting in the Lower Swansea Valley by Emlyn Evans, former Works Manager, Swansea Vale Works, Imperial Smelting Corporation (N.S.C.) Ltd, kindly made available by the author.

An outline of the
industrial history of
the Lower Swansea
Valley

China. Be that as it may, in the 'English process', as it was called, the metallic vapour was drawn downwards from large jar-like receptacles the form of which might well have originated in the Far East. It was, however, in Germany and Belgium that the greatest developments in zinc smelting took place during the hundred years following Champion's discovery. As might be expected, it did not take long for the smelters in the Swansea Valley to try their hands at zinc. The first attempt seems to have been made at the Upper Bank Works in 1757 by Chauncey Townsend, the alderman coal owner. The use of the metal was stimulated first in 1780 when the production of brass by a direct alloy of copper and zinc was patented and later in 1805 when it was discovered how to roll zinc into sheet. In 1832 George Frederick Muntz invented a copper-zinc alloy, which replaced copper sheathing and accessories on ships. Muntz metal was followed in 1837 by a process for coating iron sheets with zinc and it was this galvanizing process which completely revolutionized the demand for it. Galvanized sheets were exported in their millions to the New World where the shack towns of the frontier were springing up. Some idea of this expansion in production is given in the following table:

World production of spelter (tons)

1830	1837	1845	1890
less than 5,000	17,000	29,000	342,000

Source: E. A. Smith, 1918

After 1757 the next reference to spelter production in the Swansea district is at the Cambrian Spelter Works of Evan John of Llansamlet in 1836, using the English process (Table 2.2). In 1841 Vivian and Sons converted the old Birmingham Copper Works into a spelter works, starting with the English process, but changing later to the Silesian process and finally to the Belgian.

This progression was due to the improvement in efficiency between the processes. In the English process twenty-five tons of coal were used to produce one ton of zinc. This fell to twelve tons of coal with the Silesian and to six tons with the Belgian. In the latter processes the charge, consisting of roasted ore and coal, was placed in a series of horizontal retorts made of refractory clays arranged in a furnace setting which were then carefully heated and the zinc distilled off as a vapour which was condensed to liquid zinc.

Zinc is an extremely difficult metal to smelt; temperatures are critical and the risk of oxidation high. Furnace management required a high level of skill and working conditions were onerous. At various times German and Belgian workers were employed in the Swansea Zinc works, initially because of their familiarity with the furnaces, but later it is said because of the difficulty in obtaining local labour to work in such harsh conditions. The works operated a twenty-four-hour shift involving Sunday working, which was unpopular with the predominantly nonconformist Welsh labour force.

In spite of such difficulties the number of works in the Swansea Valley grew until in 1922 there were six in operation, employing some 2,000 workers; four of them were sited together, east of the river (Figure 2.3). A chronology of the works is given in Table 2.2. Between 1860 and World War I, fourteen works in western South Wales ceased to smelt copper ores and eleven started to smelt zinc ores. Swansea became the principal centre of zinc production in Great Britain and by 1914 was smelting 54,000 metric tons, 20 per cent of the national total. This concentration of production tended to give rise to the complaint, already familiar in the case of copper, that the smelters combined to keep ore prices low and metal prices high.

Table 2.2 A chronology of the spelter or zinc works in the Lower Swansea Valley

after Emlyn Evans and R. O. Roberts

Site no. on Fig. 2.3	Name of works	Names and dates of firms operating the works	
5	Upper Bank or Plas Uchaf (spelter) (spelter)	Pre-1924 (See Table 2.1) (a) British Copper Manufacturers Ltd. (b) I.C.I. Ltd	1924–8 1928–30
13	Morriston Spelter Works on the site of the Birmingham Copper Works (Site 12). In 1868 the Works were extended to include the site of the former Forest Copper Works (Table 2.1, Site 13).	Messrs Vivian & Co.	c.1841–1924
15	Swansea Vale (spelter)	(a) Swansea Vale Co. Ltd (b) National Smelting Co. Ltd (c) Imperial Smelting Corporation (N.S.C.) Ltd	1876–1924 1924–64 1964 to date
16	Villiers (spelter)	(a) Villiers Spelter Co. Ltd (b) British Extraction Co. Ltd	1873–1904 1904–c.1929
17	Glamorgan Works (spelter) (treatment of zinc sludges)	(a) Swansea Zinc Ore Co. (b) Anglo-French Mineral Co. Ltd (c) Swansea Smelting Co. Ltd (d) Glamorgan Spelter Co. Ltd	?–1887 1887–96 1897–1905 1905–7
18	Cambrian (spelter) Dillwyn (spelter)	(a) Evan John (b) Dillwyn & Co. Ltd (c) Dillwyn & Co. Ltd	1836 c.1858–1902 1902–26

The principal weakness of the smelting firms, one which was to recur again later in the tinplate industry, was their resistance to change. Welsh smelters were unwilling to try out new methods until they had been proven and widely accepted abroad, by which time they found themselves unable to make up lost ground. Unlike the Germans, who encouraged the exchange of ideas and scientific information between managers and technical staff, they were on the whole suspicious of the scientific metallurgist. (Vivian and Sons were an exception.) South Wales followed the German and Belgian industry in gas firing of furnaces and the use of hydraulic presses and mechanically rabbled roasters, and yet in spite of this the greatest breakthrough of all—the production of zinc by a blast-furnace process—was developed in Great Britain.

John Percy, the celebrated metallurgist, writing in 1861, said: 'While I do not venture to predict that the blast furnace will never be successfully applied to the extraction of zinc from its ores, yet I confess I do not see much reason to anticipate improvement in that direction.' A hundred years later, the first commercial blast-furnace plant in the world had started producing zinc at the Swansea Vale Works.

An outline of the
industrial history of
the Lower Swansea
Valley

The zinc industry in Swansea flourished between 1840 and 1914. During the 1914–18 war large capacity plants in America, Canada and Australia, using electrolytic processes and situated in proximity to ore fields, came into production, and after the war were in a position to meet European demand. With the exception of the Swansea Vale Works, which had been modernized in 1916 with Government help, all the other works, Villiers, Dillwyn, Upper Bank and Morriston, closed between 1924 and 1928, leaving sites occupied by buildings which steadily deteriorated. Today the Swansea Vale Works, producing zinc, lead and sulphuric acid, retains the valley's historical connection with the industry.

Air Pollution*

The Welsh process of copper smelting involved, as we have seen, a series of roastings to drive off the sulphur in the ore. Both copper and zinc ores contained varying proportions of sulphur and the smelting of both metals produced a large quantity of fume, consisting of sulphur dioxide, sulphurous and particulate sulphuric acid.† According to Percy, about 92,000 tons of sulphurous acid a year or 65,900 cubic metres a day were released into the atmosphere by the Copper Works in 1848. Since the prevailing wind was south-westerly, the Llansamlet and Bonymaen areas were the worst hit. Crops were ruined and cattle affected. Visitors to the town were not impressed. 'The volume of smoke from the different manufactories contribute to make Swansea, if not unwholesome, a very disagreeable place of residence', said the Rev. J. Evans in his tour through South Wales published in 1804.

Between 1822 and 1841 a series of indictments for nuisance were brought against individual copper firms by local farmers, but so important was the industry to Swansea that none was successful.‡ A contemporary medical report even maintained that 'copper smoke' was beneficial and that a good concentration of it gave protection from disease.

Nevertheless, the smelters were sensitive and made many attempts to reduce the noxious effects of the vast outpouring from their furnaces. Under the aegis of the Royal Institution of South Wales a fund was raised to be awarded to whichever individual or company was considered by the judges to have done most to reduce the nuisance. The work of J. H. Vivian at the Hafod and of Bevington Gibbin at the Rose Works was especially commended; both used a form of water filter. Sir Humphry Davy and Michael Faraday were associated with the investigations, but it was not until Vivian and Sons adopted Gerstenhofer's process about 1865 that any sensible improvement was made. This was stimulated by the economies which could be obtained from the efficient treatment of fume. The value of sulphur that was lost to the atmosphere in the Swansea Valley every year was estimated at £200,000.

The continuous envelopment of the valley in fume for nearly a hundred years resulted in almost a complete destruction of its vegetation. The indigenous sessile oak and birch woodland of Kilvey Hill and all grass and heather in the area disappeared. The topsoil, no longer held by plant roots, was washed off the valley sides leaving the subsoil to be eroded into gullies. The area became a virtual desert and the effects are still visible today. (Plate 5)

---

* *Sources:* Bibliography nos. 3, 8, 12, 21, 24, 33.
† Particles of acid in suspension in the air as droplets measured by the mass concentration of all acid per cubic metre of air.
‡ See particularly Lawyer's Briefs in lawsuits involving Grenfell and Co., Middle Bank, *circa* 1830 and Vivian and Sons, Hafod Works, 1833. Library, Royal Institution of South Wales and University College, Swansea.

After the closure of the copper works, fumes continued to be produced in the Llansamlet area by the group of spelter works located there. During World War I, when the need for zinc was acute, smelting operations were intensified and this resulted in damage to neighbouring farms. Complaints were investigated by the Ministry of Agriculture and the Ministry of Munitions jointly, and a report prepared. (*Report of a visit to Llansamlet on 28 September 1918 for the purpose of investigating the allegations of Damage to Crops and other vegetation by fumes from the British Metals Extraction Co. Ltd.*) This confirmed the damage to crops and vegetation. After the war the Swansea Vale Works continued smelting and it appears that, until the introduction of the blast-furnace process in 1961, complaints were received from time to time of damage to neighbouring gardens, particularly to tender vegetables such as young beans. The present levels of atmospheric pollution are discussed in Chapter 5 and the Appendix.

Tinplate*

It was at Pontypool, between 1650 and 1670, that in Britain an iron bar was first rolled into a sheet and then coated with a layer of tin. From the eastern edge of the coalfield the industry moved west, first to Kidwelly by 1750 and later up and down the river valleys until by 1880 out of sixty-four tinplate works in South Wales, forty-one were located west of Port Talbot. By 1913 four out of every five tinplate workers in Great Britain were employed within a radius of twenty miles of Swansea.

The first tinplate works in the Lower Swansea Valley was built in 1845, a century after the works at Kidwelly, and on the site of a grist mill at Upper Forest (Figure 2.3). This was the forerunner of ten others, the Landore (1851), the Cwmfelin (1858), the Beaufort (1860), the Cwmbwrla (1863), the Worcester (1868), the Morriston (1872), the Duffryn (1874), the Midland (1879), the Birchgrove (before 1880) and the Aber (1880). Tinplate production, like copper and spelter, required coal but not in such large quantities. It also needed iron bar and later steel, but water was essential first for driving the rolls, hence the grist mill site of the Upper Forest works, but even after steam, for the constant washing of the plates in the tinning process. So we find the tinplate works in western South Wales located in the river valleys of the Afan, Neath, Tawe, Loughor and Gwendraeth. Again the Tawe was a location factor for the industry but, whereas with copper it was the navigation of the river that was important, for tinplate it was the quantity and to a lesser extent the quality of its water that mattered.

Consequent upon the coming into Wales of English ironmasters from the Weald and the Forest of Dean in the sixteenth and seventeenth centuries, ironworks with their associated blast furnaces, fineries and forges were well represented in the region. These ironworks attracted tinplate mills in which the pig iron was reheated in their own furnaces to produce 'puddled' iron suitable for rolling. A mill consisted basically of three departments—the furnaces, the rolls and the tin house. The separation of the three processes of heating the bar, rolling it and finally tinning it, was a characteristic of the British industry that lasted for two hundred years; a system as unchangeable as the laws of the Medes and Persians. The mill team—furnaceman, rollerman, doubler, behinder, first and second helper—

* Sources: Bibliography nos. 6, 9, 17.

An outline of the
industrial history of
the Lower Swansea
Valley

was a unit that seemed as unalterable as the processes they served. Invariably it was a social unit as well, linked by relationship and religion, serving the chapel and the family when the shift was done.

A small works like the Worcester with two mills could be set up for £6,000—a sum within the reach of local businessmen. This was therefore an industry in which Welsh finance played a significant part, and names like William Williams, Daniel Edwards, and John Jones of the Worcester, John Jones Jenkins of the Beaufort, and Daniel Griffiths of the Aber, tell their own story.

The development of the industry in the Lower Swansea Valley area was dramatic. From five mills in 1845 it grew to 106 mills by 1913. Fortunately this period of growth coincided with the decline of the copper industry, so that skilled labour was easily absorbed. Morriston, founded as a village for copper men, became a tinman's suburb. The Swansea Royal Jubilee Metal Exchange was established in 1887 and by 1890 Swansea had become the business centre of the tinplate trade in the United Kingdom.

This was a high water mark. In July 1891 the United States Government imposed a tariff to protect its own developing tinplate industry from British competition. This increased the price of imported tinplate in the U.S.A. by 70 per cent and stimulated tinplate production in America; although the loss of the American market between 1891 and 1913 was more than compensated for by increased exports to Europe and the Far East, the growing potential of the American industry was ominous. The opportunity to challenge its British counterpart came in 1914. On the outbreak of war, while British exports of tinplate were reduced as the industry was diverted to war production, American production stepped in to meet the needs of Britain's traditional markets overseas. In spite of this the resilience of her industry and an increasing world demand enabled Britain to recover her prewar export position by 1925.

The long period of growth up to 1890, the industry's powers of recovery first after the loss of the American market and then after the First World War; its traditional ability to adjust itself without radically changing its production methods, had inclined its leaders towards an obstinate conservatism which was in general suspicious of technical innovation or methods of scientific control. Engineering and analytical staff were regarded as a luxury, and research a waste of money. All that was needed were 'practical men in sympathy with their rolls'.

The first hot strip mill went into production at Ashland, Kentucky, in 1923. The mechanized integration of the separate processes of the traditional method of tinplate manufacture, which had been sought in America since 1920, had at last been achieved. The influence of this technological breakthrough on South Wales and the Swansea Valley in particular was eventually far-reaching, but so buoyant was world demand, and so capable was the British industry of meeting the needs of specialized markets, that it was again able to hold off the new challenger for another sixteen years. At the same time, by means of redundancy schemes and amalgamations, the way was being prepared for a fresh structure. The movement towards larger units is best illustrated by the history of the firm of Richard Thomas and Co. which was registered in 1889, and had by 1937 acquired 224 out of a total of 518 mills in South Wales. Under the powerful leadership of Sir William Firth, the Company set itself to gain sufficient output capacity to justify its taking this last logical step, the building of the strip mill.

The first British strip mill at Ebbw Vale came into production in 1938. This, with the previous acquisition of pack mills in South Wales by Richard Thomas and Co., and the closure of many of the older works under the Tinplate Redundancy Scheme, resulted in the eventual closure of all the traditional pack mills in the Lower Swansea Valley, a process that was hastened by the building of a second hot strip mill at Port Talbot by the Steel Company of Wales in 1947. One by one the old works in the valley went out of production, the last being the Duffryn which closed in 1961. A chronology of the works in the valley is given in Table 2.3.

Table 2.3

A chronology of the steel and tinplate works in the Lower Swansea Valley based on E. H. Brooke's chronology of the tinplate works of Great Britain

Site no. on Fig. 2.3	Name of works	Names and dates of firms operating the works	
21	Landore Siemens Steel Works	(a) Landore, Siemens Steel Co. Ltd	1869–c.1888
	Swansea Haematite Works	(b) Baldwins Ltd	1902–45
	Landore Steel Works	(c) Richard Thomas & Baldwins Ltd	1945 to date
22	Landore Tinplate Works	Landore Tinplate Co.	1851–92
23	Cwmfelin Tinplate Works	(a) Messrs David Davies & Son	1858–68
		(b) Cwmfelin Tinplate Co.	1883–96
		(c) The Swansea Tinplate Co.	1896–1905
		(d) Cwmfelin Steel & Tinplate Co. Ltd	1905–18
		(e) Richard Thomas & Co. Ltd	1918–45
		(f) Richard Thomas & Baldwins Ltd	1945–6
24	Cwmbwrla Tinplate Works	(a) The Swansea Iron & Tinplate Co.	1863–70
		The Swansea Tinplate Co.	
		(b) E. Morewood & Co.	? –1898
		(c) Richard Thomas & Co. Ltd	1898–1941
14	Beaufort Tinplate Works	(a) Beaufort Tinplate Co.	1860–1904
	(See also Table 2.1)	(b) Beaufort Works Ltd	1905–46
25	Morriston & Midland Tinplate Works	(a) Messrs D. Glasbrook & Co. Morriston Tinplate Works	1872–99
		(b) Messrs D. Glasbrook Co. Midland Tinplate Works	1879–99
		(c) Morriston Tinplate Co. Ltd	1899–1953
26	Upper Forest Works	(a) W. Hallam & Co. et al	1845–78
	Worcester Works	(b) Llansamlet Tinplate Co.	1869–78
	Upper Forest & Worcester Works	(c) W. Williams & Co.	1878–98
		(d) Upper Forest & Worcester Steel and Tinplate Works Ltd	1898–1958
27	Duffryn Steel and Tinplate Works	(a) Daniel Edwards & Co.	1874–95
		(b) W. H. Edwards & Co.	1895–1920
		(c) Duffryn Works Ltd	1920–3
		(d) Richard Thomas & Co. Ltd	1923–45
		(e) Richard Thomas & Baldwins Ltd	1945–61
28	Aber Tinplate Works	(a) Foxhole Tinplate Co.	1880–1901
		(b) Aber Tinplate Works Ltd	1901–18
		(c) Richard Thomas & Co. Ltd	1918–46
29	Birchgrove, Steel & Tinplate Works	Richard Martin & Co.	1880–95

Steel*

In 1856 Henry Bessemer invented a process for making cheap steel in bulk. This was significant because, since the turn of the century, the demand for rails to serve the growing network of lines throughout the country was placing a heavy strain on the production of wrought iron. Bessemer steel bars replaced wrought iron bars, and from 215,000 tons in 1870, production rose to 1,044,000 tons by 1880. Meanwhile, also in 1856, C. W. Siemens and his brother Frederick were developing a regenerative open-hearth furnace which was finally perfected at the Sample Steel Works in Birmingham in 1866. In 1867 a site was obtained at Landore in the Swansea Valley, where in 1868 a commercial open-hearth steelworks was built by the Landore Siemens Steel Company. This works came into production in the middle of 1869 and produced seventy-five tons of steel a week. By July 1870 more than 100 tons of steel rails a week with castings and forge steel were being produced, and in 1871 a larger site was taken on the east bank of the river, the present site of Richard Thomas and Baldwins' foundry. Here a new and larger steel-making plant was developed with its own blast furnaces which, by 1873, was making 1,000 tons of steel a week and was considered to be, with Krupps of Essen, one of the four largest steelworks in the world. Over 2,000 men were employed at the works in 1874.

By 1900 more steel was being produced in Great Britain by the Siemens open-hearth process than by the Bessemer converter. The Siemens open-hearth furnace had special advantages for the tinplate industry. It was comparatively uncomplicated by machinery and was more economical for small-scale working. Open-hearth furnaces were installed in the majority of the tinplate works in the Swansea Valley.

Open-hearth furnaces in the Lower Swansea Valley 1875–1961

Landore Siemens Steel Co.	24
Birchgrove Steel and Tinplate Co.	2
Swansea Tinplate Co., Cwmbwrla	2
Cwmfelin Tinplate Co.	5
Upper Forest and Worcester Steel and Tinplate Works Ltd	8
Duffryn Steel and Tinplate Works Ltd	5
Total Swansea Valley	46 furnaces
Total West South Wales	52 furnaces

Sources: E. H. Brooke and W. E. Minchinton

This was an unusually heavy concentration of steel-making capacity in one area and is probably accounted for by the early Siemens development at Landore. The typical tinplate firm in west South Wales did not make its own bar but obtained it from one of the integrated steel and tinplate works, or from the Landore Steel Company. Just as the tinplate works were dependent on the steel-making plants, so the fortunes of steel in South Wales were linked with those of the tinplate industry. The closure of the handmills was accompanied by the transfer of steel-making capacity from a number of dispersed small units to the modern, fully integrated large-scale plants of the Steel Company of Wales at Port Talbot, and of Richard Thomas and Baldwins at Newport. In the Lower Swansea Valley the blast furnaces of the Landore Siemens Steel Works shut down in 1888, and the Duffryn Works, the last of the open-hearth steel-making plants, closed in 1961.

* Sources: Bibliography nos. 2, 6, 22, 31.

Subsidiary Industry*

Associated with coal, copper, spelter, steel and tinplate there was a considerable range of subsidiary industry in the valley which should be noted briefly. Along with coal there were briquette or patent fuel works. Briquettes had been made successfully in Pembrokeshire in 1727. The first works in the Swansea area were those of Messrs Warlich and Co. of Deptford which began production in 1847 and were followed by several others. The briquettes, which were manufactured from small coal bound with pitch under heat and pressure, came to be used by the Navy and were in demand in Europe for domestic and industrial heating. In 1855 Swansea was exporting 60,882 tons or three-quarters of the total United Kingdom export, by 1879 this had risen to 162,167 tons and in 1952 to 241,778 tons but with the development of oil-fired boilers, demand eventually fell off and all the works in the Swansea area have now closed.

The copper industry produced copper sulphate, which was used for vine spraying in Europe, and sulphuric acid, which was employed to make superphosphates. Sulphuric acid was manufactured by a number of chemical and zinc works in the valley and was used by the tinplate industry for pickling sheets prior to tinning. Zinc chloride was also made and used as a flux in the tinplate industry, and so was zinc oxide which was used largely by the pharmaceutical industry. All the smelting industries required refractories for furnace linings. At first these were imported from Stourbridge and Flintshire but as the coal mines were deepened suitable refractories were obtained in the region, for example, *Dinas* bricks were made near Neath in 1820. Later refractories were produced by works established in the valley itself, one of which is in operation today. Foundries and engineering works were set up to serve the steel and tinplate industry. The Millbrook Engineering Co. Ltd was founded in 1825. It made pickling and tinning machines for the tinplate industry and had an established reputation for casting and machining hollow chilled rolls.

Perhaps, however, the most important industry using steel in the valley, apart from tinplate, was the production of tubes. In 1889 the Landore Siemens Steel Company acquired the British patent rights of the German Mannesman process for the manufacture of seamless steel tubes. A new company was formed to develop this patent in Swansea: this was the Mannesman Tube Company in which the Siemens family were shareholders. The Company continued until 1899 when the Mannesman brothers, Max and Reinhard, acquired a majority share interest in the works and formed the British Mannesman Tube Company Ltd. At this time the works employed about 300 men and produced between 3,000 and 4,000 tons of steel tubes a year. By 1919 the number of employed had risen to over 1,500 and the works was producing over 35,000 tons of tubing annually. After passing under the control of the Custodian of Enemy Property during 1914–18 and then reverting to their German owners, the works were finally acquired by Stewart and Lloyds in 1938,† and were eventually closed in 1960, leaving a bare twenty-six-acre site in the centre of the valley. This was a site without road access served only by rail, a factor which contributed towards the closure of the works.

---

* *Sources:* Bibliography nos. 5, 16, 32.
† The help given by Mr G. R. Goldsworthy, Area Training Officer (retd) of the Company, in preparing this section is gratefully acknowledged.

31

An outline of the
industrial history of
the Lower Swansea
Valley

Silver and lead were smelted at White Rock and also at the Silver works of Dillwyn and Company before the site was acquired by the Siemens Company (Figure 2.3). A small combined copper and arsenic works was built about 1866 near Swansea Vale Junction and continued until 1905. A nickel and cobalt works was established at Hafod Isha. All this serves to illustrate the fact that the smelting and steel-making complex in the Lower Swansea Valley generated a considerable growth of secondary industry which was dependent upon it.

It is not perhaps surprising that in the course of the valley's long metallurgical history efforts have been made to resmelt the slags that had been discarded from earlier processes, which could reasonably be expected to be less efficient than their successors. One of the earliest of these was the Nant-rhyd-y-Vilias Works founded at Landore in 1814 to extract copper and iron from old slags and the most recent was Western Metallurgical Industries Ltd, formed in 1952, to extract zinc-lead residues from tips in the Morriston area. In neither case were the operations successful and so far as is known, no process for extracting metallic residues from the tips has yet been commercially viable.

Canals and Railway *

We have been concerned with the history of industry in the valley, but that industry was served by transport and by men, and both have left their mark on the valley's landscape. After early wagonways and tramroads, of which most traces have disappeared, a short canal was built about 1784 by John Smith to link his collieries at Llansamlet with his coal wharves at Foxhole. More important, however, for the valley then and now was the building in 1798 of a canal along the western edge of the Tawe, from the docks to Henneuadd near Ystradgynlais, a distance of 16½ miles. In its active lifetime—from 1798 until about 1930 —this canal served pits in the centre and on the northern rim of the coalfield, and not only made available large supplies of coal for the valley smelters and steel furnaces, but was instrumental in making Swansea the premier coal port of South Wales until overtaken by Newport in 1828 and by Cardiff in 1850. The history of this enterprise has been fully documented elsewhere, but it should be noted here since, in its present disused state, the canal forms an important physical barrier to the future development of the area.

In common with industrial regions elsewhere in Great Britain, Swansea has inherited an uncoordinated network of railway lines which today complicate substantially the redevelopment of its valley. The South Wales Railway from Cardiff was the first to be opened. This was in 1850, the line being carried over the river Tawe by Brunel's wooden viaduct. Two years later the Swansea Vale Railway Company took its line from the docks alongside the Smith Canal on the east side of the valley to the Graigola Collieries, and in 1861 to Ystradgynlais.

In 1871 the Swansea Vale Company split the valley down the centre with a second line to Morriston. This fragmentation was completed by the G.W.R. in 1881 with a line from Landore to Morriston, leaving the valley effectively divided by river, railway and canal into six segments. The implications of this are considered in Chapters 7 and 11.

* *Sources:* Bibliography nos. 13, 23.

Population

The growth of industry on the valley floor was accompanied by a rapid increase in the working population. From 21,533 in 1851 the population of the Borough rose to 48,114 in 1891. The valley settlements shared in this expansion. Morriston grew from 322 in 1801 to 1,215 in 1851 and to 8,389 in 1891. The *Swansea Guide* of 1833 'calculated that the Smelting Establishments on the Swansea River support a population of from eight to ten thousand souls and cause the circulation of two thousand to three thousand pounds weekly'.

Living and working conditions were harsh. The houses, large numbers of which still stand, were small terraced cottages with slate roofs and walls of stone or of a mixture of stone and slag blocks. The population grew faster than houses could be built for them. In eleven houses with eighteen sleeping rooms, were 106 people.* Cholera swept through these settlements like fire.

In the works, women and children were employed in manual work as they were in the mines.† The industrial population was mixed, Irish Catholic, Welsh nonconformist, English, German and Belgian,‡ while through the shipping in the port contacts were made with the world at large.

The rise and fall of industry in the Lower Swansea Valley is graphically illustrated in Figure 2.4.§ Today what is left after nearly two and a half centuries of industrial occupation is over 800 acres of waste land out of a total of 1,174 acres within the formal Project area as defined in Chapter 1 (see Table 2.4). It is a lunar landscape of tips, a blitzed landscape of

Table 2.4 Land use in the Project area

Type of land use	Area in Acres	% of formal Project area
Operational industry	198	17
Empty and vacant buildings	67	6
Cleared sites	24	2
Residential land	31	3
Tips	298	25
Derelict buildings	38	3
Marsh	67	6
Railways	96	8
Roads and tracks	3	—
River, canal and open water	43	4
Unused land	309	26
Total: Formal Project area	1,174	100%

derelict industrial buildings, intersected by a nineteenth-century network of canals, railway lines and sidings. Yet in this landscape are islands of active industry employing nearly 3,500 men and women (Table 2.5). Most of the land is still privately owned and, although the free-hold title to over 79 per cent of it is in the hands of only six owners, there are about fourteen leasehold interests for terms ranging from three to eighty years. Table 2.6 illustrates

---

* *Cambrian*, 21 April 1854.
† 'The women are chiefly engaged in wheeling the ore in barrows to be crushed and receive 9s. or 10s. per week; children earn from 3/6d. to 6/6½d., furnace men from 28s. to 32s.' See ref (9).
‡ In 1851, 13,437 had been born outside the Borough.
§ This figure is based on the thesis by H. W. E. Davies.

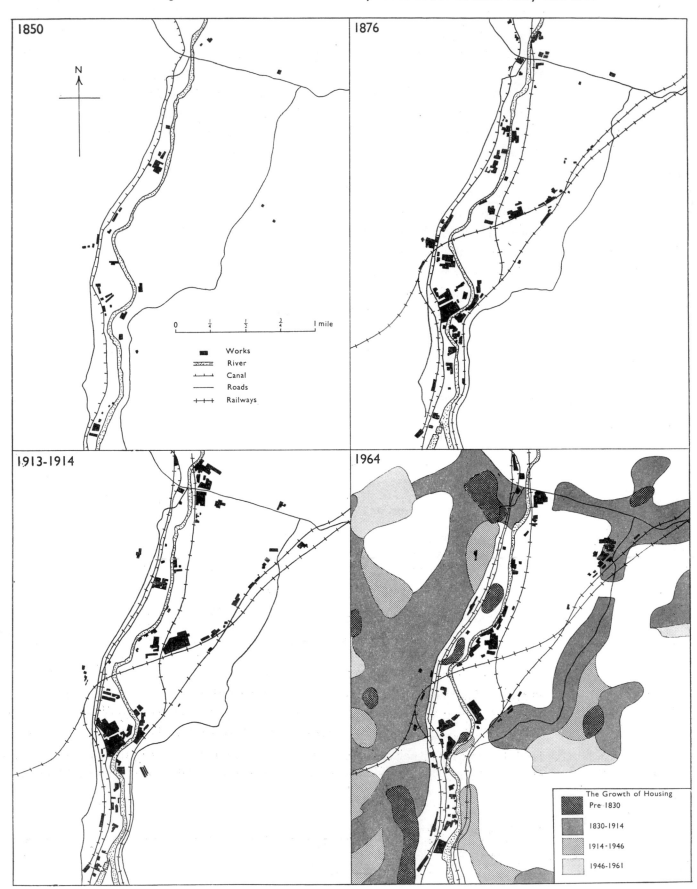

Figure 2.4 The rise and fall of industry in the Lower Swansea Valley 1850-1964

1850

N

0   ¼   ½   ¾   1 mile

■ Works
≈ River
╫ Canal
— Roads
╁ Railways

1876

1913-1914

1964

The Growth of Housing
Pre 1830
1830-1914
1914-1946
1946-1961

Table 2.5 Principal industrial land use 1964

Plot No.	Name of occupier	Type of business	Male	Female	Total
6	Steel Company of Wales Ltd	Manufacturers of tinplate packing materials	50	82	132
8	Swansea Foundry & Engineering Co. Ltd	Iron and brass founders and general engineering	151	5	156
9, 15	Birds (Swansea) Ltd	Scrap merchants and demolition contractors	38	2	40
12	Provincial Tyre Co. (S. Wales) Ltd	Tyre distributors	4	1	5
13	Coca-Cola Northern Bottlers Ltd	Storage	6	1	7
13	Bryn Demery Coaches	Garage and distribution	45	1	46
16	Wales Gas Board	Gas storage	9	1	10
16	G.A.T. Plant	Plant repair	6	1	7
16	Aberweld	Engineers	2	—	2
16	A. B. Evans & Co. (South Wales) Ltd	Engineer's merchants	3	5	8
16	Jones & Andrews	Joinery manufacturers	8	1	9
16	J. W. Faull	Steel stockholders	16	5	21
16	Abertawe Concrete Products Ltd	Agents for sectional buildings	1	—	1
16	Merlin Reinforced Plastics Ltd	Reinforced plastic moulders and plastic fabricators	11	—	11
16	W. Walters & Son	Engineers	1	—	1
16	Civic Transport Co. Ltd	Haulage contractors	7	1	8
16	British Insulated Callender's Construction Co. Ltd	Electrical and civil engineering contractors	37	—	37
17	Imperial Smelting Corporation (N.S.C.) Ltd	Zinc, lead and sulphuric acid manufacturers	760	61	821
19, 21	Morris Bros	Haulage contractor, civil engineers, luxury coach proprietors	14	—	14
20	Geo. Cohen Sons & Co. Ltd	Scrap iron, steel and metal merchants	45	2	47
	Geo. Cohen Machinery Ltd	Machinery merchants	34	2	36
	Metalclad Ltd	Iron founders and engineers	85	10	95
	Geo. Cohen (600 Group) Ltd	Transport	6	—	6
24	Richard Thomas & Baldwins Ltd	Iron founding, engineering and brick manufacturing	618	37	655
29	John & Prosser	Scrap merchants	6	—	6
35	R. Parkhouse & Sons	Haulage contractors	17	3	20
47	Shorts Auto Electrical Services	Vehicle and plant electrical specialists	5	—	5
47	Riverside Tool and Engineering Co. (Swansea) Ltd	Tool making and general engineering	5	—	5
49, 50, 51	Yorkshire Imperial Metals Ltd	Casting and rolling non-ferrous metals	274	29	303
52	Addis Ltd	Brush and plastic ware	150	150	300*
53	Aeron Thomas & Son Ltd	Joinery manufacturers	48	2	50
57	Blackvale Products Ltd	Road metalling material	7	—	7
58	White Rock Metals Ltd	Scrap merchants	8	—	8
61	South Wales Sand & Gravel Co. Ltd	Suppliers of slag	6	—	6
62	Bernard Hastie & Co. Ltd	Thermal insulation and sheet metal workers	143	22	165
63	Watney Mann (South Wales)	Beer, wine and spirit suppliers	15	—	15
64	South Wales Patent Metal Box Co. Ltd	Manufacturers of containers for packing tinplate and metal strips	42	29	71

An outline of the
industrial history of
the Lower Swansea
Valley

Table 2.5—*contd.*

Plot No.	Name of occupier	Type of business	Number of employees Male	Female	Total
65	Cambrian United Dairies Ltd	Milk bottling and distribution depot	190	45	235
72	Swansea Steel Products Ltd	Steel stockists	30	1	31
73	Nash Foundry Co. Ltd	Iron founders	4	—	4
74	Road & Rail Wagons Ltd	Railway wagon repairing	53	3	56
		Grand totals	2,960	502	3,462

* by 1966

the position in September 1961; subsequent changes are illustrated in the Appendix to Chapter 11 of this report. The physical fragmentation of the valley is therefore overlaid with multiple legal interests which further complicate its redevelopment.

Table 2.6 Land ownership in the Lower Swansea Valley, September 1961

	Land Acres to nearest acre
A *Freehold interests*	
Richard Thomas & Baldwins Ltd	155
National Smelting Co. Ltd	125
Principality Property Co. Ltd	179
The Somerset Trust	173
Yorkshire Imperial Metals Ltd	114
George Cohen Sons & Co. Ltd	74
Total	820
Vivians White Rock Ltd	30
Birds (Swansea) Ltd	29
Davies, Middleton & Davies Ltd	29
Aeron Thomas & Son Ltd	25
British Railways	24
R. Parkhouse & Sons Ltd	20
Swansea Brick Works Ltd	11
Bernard Hastie & Co. Ltd	8
Owning five acres or less: 14 owners	41
Total (excluding railway lines and river)	1,037
B *Leasehold interests*	
Richard Thomas & Baldwins Ltd	86
Wales Gas Board	38
Blackvale Products Ltd	32
South Wales Sand & Gravel Co. Ltd	16
Yorkshire Imperial Metals Ltd	15
A. H. Thomas Metals Ltd	5
Swansea Foundry & Engineering Co. Ltd	3
Less than 3 acres: 7 owners	8
	203

C *Licences for hardcore extraction*
In addition to the above, approximately 90 acres of tip are excavated for hardcore under licence by a number of contractors.

Such a situation is not peculiar to Swansea or to South Wales. Derelict land is the unhappy heritage of unplanned industrial occupation and is a feature of many areas of Great Britain. It is part of the national problem of obsolescence—of old buildings, of antiquated layouts, of depressing ugliness—that began to appear at the turn of the nineteenth century and intensified as mining and heavy industry declined. It is a problem that calls for vigorous action. This, however, is the situation in the Swansea Valley and the reasons why it continues are now considered.

Bibliography

1 W. O. Alexander, *A Brief Review of the Development of the Copper, Zinc and Brass Industries in Great Britain*, Murex Review, 1955, Vol. I, No. 15.
2 W. Alexander and A. Street, *Metals in the Service of Man*, Penguin Books, 1964.
3 J. T. Barber, *A Tour Throughout South Wales and Monmouthshire*, J. Nichols & Son, 1803, p. 25.
4 D. B. Barton, *Copper Mining in Cornwall and Devon*, Truro, 1961.
5 *The British Mannesman Tube Company Ltd. A Brief Historical Sketch*, 1915. (Anonymous pamphlet, University of Swansea College Library.)
6 E. H. Brooke, *Chronology of the Tinplate Works of Great Britain* and Appendix. 2 vols., Cardiff, 1944 and 1949.
7 N. Brown and C. Turnbull, *A Century of Copper*, London, 1899.
8 C. F. Cliffe, *The Book of South Wales, the Bristol Channel, Monmouthshire and the Wye*, 2nd edn., G. F. Carrington, 1848.
9 H. W. E. Davies, 'The Development of the Industrial Landscape of Western South Wales during the nineteenth and twentieth centuries', unpublished M.Sc. (Econ.) Thesis, University of London, 1955.
10 Rev. J. Evans, *Tour Through South Wales*, London, 1804, p. 168.
11 George Grant-Francis, *Charters Granted to Swansea*, London, 1867, p. 7. Charter of 1305 from William de Breos, Lord Marcher of Gower, to the Burgesses of Swansea.
12 George Grant-Francis, *The Smelting of Copper in the Swansea District*, 2nd edn., London, 1881, p. 153.
13 Charles Hadfield, *The Canals of South Wales and the Border*, London, 1960.
14 H. Hamilton, *The English Brass and Copper Industries to 1800*, London, 1926, p. 336.
15 J. R. Harris, *The Copper King*, Liverpool University Press, 1964.
16 W. H. Jones, *History of the Port of Swansea*, Carmarthen, 1922.
17 W. E. Minchinton, *The British Tinplate Industry*, Oxford, 1957.
18 Morris MSS., University College of Swansea Library.
19 J. U. Nef, *The Rise of the British Coal Industry*, London, 1932, 2 vols., Vol. I.
20 H. O'Neill, *Metallurgia*, December, 1956, p. 269.
21 John Percy, *Metallurgy (Copper)*, London, 1861.
22 W. Pole, *The Life of Sir William Siemens*, John Murray, 1888.
23 H. Pollins, 'The Swansea Canal', *The Journal of Transport History*, Vol. I.
24 *Proceedings of the Subscribers to the Fund for obviating the inconvenience arising from the smoke produced by smelting copper ores*, Swansea, 1823.
25 F. H. T. Rhodes, *The Evolution of Life*, Penguin Books, 1962.
26 R. O. Roberts, 'Development and Decline of the Non-Ferrous Metal Industries in South Wales', *Cymmrodorion Transactions*, 1956.
27 R. O. Roberts and D. Elwyn Gibbs, 'Early Copper Smelting in West Glamorgan', *South Wales and Monmouthshire Record Society*, IV, 1955.
28 J. D. Scott, *The Siemens Brothers*, London, 1958.
29 E. A. Smith, *The Zinc Industry*, London, 1918.
30 Swansea. *The New Swansea Guide*, Swansea, 1823, p. 32.
31 *Transactions South Wales Institute of Engineers*, Vol. IX, 1874–5, p. 117.
32 D. Trevor Williams, *The Economic Development of Swansea and of the Swansea District to 1921*, University of Wales Press Board, 1940.
33 Thomas Williams, *Report on the Copper Smoke*, Swansea, October 1854, p. 101.

Authorship

This chapter was written by K. J. Hilton. R. O. Roberts helped with material on the copper industry and Emlyn Evans with material on the zinc industry in the Lower Swansea Valley.

3 A case history of derelict land in Swansea 1900 to 1966

At the turn of the century, then, the Lower Valley was prosperous but ugly, prosperous because steel, tinplate and spelter with ancillary industry had taken over from copper, ugly because the meadows on the valley floor were submerged beneath man-made mountains of ash and slag and its flanks swept by fume and covered with sooty fall-out from the furnaces.

There is little evidence that the ugliness of this landscape troubled the consciences of those who were concerned with the business of creating it. The ground landlords and most of the entrepreneurs lived out of the sight and smell of the works, the employees and the townspeople accepted conditions into which most of them had been born and to which they were accustomed. It is the visitors to whom we are principally indebted for critical descriptions of the area.*

It was an age of *laissez faire*; the same kind of situation existed in Staffordshire and the Black Country, in Lancashire, Derbyshire and Shropshire, wherever coal was mined and metal smelted and forged. It was an attitude of mind that persisted until the conscience of society at large stirred, and slowly, but oh so slowly, public controls attempted to check the private spoliation of earth and river and sky.

In Swansea, as early as 1764, the burgesses resolved to keep the smoke of industry out of the town, but once the Lower Valley was given over to smelting its subsequent inclusion within the Borough did not alter the situation. Long usage had established a valuable prescriptive right to create noise, dirt and smell, which legal action failed to destroy.† In other parts of Great Britain, especially in the mining districts, leases sometimes laid down in detail conditions for the eventual restoration of sites on the termination of working, including the removal and retention of soil for this purpose.‡ Generally speaking, little was attempted in Swansea or elsewhere, either by the landlords or their lessees, to modify in any way the harsh effects of industrial occupation on the landscape, and by implication on the lives of the people who inhabited it. Even when legislation was introduced which was intended to help reclaim derelict industrial land, little was achieved. Attempts by local authorities and Government Departments were frustrated. Some idea of the extent of the national problem and of the pace of reclamation is given in Chapter 13 but it will perhaps be

---

* 'Landore, a spot rich in the renown of its metal and chemical works, but to the casual visitor, ugly with all the ugliness of grime and dust, and mud and smoke and indescribable tastes and odours. S. C. Gamwell, Swansea and District Guide', Swansea, 1880.
† (*a*) See a lawyer's brief for the defence in an action taken against Messrs Pascoe, Grenfell and Sons, c. 1830. Original in the Royal Institution of South Wales, Swansea.
(*b*) 'Swansea smelters enjoy the privilege of pouring dense volumes of thick sulphurous and arsenical smoke from comparatively low chimneys into the atmosphere. . . . This privilege has now in lapse of time become an established right which would not readily be conceded in many other parts of the Kingdom.' John Percy, *Metallurgy* 1861.
‡ Lease dated 1 June 1843 to Richard Blundell by the Trustees of Francis Duke of Bridgewater, quoted in 'Rehabilitation of Derelict Land in the Wigan District', J. K. Molyneux, University of Birmingham, M.A. thesis, May 1961.

A case history
of derelict land
in Swansea
1900–1966

helpful here, using the Swansea experience, to consider the more important reasons which explain why so little has been achieved in the Lower Swansea Valley and elsewhere up to the present.

The first serious effort to tackle the waste land of the Lower Swansea Valley was made by a public officer, George Bell, the Borough Surveyor, who in 1912 presented a report* to the Council in which he proposed that there should be a comprehensive scheme to utilize the tip waste, to create new industrial sites, that the tinplate works in the north of the valley be linked with the docks by a new road and tramway and that industrial housing on 'garden suburb lines' should be developed on the side of the valley at Cefn Hengoed. It will be apparent from the fact that nothing followed this imaginative proposal that Mr Bell was ahead of his time.

Shortly afterwards Britain was involved in the First World War, much of the heavy industry in the valley turned over to war production and all thoughts of its redevelopment were necessarily put aside. After the war there was, as we saw in Chapter 2, a steady revival in the tinplate industry, but coal mining in the valley closed down finally and spelter production contracted into a single works. Between 1920 and 1930 most of the older copper and spelter works closed leaving groups of brick and stone buildings to deteriorate in wind, weather and at the hands of vandals (Plate 6). Around them lay huge piles of furnace debris, no longer actively increasing but static, silent and barren. By the twenties the Swansea canal was semi-derelict, and the last barge was seen in the thirties. This was a time when the process of industrial closure began, a process which gradually overtook the whole area including, by 1960, all the steel and tinplate works.

In spite of the fact that the acreage of industrial waste land in this area increased steadily after the First World War, no further attempt seems to have been made either to improve its services and surroundings or to stimulate the fresh use of old sites. This reflects the inadequacy of the national policy for such areas at this time, and if local feeling was strong, it was not strong enough to persuade the local authority to 'go it alone'. The forging of Government policy for the reclamation of derelict land developed slowly in the fierce heat of unemployment which struck the older industrial regions in the thirties on a scale which had never been experienced before.

In 1932, 36·5 per cent of the working population of Wales was unemployed, in South Wales and Monmouthshire the figure was 41 per cent in July, topped only by West Cumberland with 46 per cent. In the Swansea area the peak was reached earlier, in September 1931, with 24·2 per cent unemployed. Swansea was comparatively well off. It was situated in the western anthracite part of the coalfield. Demand for anthracite was maintained, and serious unemployment due to cyclical movements was avoided.

To meet this situation, the Government first investigated the conditions of the depressed areas and followed this in 1934 with the Special Areas (Development and Improvement) Act 1934, under which two Commissioners were appointed, one for Scotland and one for England and Wales. The Commissioners were given wide powers and a special fund of two million pounds to enable them to take immediate action to relieve the social and economic conditions of these areas.

Unfortunately Swansea's *relative* prosperity excluded it along with Cardiff and Newport

* See Appendix, p. 44.

A case history
of derelict land
in Swansea
1900–1966

from the provisions of this legislation. From the beginning, therefore, the derelict land of the Lower Swansea Valley was placed outside the powers that were available to deal with it. The anomaly of the situation was referred to by the Commissioner for England and Wales in his first report, in these terms:

'In Wales, however, the exclusion of important cities and towns such as Cardiff, Newport and Swansea, has created an artificial boundary within an established region.'

In his second report, the Commissioner drew attention to the fact that in Wales the largest acreage of derelict land lay outside the special area and so could not be touched.

Grants for clearing derelict sites were approved by the Commissioner on condition that there were reasonable prospects of industrial development following the clearance.* This condition should be noted since it has influenced the interpretation of subsequent legislation and has limited in consequence the action which it has been possible to take to deal with derelict land. In order to qualify for grant-aid, derelict land not only had to be within the aid area but its reclamation had to be justified in these strict terms. Because Swansea, as we have seen, was outside the South Wales Special Area in the thirties, nothing was done in the valley between the Wars. With the outbreak of the Second World War in 1939, new legislation was postponed.

In spite of these setbacks, the experience gained in the administration of the Special Areas Acts was valuable. It had shown that more rather than less Government intervention was required. This was confirmed in 1940 by the Royal Commission on the Distribution of Industrial Population (the Barlow Report) which recommended a considerable extension of Government investment in providing the infrastructure for industrial growth in the Special Areas, as well as action to limit the industrial growth of the conurbations especially in the London region. This report influenced Government policy which was presented in a White Paper on Employment in May 1944, and to which effect was given in the Distribution of Industry Act, 1945.

The Act marked an important step forward. The old Special Areas were grouped into larger regions in which Swansea, Newport and Cardiff were finally included, so removing the earlier anomaly. The Board of Trade was given wide powers over industrial location and for the first time the reclamation of derelict land was made a special object of grant-aid. On the face of it, the Act seemed to provide a sufficiently satisfactory combination of powers and grants to enable a start to be made to strengthen the economies of the older industrial regions, to broaden their industrial base and to clear up the mess of the Industrial Revolution.

While the Government was working out a national policy, Swansea Borough Council, as the end of the war approached, also began to think of the employment needs of its demobilized population; memories of the thirties were still poignant. Thoughts were therefore turned towards the development of a light industrial estate on the lines of those developed before the war at Slough and Treforest. A report by the Borough Engineer presented in 1943 recommended, first, that the derelict sites in the Lower Swansea Valley should be acquired and cleared with *Government help* so as to improve the amenities of the

* Cmd 4957, 1935, paragraphs 34 and 55.

A case history
of derelict land
in Swansea
1900–1966

area and to provide sites for new industry, and secondly, that the Council should consider the development of a light industrial estate. The Council proceeded to act on the second proposal first. A site of 230 acres at Fforestfach, north-west of the town centre, was acquired (Figure 3.1) and the first turf cut by His Majesty King George VI on 15 November 1945.

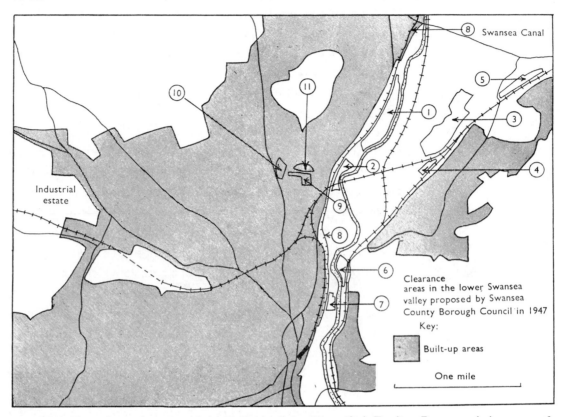

Figure 3.1 The relative location of the Valley and the Fforestfach Trading Estate and the areas of redevelopment proposed by the Swansea Borough Council between 1945 and 1960

Meanwhile, in June 1945, the Distribution of Industry Act had given the Board of Trade all the powers necessary for the development and management of industrial estates, so that it was appropriate that the Board should take over responsibility for the Fforestfach estate, and this was eventually done.

The acquisition and clearance of derelict sites in the Lower Swansea Valley was to prove more difficult. Section 5 of the Distribution of Industry Act empowered the Board to acquire *derelict* land in Development Areas, and to carry out such work as appeared expedient to enable the land to be brought into use or for improving the amenities of the neighbourhood. The Board was also able, with Treasury consent, to make grants towards carrying out such work (Section 5.3).

Swansea County Borough was a scheduled Development Area, and it seemed to the Council in 1945 that there was at last a reasonable prospect of obtaining some Exchequer help with the site clearance in the valley. These hopes came to nothing, mainly for two reasons. First, like the Special Areas Acts, one of the conditions which had to be met in the administration of the 1945 Act was that the measures taken were necessary for the relief of unemployment in the Area. In the light of employment opportunities which would be created by the decision to develop an industrial estate at Fforestfach, and of the already

A case history
of derelict land
in Swansea
1900–1966

relatively low level of unemployment in the County Borough, additional expenditure on the preparation of industrial sites in the Swansea Valley was not considered to be justified. The fact that Swansea was a *scheduled* Development Area was of little consequence.

But there was a second and more cogent reason which had an important bearing on the way in which the Distribution of Industry Act was administered, and accounted in no small measure for the parsimony with which the Board of Trade and the other Government Departments concerned were obliged to act. Between 1950 and 1959 the country experienced an acute economic crisis which obliged the Government to reduce capital expenditure. Grants for the reclamation of derelict land were severely limited, so that during this period the legislation which promised to achieve so much could not be applied effectively.

In 1959 restrictions on capital expenditure were eased and local authorities invited to submit reclamation schemes for completion by the end of March 1960.* Difficulty was now experienced from the fact that the legal interpretation of the term 'derelict' used in Section 5 of the Act meant that the land was of no value to the owner. Since all the derelict sites in the Lower Swansea Valley were in private hands it proved impossible for the Corporation to induce the owners to make this declaration. Eventually, in order to enable some advantage to be gained from the legislation before it was repealed, the Council was able to satisfy the legal niceties in respect of a coal tip which it owned outside the Swansea Valley and this was eventually levelled.

This was the only clearance which it was possible to carry out under the Act in Swansea between 1945 and 1960. Although schemes for eleven sites in the valley area were prepared at various times by the Corporation, at the invitation of the Board of Trade in 1947 and of a Government Committee under the Chairmanship of Lord Lloyd in 1953 (Figure 3.1), nothing was achieved there.

The Distribution of Industry Act was replaced by the Local Employment Act, 1960. Although in some respects an improvement on its predecessor—the definition of derelict land for example was widened to include land that was also neglected and unsightly—the Act marked a reversal of regional location policy. Instead of Development Areas, there were to be smaller Development Districts based on employment exchange areas which in the words of the Act included 'any locality in Great Britain in which in the opinion of the Board of Trade a high rate of unemployment exists or is to be expected . . . and is likely to persist whether seasonally or generally'.

Swansea with its relatively low rate of unemployment could not qualify as a Development District although there was a net outflow of labour from the County Borough which resulted from a lack of employment opportunity in manufacturing industry within it. There were other criticisms of the policy; it was too flexible and resulted in areas listed one year being removed in the next. By 1963, however, a regional policy developed again from studies of the economies of Central Scotland and North-East England. After the change of government in 1964, this trend was strengthened, and in October 1965 Swansea qualified once more for grant-aid under the Act. In January 1966 the Government presented its policy for industrial growth and location† which returned to the Development Area policy of the 1945 Act.

---

* Ministry of Housing and Local Government Circular No. 22/59.
† Cmd 2874, *Investment Incentives*, January 1966.

A case history
of derelict land
in Swansea
1900–1966

So far as the reclamation of derelict land is concerned, the situation remains unchanged. Grants are only available if the land is in a Development Area, although these areas now include nearly all such land in Great Britain, and then only if its reclamation provides employment. The reclamation of derelict land is still not an end in itself although it is the Government's intention to introduce legislation to accomplish this.* It is hoped that the level of the new reclamation grant will be sufficiently high, and its administration sufficiently uncomplicated, to induce local authorities to act quickly so that the Lower Swansea Valley may finally be dealt with.

Besides the legislative deficiencies which have been discussed, there have been special local reasons which have contributed to inaction in the valley. From what has been said, it might appear that the Corporation has lacked initiative in dealing with what is, after all, a local problem. Let us therefore consider the valley in the light of the local situation.

First there is no shortage of land in the County Borough. With 7·8 persons to the acre, the local authority did not need to use derelict land for housing even if the Swansea Valley site was suitable in other respects, which it was not.

Although industrial sites could have been prepared in the valley there was little prospect of their being taken up: there were sites at Fforestfach with all services available which could not be let. It would be unrealistic to expect the Council to prepare industrial sites with little hope of a financial return on the rate expenditure involved. Besides, when the Fforestfach estate was acquired there was less than sixty acres of waste land in the Lower Swansea Valley that could have been used and not all of this was on one site. Industry which has since closed was actively tipping in 1943.

Admittedly something could have been done to improve the appearance of the area: derelict buildings could have been removed and trees planted, but this would have made it necessary for the Council to have acquired the land, or else to have spent the rates on imimproving land in private hands. This is to ignore the fact that there has persisted in Swansea a measure of resentment against those who blighted the land and then withdrew with their fortunes to other parts of the country. The result has been a reluctance to spend rates largely from working-class pockets to put right the depredation created for private profit.

Finally, the size of the area, the vast quantities of its debris, its physical fragmentation, its multiple ownership, all contributed to a feeling that the cost of the physical redevelopment of the area was, in the circumstances, beyond the resources of the County Borough. Government help was looked for and, as we have seen, was not forthcoming.

And so the situation has stagnated and in 1961, when the Project was set up, it seemed likely that it would continue like this indefinitely. A study of the area was an attempt to break through to a new phase of action that would be based on a full understanding of the area's problems, physical, social and economic. The study therefore is seen as simply the first stage in which information is gathered and interpreted, leading, we hope, eventually to the renewal of this devastated land. The following chapters summarize the results of this study.

---

* Cmd 2923, *Local Government Finance, England and Wales*, February 1966, para. 18.

Authorship   *This chapter was written by K. J. Hilton. The author is indebted to L. N. Hopper for his comments on the text and to the Town Clerk of Swansea for permission to read the Corporation's files on the Landore area.*

Appendix

'FLOREAT SWANSEA'

18th January 1912

To the Parliamentary and General Purposes Committee

Mr. Chairman and Gentlemen—

(1).—It is a singular fact that, in the valley of the river Tawe, surrounded by very important works and almost in the heart of industrial Swansea, a tract of land of about 200 acres in extent should still retain its primitive condition. There are no public roads across the land except one very unsatisfactory footway along which thousands of workers pass daily to and from their labours—and this very often is rendered impassable by flood water—and it seems to have been no one's business to see to it that proper intercommunication is afforded and that its development should be conducted on right lines. The land referred to lies between Landore, Morriston, Llansamlet and the Great Western Railway, and is mainly at a level of 20ft. above the sea. On this account the land is subject to flooding from tidal waters from the River Tawe and the flood water from the river and its tributaries above. The sub-soil is alluvial deposit overlying glacial drift below which is strong clay and the coal measures, and it has been proved to demonstration that the whole would form a stable foundation for anything that could be put upon it. The ownership of the soil is vested in His Grace the Duke of Beaufort and the Earl of Jersey, and except for grazing purposes the land is lying idle and practically derelict.

(2).—Signs, however, are now apparent that some of the land is being dealt with for the extension of works, but without any comprehensive scheme for its systematic and proper development, and it is in view of this that I beg to submit for the consideration of the landowners and the Corporation a sketch scheme which, if carried out in a broad-minded and energetic manner, would be to the advantage of all concerned.

(3).—The plans and sections accompanying this report* indicate intercommunication roads across the land which would effectually open it out for development, and provide means of through traffic and communication between important places and the various existing works, and for the many thousands of workers now engaged at the works and those to be hereafter established.

(4).—The level of the land would be raised by at least 15ft., and this could readily be done by the use of the waste products from the works, which at the present time are disposed of in unsightly heaps, to the detriment and inconvenience of the works owners and their neighbours. This level would be above the influence of the tidal waters, and, by the construction of a large culvert, the water of the Ffrendrod Brook and the flood waters from the river would be safely carried away. The water of the Ffrendrod could, however, be made use of as required for works purposes in cooling ponds, etc., and would be of great value in

---

* Not reproduced.

this respect. The existing main road from Morriston to Llansamlet and Neath should be raised above the flood level, and the development of the land in the valley northwards of this main road could be continued as far as Glais, so as to form one comprehensive scheme.

(5).—A trunk roadway could be obtained from a point on the proposed road between Landore to Llansamlet, passing over the Great Western Railway main line, and the Midland Railway, to Upper Bank, and from thence along existing roads, which should, however, be widened, through Foxhole, Pentreguinea and St. Thomas to the Docks. Two immensely valuable benefits of this trunk road would be easy access to the Docks for the vehicles conveying tinplates and other products, and the freeing of the chief business streets of the town of a large part of the heavy haulage traffic.

(6).—The saving in distance from Llansamlet to the Docks by the construction of this road would be about one and one-third miles, and the saving in distance from Llansamlet to Landore by the construction of the roadway shown on the plan instead of along the Morriston route would be one-third of a mile, and the gradients over each would be most favourable. Along the new roadway from Landore to Llansamlet, which should have a width of 120ft. to be in proportion with its length and importance, trunk water and gas mains should be laid for supplies to the works and the suburban districts eastwards, also pipes for electricity, telegraph and telephone cables. A double line of tramway should be laid the whole way for communication with the works and beyond. By this means the workers living in Landore and Llansamlet, etc., would be conveyed to and from their work cheaply, safely and comfortably, and members of their families would be able to convey their food also by this means.

(7).—For the hive of additional workers drawn to the valley by the anticipated establishment of the new works, dwellings could be provided on the hill side at Cefn Hengoed, which is an admirable site for the purpose, and it should be laid out on Garden Suburb lines with all the institutions which are necessary for the well-being of man.

In these scientific days it need not be feared that this site would be prejudiced by the smoke arising from the manufacturing processes in the valley adjoining, as all deleterious constituents of the fumes are now extracted for profitable purposes before discharge into the atmosphere. The ultimate smoke emitted, composed principally of carbon, we are fortunately well used to, and is only regarded as good evidence of the prosperity of the district. This place is most conveniently situated for the dwellings required, and although at present beyond the boundary of the Borough, it must soon—to meet the necessities of expansion—be added to the area under the control of the Council. Swansea is rapidly outgrowing its present boundaries. With the communication roads laid out as suggested, and with tramways, Cefn Hengoed would be in close touch not only with the existing and future works, but also with Llansamlet, Morriston, Landore, St. Thomas, and Swansea, and its inhabitants would be able to reap for themselves and their families full benefit of all the institutions of Swansea for business, education, and the recreations and pleasures of life.

(8).—I now beg to suggest that after this scheme has received the careful consideration of your Committee and the Corporation, and, if approved in principle, it should be formally submitted to the landowners and their agents, and the proprietors of the works, with a view to arrangements being made for carrying it into effect. Whether the Corporation would, in the event of the scheme being approved, pursue a pushful policy in the attraction of works to the sites is a matter worthy of favourable consideration. Industries occupy a high position

A case history
of derelict land
in Swansea
1900–1966

among the prime causes of the growth of towns and cities. They have inherently a high rateable value, but they also produce a contingent rateable value in so far as extra dwellings, shops and other premises are required by those engaged at the factories. I understand that in America the advantage of securing the establishment of works within the areas of cities is so appreciated that land is often given for the purpose, both rent and rates free, for a period. There should be no dearth of works for the occupation of our sites, for not only are there new works constantly being started in the country, but there are the works which find it necessary to move to the ports, so as to relieve themselves of the more or less heavy railway freightage appertaining to inland sites. I believe there is a growing tendency to remove, and therefore towns like Swansea stand to gain thereby, whilst, of necessity, the inland towns from which the works depart must correspondingly suffer. Apparently a city in the North has already acutely felt the loss, due to the closing of a number of its works on account of remoteness from docks.

(9).—Swansea, with its splendid juxtaposition of perfect sites and magnificent docks, its copious water supply and proximity to the coalfields, has all the facilities necessary to successful manufacturing, and, surely, it but requires that its advantages be better known throughout the country and abroad also for its call to be strongly felt. The only objection of which I am aware that industrial site prospectors detect in regard to the Borough is that of rates, but, without erring on the side of optimism, I venture to suggest that the future will see conditions operating to lower rather than raise the local rates.

Possibly your Committee may deem it justifiable, if not necessary, civic advertising, for the Council to circulate attractively prepared hand maps displaying the features and advantages of Swansea for industrial and commercial purposes.

Your obedient servant,

GEORGE BELL,

Borough Surveyor.

References

W. H. Beveridge, *Full Employment in a Free Society*, London, 1944.
A. E. C. Hare, *The Anthracite Coal Industry of the Swansea District*, University of Wales Press Board, 1940.
The Second Industrial Survey of Wales, Cardiff, 1937.

Government publications

An industrial survey of South Wales made for the Board of Trade by the University College of South Wales and Monmouthshire, H.M.S.O., London, 1932.

Reports of Investigations into the Industrial Conditions in Certain Depressed Areas, Cmd 4728, 1934.
The First Report of the Commissioner for the Special Areas (England and Wales), Cmd 4957, 1935.
The Second Report of the Commissioner for the Special Areas (England and Wales), Cmd 5090, 1936.
Report of the Commissioner for the Special Areas in England and Wales for the year ended 30th September 1937, Cmd 5595, 1937.
Report of the Commissioner for the Special Areas in England and Wales for the year ended 30th September 1938, Cmd 5896, 1938.
The Report of the Royal Commission on the Distribution of the Industrial Population, Cmd 6153, 1940.
Employment Policy, Cmd 6527, 1944.
Distribution of Industry, Cmd 7540, 1948.

4 Geology, soil mechanics and foundation engineering

The purpose of the geological survey was to describe the surface and subsurface geology of the Project area and of its immediate surroundings, with particular reference to problems of foundation engineering.

The civil engineering investigations which followed were primarily concerned with the three main foundation problems that emerged: namely the effect of large areas of soft and compressible natural deposits; the influence of fill material, mainly industrial waste, and the dangers from abandoned coal workings, on the foundation of possible future building areas.

The area was first mapped in the field using aerial photographs at a scale of 1/5000. Although this was adequate on the sides of the valley where the rock is abundantly exposed or only buried to a shallow depth, surface mapping provides little information about the deposits of superficial material that underlie the flat valley floor, covering the greater part of the Project area.

A comprehensive collection was made of all available records of previous subsurface investigations in the area. These included the records of the Coal Board, the detailed records of the Swansea Main Drainage excavations and over sixty other boreholes that have been drilled for various purposes by different concerns. The information obtained from these sources gives a clear picture of the subsurface solid geology, particularly in relation to the coal seams and it also gives an indication of the types of drift material to be found on the edge of the Project area. Unfortunately there was very little information from the centre of the valley.

In order to remedy this the Project undertook a series of geophysical traverses using a gravity meter and a shallow depth seismic instrument, both of which were kindly lent by the University College of Cardiff and operated by Dr D. E. T. Bidgood of that College. These traverses across the alluvial floor of the valley provided an indication of the nature of the deposits likely to be found under the recent marsh and peat surface. They also revealed the approximate shape of the buried valley in the solid rock.

On the basis of the geophysical investigations and the conclusions drawn from all other available sources the Project sank five boreholes in the area—two were duplicated making a total of seven, of which four reached the rock floor of the buried valley. The data derived from these boreholes greatly increased the amount of information available about the superficial deposits and their engineering properties and it also served to correlate the geophysical results.

Coal mining and the valley sides

The Project area lies almost entirely on a flat alluvial plain at the bottom of a comparatively steep-sided valley. The valley floor is about twenty feet above the sea level, but the surrounding hillsides rise to four hundred feet or more. The mouth of the river Tawe has to flow through a narrow gorge between Kilvey Hill and Townhill and here the bare rock hillsides descend steeply, almost into the river; it is only at the north of the Project area that the flat valley floor spreads out to a width of half a mile or more. Even here the hillsides are often steep and bare rock is exposed.

The Project area lies at the southern upturned edge of the great basin of Carboniferous rocks which forms the South Wales Coalfield. At the south of the area the Kilvey-Townhill ridge rising steeply from the sea, is formed of hard Llynfi Sandstone which lies at the top of the Lower Coal Series. North of this there is a shallow gully following the outcrop of the Dyfatty Seam which forms the boundary between the Lower Coal Series and the Pennant Series; then the land rises again over the massive, frequently crossbedded sandstones which form the bulk of Kilvey Hill and which outcrop in great scars down the sides for some way to the north.

In this southern part of the area the rocks are inclined northwards at angles of between thirty and forty degrees to the horizontal, but farther north the dip becomes less steep and in the Morriston and Llansamlet areas is almost negligible, certainly less than five degrees. This has meant that a coal seam exposed on the sides of the valley, or even on the steeper-dipping Kilvey Hill, could be mined with comparative ease from the surface. Further, where coal seams were mined from shafts sunk to depths of a thousand feet or more, the roads radiating from the shafts could run almost horizontally along the seams.

Mining of the local coal began in the fourteenth century on the exposed seams on Kilvey Hill and by the time the last pit in the area closed a few years ago most of the workable coal had been removed from the area. With the exception of a barrier left to the west of Callands Pit, it is unlikely that further mining will be attempted, particularly as all the old workings are now flooded.

The coal seams which were most extensively worked were, in their correct sequence and with their approximate depths in feet below ground level on the Morriston-Llansamlet road:

Four Feet Seam	150
Five Feet Seam	530
Six Feet or Graigola Seam	900
Three Feet Seam	950
Two Feet Seam	1,080
Hughes Seam	1,800

Owing to the occurrence of large faults running NNE–SSW, different levels of rock are exposed on different parts of the valley sides. Thus, although even the Four Feet Seam underlies the Morriston-Llansamlet road, the stratigraphically lower Five Feet Seam is exposed in old open-cast workings at about 300 ft above sea level around the top of the Morriston hillside on the west of the valley.

These extensive underground workings were serviced from numerous pits and adits scattered around the valley. Many of these have been filled in and there remains no record of them; others have been more recently closed and cemented over and their site can be found today. The main coal mines were at Pentre, where within a small area there were five important pits and numerous subsidiary shafts from which the Five Feet, Six Feet, Three Feet and Two Feet Seams were worked over an extensive area. There were several pits near the present Wychtree Bridge, below Morriston, including the Copper Pit and Herring Pit; and on the other side of the valley there were a number of collieries at Llansamlet. Of these, one, Marsh Pit, was near the centre of the valley and must have provided a good section of the superficial deposits overlying rock, but no record of these has been found.

In an area so extensively undermined by old coal workings, the possibility of subsidence, owing to collapse of overlying rock into old workings, has to be considered. In fact there have been no reports of subsidence of this kind in the area, and this has been attributed to the strength of the Pennant sandstone; but it is also considered that the flooded condition of these pits has been an important factor in preventing subsidence of the roof rock.

In order to appreciate the possible subsidence at ground level arising from the collapse of abandoned underground workings, it is necessary that the nature and extent of the worked coal seams near the surface is known. On the final closure of the pits in the area, the National Coal Board collected the available plans and these give a general picture of the extent of the workings. These plans have been summarized and the known extent of the underground workings is shown in Figure 4.1.

It is essential that prior to any construction work being carried out in the area, old pit shafts, adits and air vents should be accurately located as the discovery of these by heavy plant during site clearing operations would be a very late stage to take precautions against shaft failures and could increase considerably the cost of construction. The present position regarding information as to the location of these shafts, etc., is summarized in Figure 4.1. These locations are based on the preliminary geological report and on a map prepared by the Mineral Valuer, Wales (1964). It is not claimed that this gives a complete record of all disused shafts but it pinpoints the areas in which such features are most likely to be found. For a particular construction project where there is any doubt as to the possibility of these openings existing, it is suggested that a resistivity survey using constant separation traverses should be employed as an aid to exact location.

A comprehensive survey of existing buildings in the Project area has been carried out in order to ascertain whether there is any evidence of settlement which could be attributed to mining subsidence. Although evidence of relative movement was found in five areas, in all cases it could be reasonably assumed that the settlement and resulting structural cracks were due to factors other than mining subsidence. A typical example of differential movement attributable to causes other than mining subsidence in an area where extensive underground workings are known to exist is the case of the National Smelting Company's Swansea Vale Works (Plot 17). This works is sited in the vicinity of the Marsh, Fire Engine, Garden and Six Pit mining complex where the Five Feet Seam is at approximately −200 ft O.D. and site level is in the region of +60 O.D.

Boreholes sunk by civil engineering contractors in this area show that the fill, consisting

Figure 4.1 The extent of coal workings

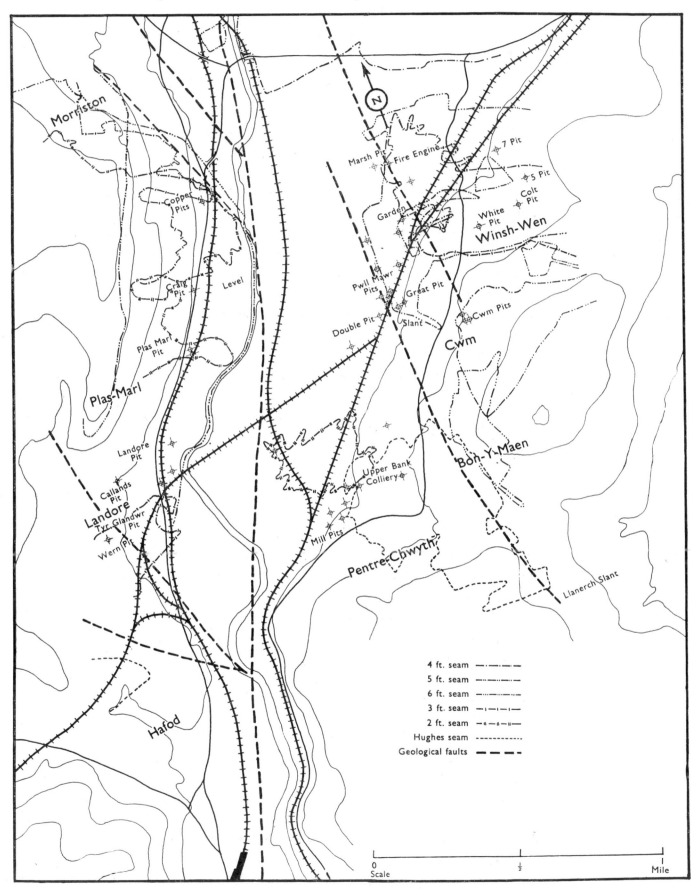

Morriston

Copper Pits

Craig Pit

Level

Plas Marl Pit

Plas-Marl

Landore Pit

Callands Pit

Landore

Tyr Glandwr Pit

Wern Pit

Hafod

Marsh Pit · Fire Engine

7 Pit

5 Pit

Garden Pit

Colt Pit

White Pit

Winsh-Wen

Pwll Mawr Pits

Great Pit

Cwm Pits

Double Pit

Slant

Cwm

Boh-Y-Maen

Upper Bank Colliery

Mill Pits

Pentre-Chwyth

Llanerch Slant

4 ft. seam	—·—·—
5 ft. seam	———
6 ft. seam	···———···
3 ft. seam	—ı—ı—ı—
2 ft. seam	—ıı—ıı—ıı—
Hughes seam	··············
Geological faults	— — — —

0 Scale   ½   Mile

mainly of spelter waste, on which some of the present buildings are constructed is up to 40 ft thick. Below this lies a boulder clay which, when tested in triaxial compression at lateral pressures approximating to its overburden pressures, gave results indicating a high shear strength.

The foundations of buildings in this area which had been founded directly on the fill had been designed on the basis of a safe bearing capacity of $\frac{1}{2}$ ton/ft^2, but despite this modest loading, differential movement and consequent cracking has occurred. More recently piles bearing in the boulder clay have been used as foundations and there have been no reports of relative movement in these cases. On this evidence it is considered reasonable in this case to attribute structural movements to a settlement in the fill material rather than to mining subsidence, although the Works area is in the region of a mining complex as previously stated. The results of the survey of existing buildings within the Project area confirms the geologist's findings of no reported mining subsidence in the area.

The lack of mining subsidence has been attributed to the strength of the country rock, the Pennant Sandstone, and to the flooding of the underground workings. Mr D. Ivor Evans,[1] * in strongly opposing the suggested extraction of water from the Callands pit, suggested that subsidence is unlikely over waterlogged collieries. Experiments in the Soil Mechanics Laboratory at University College, Swansea, using the electrical analogue technique for the study of ground water flow, showed that if openings such as pit headings, located at depth, are pumped and the water level in such openings lowered, the hydraulic gradients set up in the region of the heading, by the inflow of water to make good the deficiency caused by pumping, can be very high. It is, however, difficult to make an estimate of the exact order of magnitude of these gradients.

Since high hydraulic gradients mean that the seepage forces transferred by viscous drag are large, this can result in high effective stresses being placed on the rock in the vicinity of the opening. If it can be reasonably assumed that the majority of the coal workings were of the pillar and stall type as opposed to the longwall method, then considerable extra stress would be thrown on the pillars as a result of the seepage forces described above.

In order to obtain an estimate of the possible magnitude of these stresses the maximum increase would be that occurring when the water was extracted from the workings at a rate greater than the inflow of compensating water. In this case the total stresses would become effective stresses and at a depth of 200 ft, for example, the increase would be of the order of $5\frac{1}{2}$ tons per square foot which gives strong support for Mr Evans's recommendation.

There is one site in the area at which water is being pumped from old workings. This is on Plot 17 where Swansea Vale Works extract about 2·8 million gallons per week from the old Six Pit. Unfortunately no records exist as to the amount of water that was required to be pumped from this pit when it was operational. Water has, however, been extracted continuously since 1961, but there has been no evidence of lowering of the ground water table and no case reported of the source running dry. It would therefore appear that the water is being replenished at a rate equal to that of extraction and for all practical purposes regarding stressing of the workings they may be considered as being continuously waterlogged.

* References are given on p. 61.

Although, on the basis of the above arguments, it would appear reasonable to expect settlement following extraction of large quantities of water from abandoned workings, it must nevertheless be recognized that the presence of water in such workings has an undesirable effect with regard to the stresses developed at depth following the placing of new structures.

This effect is probably best illustrated as follows:

With the workings dry, the initial effective stress is given by

$$\sigma = \gamma H \qquad \left\{ \begin{array}{l} \gamma = \text{bulk density} \\ H = \text{depth below surface} \end{array} \right\}$$

The increase in effective stress due to the load at its surface is $\Delta\sigma$ (say) so that an increased stress of $\dfrac{\Delta\sigma \times 100 \text{ per cent}}{\sigma}$ occurs. If, however, the workings are flooded the initial effective stress is

$$\sigma_\omega = (\gamma - \gamma_\omega)H \qquad (\gamma_\omega = \text{density of water})$$
$$\simeq \frac{\sigma}{2}$$

and the increase in effective stress becomes $\dfrac{\Delta\sigma \times 100 \text{ per cent}}{\sigma/2}$ which is twice the effect for the original case of dry workings.

It is known that there are worked seams at 84 feet below ground level at Double Pit, 151 feet below ground level at Charles Pit and 174 feet below ground level at Tir Glandwr, and it is therefore convenient to consider the effect on flooded and dry seams at depths of 100 feet, 150 feet and 200 feet below the surface of, say, four buildings with the following dimensions and loads:

(a)   100 feet × 50 feet at 2 tons/square foot
(b)   200 feet × 200 feet at 2 tons/square foot
(c)   100 feet × 50 feet at 3 tons/square foot
(d)   50 feet × 50 feet at 3 tons/square foot.

The changes in stress at depths under the centre of these areas due to the placing of these loads at the surface is given in the following table, based on a bulk density of 130 pounds per cubic foot, and a submerged density of 67·5 pounds per cubic foot.

Depth in feet	Initial effective stress ton/ft²		Per cent. increase of initial stress caused by structure							
			(a)		(b)		(c)		(d)	
	Dry	Wet	Dry	Wet	Dry	Wet	Dry	Wet	Dry	Wet
100	5·8	3·0	6·9	13·2	24·0	46·5	10·3	20·0	5·1	10·0
150	8·6	4·5	2·1	4·0	11·5	22·0	3·0	5·8	1·4	2·7
200	11·6	6·0	0·86	1·6	6·9	13·0	1·3	2·5	0·86	1·6

The above table shows that it is possible to get considerable increments of stress even down to depths of 200 feet, but the criterion is the strength of the rock compared with the probable stressing. However, whereas the proximity of the existing stressing to the ultimate strength is not known, it is possible to estimate the extent of the increase of stress which will take place. The opinion as to whether subsidence will occur due to this stressing will be a matter of engineering judgment since the known facts, regarding existing structures in the area sited over mining complexes, are limited. A study of the foundations plans and loads imposed in the area of the Swansea Vale Works would, however, serve as a useful guide and reference may be made to the company regarding the relevant details.

It is necessary to point out that care should be taken on the steep sides of the valley where quarrying and open-cast mining to an almost excessive degree, particularly in the region of Graig Brickworks, has oversteepened sides of the valley, increasing the tendency of soil creep and, more disastrously, landslip. These tendencies are clearly visible on the high roads along the sides of the valley, Trewyddfa Road and Graig Road in particular.

Coal seams, of course, form only a very small proportion of the solid rock exposed around and underlying the Project area, but they are of far the greatest economic importance. Nonetheless, the extensive outcrops of massive grey Pennant sandstone although inter-bedded with rubbly shales have been quarried and used for building stone and for road aggregate. Also associated with the Pennant sandstones is a thick bed of fireclay which is exposed at Graig Brickworks where it was extensively quarried for use in the furnaces of the neighbouring steelworks, but in common with the rest of the quarrying and mining operations in the area this is no longer worked.

The Project area is thus surrounded, and underlain at depth, by a series of rocks which generally offer good engineering characteristics and which have in the past been of considerable economic value, but the actual area of the Project itself lies almost entirely on a flat, marshy plain which from the evidence of valley sections, from boreholes sunk a few miles upstream and from other rather indirect information, appears to be of considerable thickness above the rock floor. Information about these deposits was the most vital to the Project and the least easily obtainable.

Superficial deposits

Three types of superficial deposit are found on the surface: Glacial Till (so-called boulder clay), gravel and alluvium. In fact there is so much variation within the first category that it grades from true boulder clay right through to clean gravels, frequently without any marked junction. This assorted glacial material is found over a good deal of the valley sides, especially in the northern part of the area. On the Morriston hillside it is near to true boulder clay, but at Cwm on the east of the valley the clay content is much less and the deposit is more an amalgam of stones and rock fragments, sands, earth and gravel. At Llansamlet there is a considerable surface deposit of washed gravel quite distinct from the ill-assorted till, but in fact this grades southwards into the deposits mentioned at Cwm. At Pentre there are similar great mounds of gravel which still form distinct features, even though the area has been built over. At Pentre, these gravels are probably of great thickness, but over the rest of the valley sides, although there are extensive deposits of drift, they are seldom more than about twenty feet thick and rest directly on rock.

In the centre of the valley the picture is different. Much of the valley floor is now covered with slag and other waste material, but this has been dumped on a flat alluvial flood plain which is still largely waterlogged wherever it is visible. The surface deposits here are marshy peat and riverborne flood gravels, sands and silt which are between five and ten feet thick.

On the edges of this flood plain, where the glacial deposits on the valley sides are in contact with the alluvium of the centre, we have a fairly extensive coverage of old borehole records. Generally, these have been drilled as part of site investigations for large or heavy buildings. The greatest concentration is at the site of the new flats recently erected in the Brynmelyn and Dyfatty area; there are a fair number of records from the north of the docks, and again from the Rose Tip area, the Wychtree Bridge and the Swansea Vale Works.

Not all of these boreholes were drilled down to rock, but they do give a record of the superficial deposits encountered. Unfortunately they are almost all on the edges of the flood plain and so pass through extremely variable drift deposits which are derived partly from the valley sides, partly from glacial deposition and partly from alluvial action. The result is that no two holes, however close together, show the same section, and therefore it is impossible to use their data to extrapolate over the smallest distance in any but the most general terms.

In view of this, and the fact that there were only four boreholes from the centre of the valley where results might be expected to be more consistent, a simple geophysical survey was attempted using a seismic refractometer and a gravity meter. Owing to the unsuitability of the surface deposits—slag or marsh—the seismic survey was of limited success. It did give an indication of a medium-velocity layer underlying the alluvium at between five and ten feet, and it gave an indication in three places of the depth to rock.

The gravity survey was more successful, although once again the areas of extensive slag deposits had to be avoided. Eight traverses were completed across the valley, two of them well outside the Project area in order to correlate the interpretation with known borehole data. The results gave an indication of the shape of the rock floor of the valley and of its depth which tied in very closely with that derived by deduction from exposed rock contours and other methods. The survey was most successful in the more open northern part of the area; in the south, where the valley becomes very narrow, where the topography is irregular and where there are numerous heavy buildings in a completely built-up area, the results were less certain.

The geophysical surveys were carried out on instruments loaned by the University College of South Wales and Monmouthshire, Cardiff, under the direction of Dr D. E. T. Bidgood of that College. The Project is grateful to Professor Anderson for loaning the instruments and to Dr Bidgood for his work on interpretation of the results. It was on the basis of the geophysical work, combined with all available information that had been collected, that sites for several boreholes were selected for drilling by the Project itself. The number of boreholes was also controlled by economic considerations. The detailed investigation of the whole of the area within the Project's boundaries by this method was not envisaged, due to the obvious high cost and to the fact that any potential user of a particular site would in any case carry out the more detailed investigation necessary to determine the site's suitability for the particular project in mind.

The work of drilling five exploratory boreholes was carried out under a contract which required:

(a) the collection of disturbed samples of soil for identification purposes at every change of stratum and at 2 ft 6 in intervals throughout each stratum;

(b) the obtaining of 4-in diameter undisturbed samples from each interval of plastic or organic material. and at intervals of 10 ft in such material where appropriate;

(c) *in-situ* testing of all soft plastic and organic soils using approved vanes and of all non-cohesive soils by means of standard penetration equipment at intervals of 5 ft where suitable;

(d) collection of ground water samples and the recording of water levels in the boreholes when first located, and at the commencement and completion of each day's work;

(e) the production of completed borehole logs and the transportation of all samples for identification and testing to the Soil Mechanics Laboratory of the Engineering Department at University College, Swansea.

Work started on 21 February 1964 and was completed on 12 March 1964. Seven holes were bored, six using a Shell and Auger rig (total depth 395 ft) and one by rotary drilling (160 ft deep). Despite variations, which arose during the course of the borehole operations, it was found possible, with the contractor's cooperation, to keep the total expenditure within the original tender cost.

Difficulty was experienced in obtaining 4-in diameter undisturbed samples from the softer clays and silty clays that were encountered. By using three 4-in diameter sample tubes joined together to form a tube of overall length 4 ft 6 in, the difficulty was partly overcome, but it proved impossible to obtain samples of these materials at depths exceeding 50 ft, even when using this equipment. This somewhat restricted the soils testing programme and limited to a certain extent the information on the engineering properties of the deposits, making it necessary to rely more than is usual on the results of the standard penetration tests which were methodically carried out through all strata in each borehole.

Engineering properties of the superficial deposits on the valley floor

The geological report[2] gives a general description of the nature of the superficial deposits underlying the flood plain of the Tawe and offers an explanation of the conditions under which these deposits may have been laid down. This may be summarized as the blocking of the southern end of the valley behind which a large lake developed allowing for the accumulation of silts and other fine-grained material. The succession was probably disturbed by intermittent flooding resulting in the fine deposits being interspersed with sands and gravels. An overall picture of the distribution and approximate boundaries of these lacustrine deposits is given in Figure 4.2.

The study of the engineering properties of the superficial deposits fell into two broad categories; the laboratory testing of the undisturbed samples of the fine-grained materials, and the *in situ* testing of the coarser deposits from which it was not practicable to obtain undisturbed samples.

Laboratory tests were made on the limited number of undisturbed samples obtained from the boring operations and on all these samples triaxial compression, oedometer and consistency tests were carried out. Undrained triaxial tests on these samples showed that all were of low shear strength of values between 300 and 600 pounds/ft² although stiffer material was found at the extreme north end of the Project area where a shear strength of 1,100 pounds/ft² was recorded for a sample obtained from 7 to 10 ft O.D.

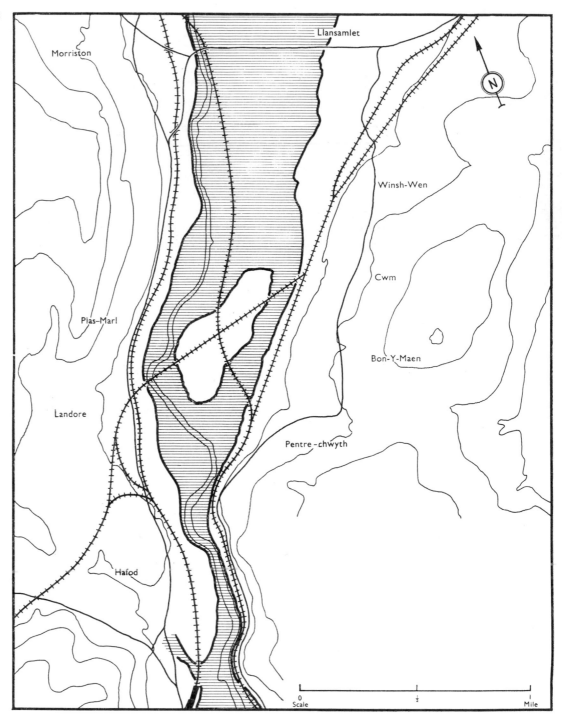

Figure 4.2 The lacustrine deposits

Oedometer tests, to determine the settlement characteristics, were carried out for pressure ranges $0–\frac{1}{4}–\frac{1}{2}–1–2–3–4$ tons/ft^2. The coefficients of compressibility (m_v) were determined directly from changes in sample thickness thus obviating the necessity for determining changes in void ratios throughout the tests, and the coefficients are reported for specific pressures rather than for pressure ranges. The coefficients of consolidation (c_v) were determined for the same pressure increments and these showed a variation with

Engineering properties
of the superficial
deposits on the valley
floor

pressure in the lower range, but there was a tendency to a constant value for pressures in excess of 2 tons/ft².

Preliminary investigations, prior to the exploratory borings, suggested the possibility of very soft layers occurring immediately below the topsoil. Since the extent of these layers was not known it was decided to specify that *in-situ* vane tests should be carried out in those upper soft layers immediately they were encountered. These tests were carried out where practicable, but an examination of the borehole logs has shown that the problem of the soft layer just below ground surface is overshadowed by the problem of the extensive soft deposits encountered at greater depth.

Standard penetration tests were carried out at suitable intervals throughout the boring operations, and in addition to their normal use of supplying information regarding the properties of sands and gravels encountered they were used to give a general indication of the condition of the silts from which it was not possible to obtain undisturbed samples.

The triaxial and consolidation tests on the limited number of samples obtained indicate that the deposits of the finer materials, that is the silts and clays, are in the main soft and highly compressible, with shear strengths of the order of 500 lb/ft² on average and co-efficients of compressibility in the range of 0·02 ft²/ton for pressures of 1 ton/ft². These figures are quoted to give a general indication, and for greater detail reference should be made to Appendix D of the detailed Study Report.[3]

It is interesting to note that the standard penetration tests taken in the vicinity of the undisturbed samples show a broad correlation between number of blows and shear strength. An examination of the borehole logs indicated that where no laboratory tests of the fine deposits were made a figure of 40 lb/ft² per blow could be a useful guide to the shear strength of these deposits.

Reference to Figure 4.2, which shows the extent of the lacustrine deposits, the results of the laboratory tests summarized in Appendix D of the Study Report[3] along with the depths of the deposits as revealed by the borehole logs quoted in its Appendix C, exhibits clearly the need for care in considering the types of structures to be erected in the valley floor area, particularly in the northern half. The presence of large quantities of tip materials which have been in position for many years will have modified and improved the shear and settlement characteristics of the alluvium, but it must always be borne in mind that these deep deposits of relatively soft compressible materials do exist and that the possibility of overstressing these layers with consequent large settlements must in all cases be carefully examined.

Engineering properties and problems associated with fill material in the Project area

A considerable proportion (approximately 50 per cent) of the Project area is covered with fill material of various kinds. These include:

Coal tip waste
Iron and steel works slag
Non-ferrous works slag
Old factory waste
Current factory waste

Current urban tipping

Rubble from ruins of industrial buildings

A large amount of the fill has probably been placed by random end tipping or conveyor tipping in thick layers; in addition many tips contain cooled molten slag. It is unlikely that the fill was originally in a very compact state, but this condition would improve with time in a varying manner, compaction generally increasing with depth.

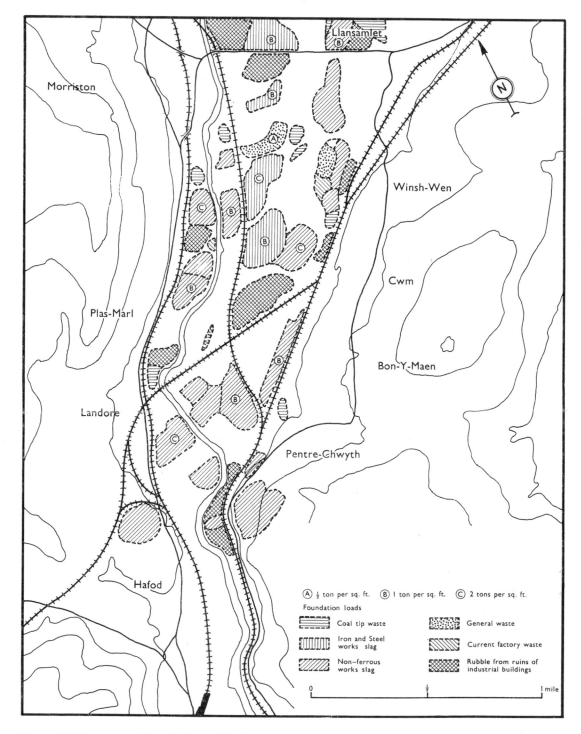

Figure 4.3 Tip materials and derived loadings

The extent of the tip areas has been surveyed and the location of these tips, with a broad classification of the material they contain, is given in Figure 4.3. For a more detailed statement of the nature of the fill material in any particular locality, reference should be made to Appendix A of the Study Report.[3]

Fill is generally heterogeneous in texture, rarely very dense and often contains a considerable proportion of voids. With the large areas involved, it was not possible to obtain extensive and detailed information of the engineering properties of the fill. Indeed, in some areas, the very nature of the fill, consisting as it does of very large inclusions of cooled molten slag, prevents a rationalized classification of engineering properties of the material. In other areas the presence of cavities due to buried cellars or old kilns makes meaningless any attempt at classification in terms of density, shear strength and settlement characteristics as would be normal practice for homogeneous fill. Further, since the report of R. D. Worrall[4] suggests the necessity of a reappraisal of existing tip levels, any large effort expended in detailed work on tip properties could not have been justified.

There are, however, areas of relatively homogeneous fill where it was possible to carry out certain density and classification tests, and the results of these tests are set out in Appendix E of the Study Report.[3] It should, however, be stated that these tests gave only a broad indication of the properties of the fill in any particular area, and in certain instances emphasized the wide variations that can occur in a relatively small area.

In any development scheme a large part of the tip material would have to be built on, or used for filling. Both cases give rise to many problems, the main of which are the difficulties associated with building on the fill material in its present state or on the fill which has been moved and recompacted. In certain areas, because of the nature of the fill, problems will arise when it will be necessary to carry foundations down through the fill to harder strata beneath.

As has been stated, fill is generally heterogeneous and wherever possible steps should be taken to reduce the extent of the heterogeneity. This is particularly so in the area where cavities due to buried cellars or old furnaces occur. Under building loads these conditions give rise to differential settlement between adjacent foundations causing the structure to crack and distort. It would be advisable to destroy old furnaces completely to ensure that they do not collapse when loaded. In any case they represent a potential source of danger, forming as they do a passage for the supply of air to the interior of tips, thus making tip fires more likely.

Many types of fill contain chemicals which are harmful to building materials, and it is important that these are adequately investigated prior to construction work below ground level. Nowadays this is routine testing in any detailed and localized site investigation, and it is anticipated that this work would normally be done before construction was contemplated in a particular area. Injurious chemicals are more likely to occur in ferrous and non-ferrous tips, household and factory refuse tips. The information collected on this aspect of the fill material in the Project area, although indicating the presence of harmful chemicals in certain areas, did not reveal concentrations such as could not be dealt with by well-established engineering practice.

A study was made of the allowable bearing capacity of the fill material in the Project area and the derived loadings are summarized in Figure 4.3. These bearing capacities, which vary from $\frac{1}{2}$ ton/ft^2 to 2 tons/ft^2, are based on a study of the type of fill material, its history and comparative tests which have been carried out. It must be emphasized that the allowable loadings given in Figure 4.3 are approximate loadings for preliminary schemes and estimates only, and must be confirmed by further investigation of the particular area in question before detailed designs are contemplated.

Apart from an assessment of the allowable bearing capacity, the location of buildings on fill material automatically gives rise to the problem of overcoming differential settlement due to the heterogeneity of the fill material itself. Such differential settlement can, if certain precautions are not taken, lead to distortion of the structure with subsequent cracking and dislocation of the services to the building. One method commonly used to overcome this problem is to use flexible construction such as lightly clad steelframed factory buildings, sectional precast concrete office buildings and houses and bungalows of light construction on fairly heavily reinforced rafts. An alternative solution is to take special precautions with the building foundations, for example by the use of large reinforced strip and pad type footings for walls and columns which will reduce the loadings on the fill and also tend to span regions of uneven settlement.

These methods of dealing with the problem of differential settlement assume no measures taken to improve the condition of the fill itself. Modern civil engineering techniques, such as grout injection into the voids of the fill, can be used to improve the bearing capacity of the fill and reduce the risks associated with differential settlement. Another method of improving the suitability of the fill for building purposes is the 'vibro replacement' method whereby stone skeleton foundations are formed within the material. Vibro replacement is a method of soil stabilization which is relatively new to the United Kingdom but it is claimed that if the normal requirement is 20 to 30-ft piles of any type, the cost of vibro replacement is of the order of half to two-thirds of that of piling. The method may be used either to transfer structural loads from pad or strip footings through soft superficial deposits to underlying suitable bearing strata, or to form a thick compact stabilized layer to distribute the structural loads and reduce differential settlements to acceptable values. It may well be that this method, or something similar which may be developed later, would be of particular use on the tip materials in the Project area.

One obvious method of overcoming the differential settlement problem is by siting buildings on the fill at positions of old demolished buildings, since these will have caused preloading on the fill and if the contemplated loadings are comparable very little settlement should occur. A survey of existing and demolished buildings was carried out and for details of these reference should be made to Appendix A and accompanying maps in the original Study Report.[3]

As has been previously stated, the removal of fill from one area and placing it in position where it is intended to build will also present its own problems. The natural ground beneath the fill may be soft and compressible and the new loadings applied by the fill itself may cause consolidation settlements. If buildings were then constructed on this new fill these would also be affected by the consolidation of the lower stratum. This problem will arise in the areas of the soft compressible lacustrine deposits revealed by the Project boreholes and shown in Figure 4.2.

If the positions of the buildings in the new fill areas are known beforehand, then the best type of filling available should underlie these positions. If possible, this fill should be granular with a reasonable grading not susceptible to being broken down by weathering. Very

Engineering properties
and problems
associated with fill
material in the Project
area

large pieces of cooled slag should not be used in critical positions because of the difficulty of adequately compacting such material.

All the fill should preferably be compacted in not more than 9-in layers, and it should be compacted to at least 95 per cent standard compaction. It would be unwise to use household refuse under building areas, as even when well compacted, this type of fill cannot be guaranteed against long-term settlements. The majority of the fill should be free draining, but if this is not possible precautions should be taken to maintain a cross fall on the fill to prevent wet spots during compaction.

The final problem mentioned in connection with the large areas of tip material was the difficulties involved in taking foundations down to harder strata. Piles or caissons will be necessary if loads are unusually heavy, or if the structure or unit to be supported is unable to withstand settlement.

Some of the fill contains large masses of cooled slag, particularly in Plots 3 and 21. It would be very difficult to drive normal diameter piles or to construct normal bored piles in these areas. If no alternative exists, then large-diameter bored piles would probably be the only practical method for deep fill. If, however, this fill is shallow, normal foundations may be taken down to natural ground using ordinary excavating equipment. Similar problems would also arise if piling had to be carried out at the positions of demolished buildings or furnaces.

The presence of harmful chemicals in the tip material might require unusual solutions for the protection of piles. In one case[5] up to 3·75 per cent sulphates have been recorded. In such conditions it may be possible to use large-diameter bored piles and to spray the sides of the holes with bitumen before placing the concrete.

Although the presence of large quantities of fill materials in the Project area gives rise to particular problems related to the properties of the fill itself, it should be recognized that the tipping of these waste materials in depth has served to reclaim large areas where the original ground surface was soft alluvium unsuitable for directly supporting even the lightest foundation loads. Providing, therefore, suitable precautions are taken, where necessary, the presence of the fill material, from a foundation engineering standpoint, may be regarded as an asset, reducing the extent of the foundation problems generally associated with deep deposits of soft alluvium.

References

1 D. Ivor Evans, letter to Borough Engineer, Swansea, 24 October 1957, concerning the proposed extraction of water from Callands Pit.
2 W. F. G. Cardy, *Report on the Geology of the Lower Swansea Valley* (Study Report No. 4).
3 H. G. Clapham, H. E. Evans and F. E. Weare, *The Soil Mechanics and Foundation Engineering Survey of the Lower Swansea Valley Project Area* (Study Report No. 5).
4 R. D. Worrall, *Report on Transportation and Physical Planning in the Lower Swansea Valley* (Study Report No. 2).
5 George Wimpey and Co. Ltd, *Report on Site Investigation for Proposed Development at the Villiers Site, Swansea*, November 1957.

Authorship

This chapter was written by Dr H. E. Evans, and W. F. G. Cardy.

The success of the geological and soil mechanics survey has been very largely dependent on the generous and willing help of numerous persons and companies.

We particularly wish to thank Professor F. H. T. Rhodes and his staff for unlimited use of space and facilities in the Geology Department, and Professor O. C. Zienkiewicz of the Division of Civil Engineering for the use of testing equipment and for their personal help and attention. In addition we must thank Professor J. G. C. Anderson of University College, Cardiff, for the loan of valuable geophysical equipment; and particularly Dr D. E. T. Bidgood who with Dr C. R. K. Blundell and J. Wilson came to the area on several occasions to operate the instruments and interpret the results. Their assistance has been greatly appreciated.

In the early stages of the investigation we received assistance and guidance from H. G. Clapham and throughout the soils survey F. E. Weare contributed largely to the site work. We are indebted to them both for their invaluable help.

Others who helped the investigation in various ways were C. Lawrence and R. O. Meek, of the County Borough Engineers and Surveyors Department, Guildhall, Swansea; Dr J. C. Stubblefield, the Director, and J. V. Stephens, of the Geological Survey; Captain J. D. Payne, Adjutant 53rd (Welsh) Division R.E. (T.A.), and Sergeant W. R. Thomas; T. Rees and W. G. Hodges, of the Steel Company of Wales; J. L. Bowen, Estate Department, Richard Thomas and Baldwins Ltd; E. S. Rees and N. B. Price, of the National Coal Board; N. S. Robinson, of British Railways, Neath; D. Allen and J. R. Williams, of the National Smelting Co. Ltd; Carey Jones; E. J. Bonney-James, Yorkshire Imperial Metals Ltd; Dr E. B. Meyrick, Medical Officer of Health, Swansea; Col R. H. Edwards, of Barry Docks; M. D. Mossman, Location Manager, George Cohen Machinery Ltd; D. C. N. McLeod, of the Ministry of Public Building and Works.

Appendix I

The preparation of the base plan

In order to show the whole of the area studied on a single sheet map, the scale of 1/5000 (approximately 12·5 inches to one mile) is the largest which can conveniently be employed. For most field studies and as a general reference document this scale is quite large enough. The choice of this scale also has the important practical advantage that much of the detail printed in black can be reduced photographically from the large-scale Ordnance Survey plans without any need for redrawing this information.

The completed base plan (in pocket at end) has been printed in two colours. The black printing represents some of the planimetric detail which is shown on the current 1/2500 scale plans of this part of Swansea. The brown printing depicts additional information which has been obtained during the work of the Project in order to supplement the detail which is customarily available on the large-scale Ordnance Survey publications. Hence the two colours of the base plan serve to distinguish that detail which is derived from official sources (and therefore possesses some measure of administrative or legal weight) from that obtained by our own work and which has no administrative or legal authority. There are three varieties of additional information: (1), the surface contours; (2) the plot boundaries and their numbers; (3) brief information about the name, nature and history of the principal industrial sites within the area of detailed survey.

Practically the whole of the area studied by the Project lies within the urban part of

Swansea which has been resurveyed by the Ordnance Survey at the 1/1250 scale since 1945 and this work has subsequently been kept up-to-date by continuous revision. Most of the remainder of the area is available on modern 1/2500 scale plans. Despite the availability of modern Ordnance Survey mapping it was desirable, for our purposes, to supplement this information. For example, from the initiation of the Project it was obvious that the network of spot heights and bench marks, which provide the only information about surface relief on the large-scale plans, would need supplementing with contours. These were particularly necessary for evaluating the quantities of material contained in the different tips and for the investigation of flood risks in certain low-lying areas. With the later prospect of afforestation on parts of Kilvey Hill, some detailed knowledge of this terrain would also be important. For these reasons it was decided to prepare a contoured plan using a contour interval of 10 ft at lower elevations and an interval of 20 ft above 200 ft. Because the only economic way of doing this work in an area of such complex micro-relief is by photogrammetric methods, the University College of Swansea obtained the service of Hunting Surveys Ltd to take a block of vertical aerial photography. This was specified to be wide-angle photography of survey quality to be taken at the nominal scale of 1/5000.

This sortie (HSL/UK/62/173)* was flown on 24 January 1962, and comprised three strips approximately aligned in the direction of the valley between Wychtree Bridge and High Street Station (Figure 4.4). There are thirty-three photographs in the block. Because there is a fair density of Ordnance Survey control (revision points and spot heights) throughout the area, we hoped that the work could be done reliably and quickly by plotting each model independently in a third-order photogrammetric instrument. A fairly new Zeiss Stereotope was available in the Geography Department and it was intended to plot 10-ft contours at 1/5000 scale with it. It so happened that this was the first survey quality photography possessing abundant height control which had ever been used in this instrument. It was immediately apparent that this particular Stereotope possessed mechanical defects which gave rise to appreciable height errors in each model. It was therefore necessary to return it to the manufacturers for overhaul, resulting in a delay of several months. Although it was eventually shown that the repaired instrument could have been used for the work of the Project by then most of the work had been done by other, rather slower methods.

During the delay the present writer began to do the plotting by Multiplex and he also gladly accepted the invitation from Mr G. Petrie (Geography Department, Glasgow University) that some of this plotting might be done in a new Wild B 8 plotter belonging to that department. Resulting from these changes to the original plan, six models in the south and east of the Project area were done in Glasgow by G. Petrie, Capt. R. O. Dugmore, R.E., Mr J. Bajulaiye, Mr N. D. Campbell and Miss A. B. Wilson. This work was all done at 1/2500 scale. The remainder of the photography used was plotted in Swansea by the present writer at scales of 1/1750 and 1/2000.†

Only a small part of the western side of the valley has been plotted. This is because this side of the valley is so densely settled that continuous contours are difficult to draw and are in any case of limited value to the work of the Project. However, Miss G. M. Brown did some

* The negatives for this sortie are now preserved in the Geography Department, University College of Swansea.
† Unlike the Geography Department in Glasgow we do not possess a modern second-order photogrammetric instrument. The Multiplex in Swansea is a home-made assembly comprising components from prewar Zeiss equipment and two Bausch and Lomb wide-angle projectors of wartime vintage.

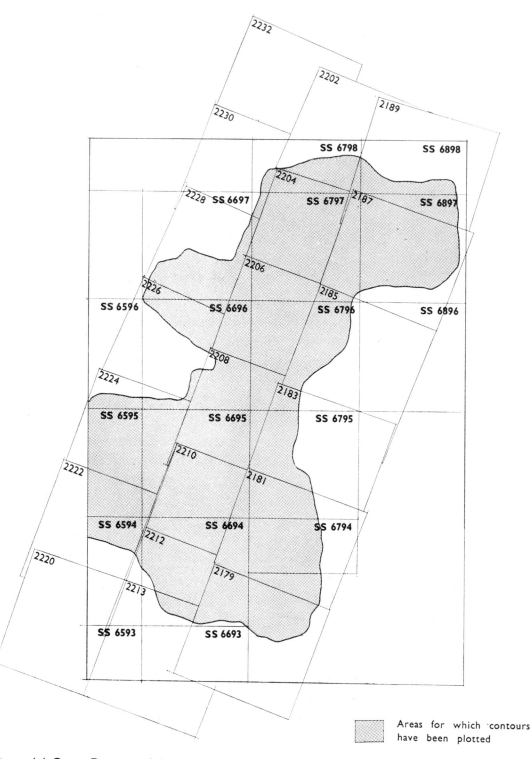

Figure 4.4 Cover Diagram of the Lower Swansea Valley

additional plotting for the western side of the valley after completion of the main work of plotting. Because most of the models contained a considerable amount of planimetric detail which was identifiable on the Ordnance Survey plans and because the majority of the models contained between twenty-five and forty identifiable Ordnance Survey spot heights, it was possible to do the work of absolute orientation of the Multiplex model with much greater care than is usual in topographical mapping with this instrument. This was done using the customary three points of known height, but repeating the tilt adjustments employing different combinations of height control until residual height errors in the model ceased to show any systematic bias. All spot heights measured, whether these were Ordnance Survey control or points of unknown height, were determined from five individual observations. On this basis, a sample of 413 heighted points shows a standard error of $\pm 1 \cdot 31$ ft for the single observation. The mean residual error for 172 points of known height in five different models after the completion of absolute orientation was $+0 \cdot 8$ ft, with a standard deviation of $\pm 3 \cdot 4$ ft. In one particularly good model with twenty-six points of known height the corresponding values were $+0 \cdot 2 \pm 2 \cdot 2$ feet. These figures all refer to models plotted at 1/2000 scale and correspond to a heighting precision of $0 \cdot 9$ to $1 \cdot 4$ per cent of the flying height. Although this order of precision could be easily excelled in modern photogrammetric instruments it is about as good as can be expected with our home-made Multiplex.

Two well-known defects of Multiplex are the grain of the much-enlarged model and the loss of illumination through the combination of anaglyph filters and spectacles needed for stereoscopic vision. These combine to cause uncertainty in placing the floating mark in the model, especially where the projected image is dark in tone. Because many of the tips appeared very dark compared with adjacent vegetated ground the stereoscopic model was frequently indistinct and it was often difficult to plot contours in just those parts of the valley where they were most needed for volume determination. After repeating one or two of the models plotted at the outset of the work and finding that much of the contour plotting was distinctly inferior to the order of accuracy suggested by deliberate measurement of spot heights, the author made it standard practice to plot each contour at least twice. The preparation of the base plan provided an opportunity for carrying out part of a more prolonged investigation of the differences in precision of height determination between using stereoscopic and pseudoscopic vision. It now seems probable that there is no significant difference in the accuracies obtained by either method of viewing. In this context the conclusion justifies the use of pseudoscopic vision for contouring where one of these combinations of filters and spectacles provides a better illuminated image than can be obtained stereoscopically.

Certainly the greater range of illumination provided by four possible combinations of filters and spectacles helped appreciably in locating contours on the darker tips.

Compilation of the base plan was done by reducing the individual photogrammetric plots to the common scale of 1/2500 in a Zeiss SEG-IV Rectifier and redrawing the contours on Ordnance Survey plans. A compilation manuscript for the whole area was prepared at this scale for Cook, Hammond and Kell Ltd, who have done all the fair drawing, photo-mechanical work and printing of the base plan.

Authorship

This appendix was written by Dr D. H. Maling, Senior Lecturer in the Department of Geography, University College of Swansea.

Appendix 2   Quantities of fill materials

A knowledge of the quantities of materials existing in the Project area is a useful adjunct to any proposal for redevelopment. The quantities of material existing above 20 ft O.D. have been estimated for the northern part of the Project area, since, at the time, it was considered that any initial redevelopment would most likely take place in this region. A method of estimation and presentation of results has been devised, which may readily be adapted to other parts of the Project area should the need arise.

The area for which estimates of quantities was made is found within the Project's boundaries north of the National Grid Line 960. This southern boundary of the region considered approximates to an east–west line passing through the southern edge of the old Mannesman Tube works. In order to present the results in a compact form the area was subdivided into a square network within the National Grid boundaries. A square of 250 metres side was chosen as the basic unit, as this was considered to be a reasonable size for evaluating quantities for preliminary estimating purposes. It was found that this size square was small enough for the intended accuracy but was not so small as to obscure the overall picture by an excess of detailed information.

Although 250 metres was chosen so as to fit conveniently into the National Grid reference system all quantities were evaluated in cubic yards which, for the present at least, is the standard unit for this type of estimate. It was assumed throughout that the minimum ground level in the area is 20 ft O.D. In the few areas such as the Nant-y-Fendrod valley where spot heights indicate levels slightly below 20 ft O.D. these were, for simplification, ignored and the area considered as being at 20 ft O.D.

The basic squares are referred to by the grid reference number of the south-west corner of the square and also numbered 1–29 (inclusive) starting from the south-west of the part of the Project area considered. Both reference systems are used in the results presented in Table 4.1, but only the square numbering system from 1–29 (inclusive) is used for the results

Table 4.1

Grid reference of S.W. corner of basic square	Square or sub-unit reference No.	Area enclosed by 20 ft O.D. contour (yd²)	Mean height (ft O.D.)	Volume of material required to change level by 1 ft (yd³)	Remarks
6650 9600	1	66,092	38·6	22,030	
6675 9600	2	74,750	48·4	24,917	
6700 9600	3	53,318	68·9	17,773	Only areas north of the railway boundary are considered
6725 9600	4	29,143	42·9	9,714	
6650 9625	5	45,560	49·6	15,187	
6675 9625	6a	19,208	61·0	6,403	West of Tawe
6675 9625	6b	43,714	24·1	14,571	East of Tawe Width of river taken as width at 20 ft contour level
6700 9625	7	74,750	42·8	24,917	
6725 9625	8	74,750	49·1	24,917	

Table 4.1—*contd.*

Grid reference of S.W. corner of basic square	Square or sub-unit reference No.	Area enclosed by 20 ft O.D. contour (yd²)	Mean height (ft O.D.)	Volume of material required to change level by 1 ft (yd³)	Remarks
6750 9625	9	57,103	40·7	19,034	Railway boundary forms eastern boundary
6650 9650	10	8,516	45·6	2,839	Area to east of canal only considered
6675 9650	11	60,888	45·0	20,296	West boundary canal, east boundary Tawe
6700 9650	12a	34,347	45·1	11,449	North of Fendrod
6700 9650	12b	27,109	43·9	9,036	South of Fendrod
6725 9650	13a	10,030	28·9	3,343	North of Fendrod
6725 9650	13b	61,503	46·8	20,501	South of Fendrod
6750 9650	14	74,750	26·8	24,917	Assumed no level below 20 ft O.D.
6775 9650	15	39,078	48·1	13,026	Railway forms eastern boundary
6675 9675	16	38,700	62·4	12,900	Canal east bank forms western boundary
6700 9675	17a	13,956	48·5	4,652	West of Tawe
6700 9675	17b	52,041	43·5	17,347	East of Tawe Width of river as at 20 ft contour
6725 9675	18	74,750	32·3	24,917	Assumed no level below 20 ft O.D.
6750 9675	19	74,750	27·9	24,917	
6775 9675	20	74,750	52·4	24,917	Contour info. scarce estimates on spot heights
6675 9700	21	11,591	49·6	3,864	Area to east of canal only considered
6700 9700	22a	23,324	45·4	7,775	West of Tawe
6700 9700	22b	39,835	26·7	13,278	East of Tawe Width of river as at 20 ft contour
6725 9700	23	74,750	26·9	24,917	
6750 9700	24	74,750	26·2	24,917	
6775 9700	25	74,750	29·1	24,917	
6700 9725	26a	31,698	46·7	10,566	East of canal West of Tawe
6700 9725	26b	19,160	20	6,387	
6725 9725	27	74,750	23·4	24,917	
6750 9725	28	74,750	23·4	24,917	
6775 9725	29	74,750	33·0	24,917	

as set out in Figure 4.5. Although maximum simplicity would be achieved by adhering to the basic square system throughout, such a system could give rise to misconceptions in certain areas. It has been found necessary, for example, to make minor subdivisions in areas where the basic square is crossed by natural barriers such as the River Tawe. In these cases the squares are divided into two parts, 'a' and 'b', with the boundaries of each part clearly marked on the map form of Figure 4.5 and noted in the remarks column of Table 4.1.

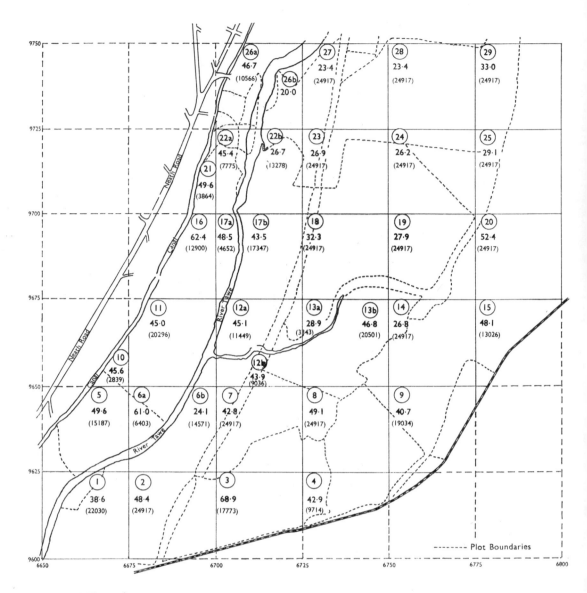

Figure 4.5 Tip volumes

Several methods, such as stating the quantity of material between adjacent contours, were considered but all suffered from the disadvantages of producing too much detail which obscured the overall pattern. In order to produce a simple final statement which would also make further calculations on readjustments of levels as easy as possible, it was decided to present the results on a mean height basis. In this method the total volume of material above the 20 ft O.D. contour within the basic square unit, or occasional sub-unit, is first estimated. This volume is then divided by the plan area of the basic square or sub-unit, giving the mean height within the unit boundaries. In this way the part of the Project area considered may be thought of as having had its irregularities of height levelled within each unit area, without material having been brought into or taken out of that area.

Since the area of the basic unit or sub-unit is known, the amount of material required to raise or lower the level in a particular unit by, say, 1 ft from the mean height may readily be calculated. The map form of Figure 4.5 presents a summary of the results obtained and a typical example is as follows.

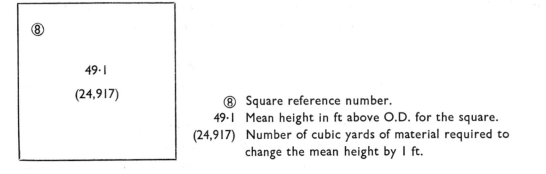

⑧ Square reference number.

49·1 Mean height in ft above O.D. for the square.

(24,917) Number of cubic yards of material required to change the mean height by 1 ft.

Where subdivisions of the basic square are used, for reasons previously stated, the subdivisions themselves are individually marked in a manner similar to the above example. This information with additional detail is also given in tabular form in Table 4.1.

Quantities of materials were estimated on the basis of the simple prismoidal formula.

If A_1 = area (square yards) enclosed by the X ft O.D. contour in the basic unit

A_2 = area (square yards) enclosed by the $(X+h)$ ft O.D. contour in the basic unit

then the volume (V) of material contained between these contours is given by

$$V = \frac{h}{3}(A_1 + \sqrt{A_1 A_2} + \sqrt{A_2})\frac{1}{3} \text{ cubic yards}$$

Measurements such as A_1 and A_2 for 10-ft contour intervals were made by planimeter on the 1/2500 contour map. This map, the details of which are given in Appendix 1 of this chapter, was prepared by Dr D. H. Maling from the aerial photographs taken by Hunting Surveys Ltd on 24 January 1962. To eliminate planimeter errors each area within a contour was determined at least twice or until consecutive planimeter readings agreed to within 1 per cent. In order to allow for volumes above the highest contour level recorded in any particular square, a fictitious contour area equal to half the area enclosed by the highest recorded contour, but at a level of 10 ft above this contour, was included where appropriate.

If the total volumes above the level 20 ft O.D. are to be evaluated on the basis of a 10-ft contour interval and the results expressed as a mean height H

Then

$$H = 20 + \frac{V}{kP_1} \cdot 3 \text{ ft}$$

where P_1 is the planimeter reading for the area enclosed by the 20 ft O.D. contour

k is the constant required to convert the planimeter reading to an area in square yards.

Similarly if P_2, P_3, etc., are the planimeter readings for the 30 ft, 40 ft, etc., contours then

$$H = 20 + \frac{1}{kP_1}\frac{10}{3}[P_1 k + \sqrt{P_1 kP_2}k + P_2 k + P_2 k + \sqrt{P_2 kP_3}k + P_3 k + \ldots]$$

$$= 20 + \frac{10}{3P_1}[P_1 + \sqrt{P_1 P_2} + P_2 + P_2 + \sqrt{P_2 P_3} + P_3 + \ldots]$$

In order to evaluate the mean height H a computer programme* was written and used with the College I.B.M. 1620 machine. It was also a simple matter to include in this

---

* H. E. Evans, *Estimation of Quantities of Materials in the Northern Part of the Lower Swansea Valley Project Area* (Study Report No. 12).

programme instructions to print out the area corresponding to the 20 ft O.D. contour for each unit or sub-unit. This enabled the information for future adjustments of levels to be readily obtained.

Since the aerial photography of 1962 quantities of material have been removed from the Project area and a summary of the latest information available (January 1966) giving an estimate of the volume removed is given in Table 4.2. All calculations were based on the simple prismoidal rule and the limitations of this method when used with certain land forms must be appreciated.* It is, however, considered that the method gives sufficiently accurate results for producing information on which future levels in the northern part of the Project area may be estimated.

Table 4.2   Excavation of hardcore January 1962–December 1965

Tip	Square ref. Nos.	Estimated weight of material excavated tons	Estimated volume removed (yd³)
Copper and spelter tip Plot 21	16 and 17a	117,262	97,718
Beaufort tip Plot 20	12a and 17b	122,529	102,108
Nicholl tip Plot 28	8	38,452	32,043

Authorship

This appendix was written by Dr H. E. Evans. The author wishes to acknowledge the kind assistance given by Dr K. G. Stagg in the formulation of the computer programme necessary to the method of quantity estimation.

---

* R. D. Worrall, *Report on Transportation and Physical Planning in the Lower Swansea Valley* (Study Report No. 2), section 3.2, Accuracy of Estimates.

5 Revegetation techniques in the Lower Swansea Valley

The Lower Swansea Valley Project's area of 1,174 acres includes about 800 acres which are completely derelict. Roughly half of this derelict land is occupied by waste tips of varied composition. They are built up of slags derived from metallic ores (copper, zinc, lead, iron, cobalt, nickel, arsenic, silver), many of which are regarded as highly poisonous to plant life, or from more innocuous wastes (foundry sand, domestic refuse, building rubble, furnace ash, coal shale). Of the remaining derelict land, there are about 300 acres of badly eroded, infertile, sandy clays, sparsely covered with grasses, principally Common Bent-grass (*Agrostis tenuis*) and Wavy Hair-grass (*Deschampsia flexuosa*), the rest being marsh or open water. The infertile soils were produced by severe sheet and gully erosion after their original vegetation cover had been destroyed by sulphurous smelter-smoke during the late eighteenth and the nineteenth centuries (Bridges, 1965). The marshy ground represents the original valley floor where the drainage has been impeded by the adjacent tips.

Clearly, any redevelopment plan for the area would have to indicate whether this derelict land, or parts of it, could if necessary be reclaimed as grassland, woodland or parkland without involving prohibitive costs. At the outset it was judged that appropriate cultivation and standard fertilizer treatments would probably permit of the establishment of grass or trees on the infertile, eroded soils, or on the more innocuous tips, all of which already bore at least a very poor vegetation cover. By contrast, the bare slag tips containing poisonous metals were considered to be a much more difficult technical problem and were treated in an experimental manner, using many small-scale trials; (the work on the eroded soils and innocuous tips was less experimental and involved larger scale plantings, see also Chapter 10, Visual Improvement). The objective of both types of study was to develop techniques for the inexpensive establishment of vegetation giving an acceptable cover and requiring minimal maintenance.

This strictly practical objective and the very limited duration of the Lower Swansea Valley Project required the rapid establishment of the planting trials. Further, it was necessary that these should only involve simple cultivation operations, relatively inexpensive, readily available substances (sewage sludge, domestic refuse, standard agricultural fertilizers) to improve the surfaces of the tips as sites for plant growth, and readily available hardy plants capable of being set as seed or easily propagated by vegetative means. Guides to the design of such planting trials were the earlier reports relating to the vegetation of coal shales (Bates, 1957; Richardson, 1957; Atkinson, 1964; Coates, 1964), pulverized fuel ash (Holliday *et al.*, 1958; Barber, 1963) and lead tailings (Evans, 1962).

A shortage of available manpower and the many difficulties (negotiatory and manual)

Figure 5.1 Vegetation trials

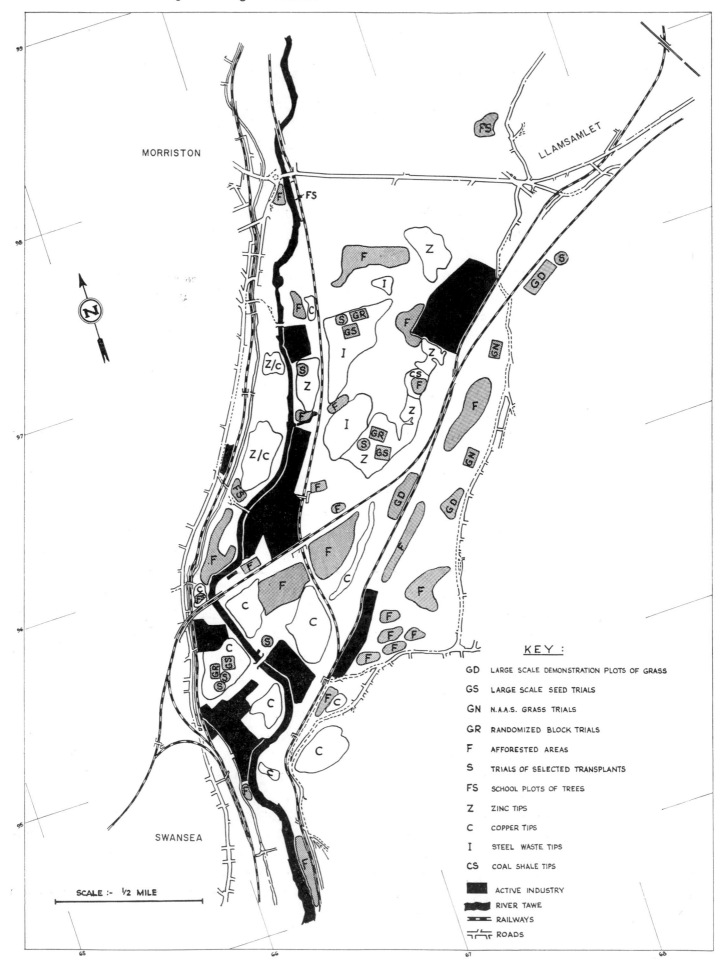

MORRISTON

LLAMSAMLET

SWANSEA

SCALE :- 1/2 MILE

KEY :

GD LARGE SCALE DEMONSTRATION PLOTS OF GRASS

GS LARGE SCALE SEED TRIALS

GN N.A.A.S. GRASS TRIALS

GR RANDOMIZED BLOCK TRIALS

F AFFORESTED AREAS

S TRIALS OF SELECTED TRANSPLANTS

FS SCHOOL PLOTS OF TREES

Z ZINC TIPS

C COPPER TIPS

I STEEL WASTE TIPS

CS COAL SHALE TIPS

ACTIVE INDUSTRY

RIVER TAWE

RAILWAYS

ROADS

which had to be overcome to establish plant trials on the tips made it necessary to limit the extent and the number of experimental areas. Despite their mixed composition, it was possible from historical evidence, visual examination, physical properties and such flora as was already present, to group the metallic slag tips into three broad classes as zinc, copper and steel tips. Trial plantings were largely confined to a large, flattened tip of each class. Subsequent chemical analyses supplied principally by the National Agricultural Advisory Service (Cardiff Sub-section) upheld the preliminary classification of the selected planting sites. The tip classes and the tip locations chosen were as follows: 'Steel slag', Duffryn tip, Plot 19; 'Copper slag', Imperial Chemical Industries tip, Plot 49; 'Zinc slag', Cohen's tip, Plot 28. The locations of these experimental areas and all other planting trials (grey stippling), together with the tips, are shown in Figure 5.1; plot numbers are shown on the base map in the end pocket of this report.

Experimental work at each of these sites commenced in 1962 and involved:

1   A study of the natural vegetation.
2   Laboratory and glasshouse studies of the physical, chemical, and biological properties of the tip materials.
3   Randomized block experiments sown to seed.
4   Larger-scale seed trials initiated in 1965 and based upon results obtained from the randomized block experiments.
5   Trials of selected transplants and seed of woody and herbaceous species (initiated in 1963).
6   Trials of grasses collected from old mining spoil areas in other parts of the United Kingdom and the Irish Republic (initiated 1963).
7   Microbiological experiments, both at the experimental sites and on tip materials brought into the laboratory.

In addition to this work on the slag tips, the investigations carried out on the more innocuous tips and the eroded soils involved:

8   Tree planting on eroded soils and on the more innocuous wastes.
9   Grass trials on the eroded soils.

The nature of the evidence from these experimental studies is outlined here under these nine headings. For more definitive descriptions of techniques, and a more detailed consideration of the findings from individual experiments, reference should be made to four study reports deposited in the Library of University College, Swansea (Hooper, 1965; Gadgil and Gadgil, 1965; Gadgil, 1965 and Salter, 1965).

1   The natural vegetation of the tips

A general survey of the vegetation present at the chosen tip areas was made in August–September 1962. The zinc tip, which had not been disturbed for sixty years, was bare except for a vegetative species of moss (*Bryum* sp.) found on slopes sheltered from the prevailing south-westerly wind. At the foot of this tip was a small pond (Plot 28) and here there grew isolated tussocks of Purple Moor-grass (*Molinia caerulea*), Yorkshire Fog (*Holcus lanatus*) and a few plants of Creeping Bent-grass (*Agrostis stolonifera*). These plants were absent from the tip itself. Zinc waste currently being tipped on Plot 17 by the Swansea Vale Spelter Works would seem to be more readily colonized than this old zinc material. Material tipped in 1963 carried, within a year, apparently healthy plants of Coltsfoot (*Tussilago farfara*), Creeping Bent-grass, Rosebay Willow-herb (*Chamaenerion angustifolium*) and Goat Willow (*Salix caprea*).

The species found on the steel and copper tips are listed in Table 5.1.

Table 5.1   Plant species recorded on the steel and copper tips, August 1962

Steel tip (Plot 19)
* *Agrostis stolonifera* (Creeping Bent)
* *Agrostis tenuis* (Common Bent)
  Artemisia vulgaris (Mugwort)
  Centaurea nigra (Lesser Knapweed)
  Cerastium holosteoides (Common Mouse-ear Chickweed)
* *Chamaenerion angustifolium* (Rosebay Willow-herb)
  Chenopodium album (Fat Hen)
* *Cirsium arvense* (Creeping Thistle)
  Coronopus didymus (Lesser Swinecress)
  Diplotaxis muralis (Stinkwort)
  Epilobium montanum (Broad-leaved Willow-herb)
  Epilobium parviflorum (Lesser Hairy Willow-herb)
* *Equisetum sp.* (Horsetail)
* *Funaria hygrometrica*
  Holcus lanatus (Yorkshire Fog)
  Lapsana communis (Nipplewort)
  Linaria repens (Pale Toadflax)
  Plantago major (Great Plantain)
* *Poa annua* (Annual Meadow-grass)
  Polygonum aviculare (Knotgrass)
  Rumex sp. (Sorrel)
  Sagina procumbens (Pearlwort)
* *Salix caprea* (Goat Willow)
* *Salix cinerea* (Common Sallow)
  Saponaria officinalis (Soapwort)
  Senecio squalidus (Oxford Ragwort)
  Senecio vulgaris (Groundsel)
  Sisymbrium altissimum (Tall Rocket)
  Solanum dulcamara (Woody Nightshade)
  Sonchus oleraceus (Sow Thistle)
  Trifolium repens (White Clover)
  Tripleurospermum maritimum (Scentless Mayweed)
* *Tussilago farfara* (Coltsfoot)
  Urtica dioica (Stinging Nettle)
  Valeriana officinalis (Valerian)
  Verbascum thapsus (Mullein)

Copper tip (Plot 49)
  Those marked with an asterisk in the above list and, in addition:
  Betula pendula (Silver Birch)
  Calystegia sepium (Large Bindweed)
  Carex panicea (Carnation Sedge)
  Polygonum cuspidatum
  Silene maritima (Sea Campion)

To describe the vegetation of the tips, two lines intersecting at 90° were marked out and square sample plots (quadrats) of 50-cm side were laid at fixed intervals along these transects. The averages for percentages of ground covered by vegetation and for number of species per sample plot were calculated and are shown in Table 5.2.

Table 5.2   Natural vegetation of zinc (Plot 28), copper (Plot 49) and steel (Plot 19) tips in 1962

Tip	Percentage of ground covered		Total no. of species recorded	No. of sample quadrats examined	Average no. of species per quadrat
	Including moss	Excluding moss			
Zinc	10	1	4	50	0·04
Copper	27	4	15	57	1·5
Steel	16	3	36	70	3·2

If moss is excluded, percentage cover is similar on all three, although there were large bare areas on the copper and zinc tips not encountered on the steel tip. The copper tip was levelled in 1949, the steel tip in 1957; the steel tip is, however, much more heavily compacted than the copper tip.

Permanent quadrats were established on the three tips in September 1962 and the exact position and extent of individual plants recorded. In September 1963 and September 1964, these quadrats were again examined and changes in coverage by established plants and invasion of the quadrats by seedlings recorded. The values obtained were used to calculate the percentages of quadrats showing decreases and increases in number of established plants and in seedlings compared with the 1962 counts. The results indicated that recolonization of the steel tip was proceeding by new seedlings and the growth of established plants, whereas the vegetation of the copper tip, although subject to fluctuation, did not change significantly during the two years. Although the records on the zinc tip were incomplete because of its disturbance in 1964, the data suggested that the vegetation was increasing slightly, but solely because of the growth of plants already established and not by seedling invasion.

2   Physical, chemical and biological properties of the tip materials

(a) Temperature

The tips are dark in colour and porous to water. During the period, March 1963 to March 1964, records were made once weekly of maximum and minimum temperatures recorded 4 inches below the tip surfaces and also at the same time, 4 inches below a grassed-over soil surface in the Botanic Garden at the University College. The data indicates that the more extreme temperatures occurred at the tip sites giving a much greater range in summer. These extremes were particularly marked for minimum temperatures. The temperature fluctuations were less marked in the steel tip (grey in colour) than in the darker zinc and copper tips. Tip material appears to resemble a black body in gaining heat rapidly from sunshine and losing heat rapidly at night. The magnitude of the consequent temperature changes is further enhanced by the exposure of the tip surface (there being no trees or local shelter and, most important of all, a lack of vegetation cover).

(b) **Moisture**

Determination of such factors as water-holding capacity (Piper, 1950) and field capacity (Lyon *et al.*, 1952) and studies on the course of drying out of the tip materials under laboratory conditions, showed, as expected, that the tip materials were somewhat inferior to soils in water retention. However, tests where transplants and seeds were grown in the tip materials under different watering régimes in the glasshouse showed that the unfavourable effects of the materials on plant growth were not mitigated by maintaining a high moisture régime. Nor was growth failure increased preferentially in the tip materials as compared with soil under conditions inducing high water stress. Although much more critical experimental work would be required to assess precisely the effects of surface drying out of the tips and their microtopography and stability in relation to plant growth and particularly to seedling establishment, our studies taken as a whole point to other factors being of much greater importance in accounting for the lack of good vegetation cover on the valley tips.

(c) **Chemical composition**

Two aspects of the chemical composition of the rooting medium are of importance to plant growth. One is the capacity of this medium to supply in a soluble form essential chemical elements, amongst which nitrogen, phosphorus, potassium and calcium are quantitatively important. The other relates to soluble elements occurring at toxic concentrations. At low concentrations, certain metals (such as copper, zinc and iron) are essential to plant growth; at higher concentrations, such metals are usually poisonous to plants and this applies particularly to copper, zinc, nickel and lead. In view of the origin of the valley tip materials, they could be expected to contain abnormally high amounts of such metals and, if sufficient of these were present in soluble form, they would be inhibitory or even lethal to plants. The importance of the chemical composition of the tip materials to their ability to support plant growth can be assessed from chemical analysis of the material itself, study of the release into solution of elements from the material and chemical analysis of the plants growing in it. It remains the task for future research to carry out extensive analyses of plants grown on the valley tips, and to this extent our present data is incomplete. Chemical data from the tips, although available, must be interpreted with caution because of the great difficulty in obtaining representative samples. Many of the valley's smelting works producing copper commonly changed over to zinc smelting and vice versa, depending on the current prices of these metals. Thus, several tips have successive layers of copper and zinc waste. Subsequent disturbance by hardcore working and re-extraction enterprises have produced a highly heterogeneous distribution of these layers so that generalization about the overall suitability of a tip surface for plant growth is virtually impossible. It should also be emphasized that regrading of the tips in any redevelopment of the valley could result in quite significant changes in the chemical composition of the tip surfaces, by exposing both materials of different initial composition and materials which have not yet been subjected to weathering.

Analytical data representing some 1,500 separate determinations of chemical elements from many of the valley tips are presented by R. Gadgil and P. D. Gadgil (1965), where the problem of tip heterogeneity is well illustrated. Here attention is concentrated upon the three principal tip types from the chosen locations, the infertile clay soil and the currently

Table 5.3 Chemical analysis of ten samples of tip material and soil from the Lower Swansea Valley (Data supplied by N.A.A.S.)

	Depth of sample (inches)	Total metal content (parts per million of oven-dry material by spectrographic analysis[1])						p.p.m. of EDTA soluble copper	p.p.m. 0.5 N acetic acid soluble zinc	Calcium carbonate	Agricultural analysis[5] (p.p.m. of 0.5 N acetic acid soluble:)			
		Copper	Zinc	Lead	Nickel	Chromium	Tin				pH	Phosphorus (P₂O₅)	Potassium (K₂O)	Calcium[2] (CaO)
Zinc waste (Plot 28)	0–3	9,000	≫9,000	≫9,000	270	27–90	2,700	470	26,000	Nil	6·3	2·6	25	Nil
	9–12	9,000	≫9,000	9,000	90–270	27–90	2,700	760	23,000	Nil	6·1	6·1	33	Nil
Copper waste (Plot 49)	0–3	6,000	6,000–8,000	6,000	180	18–60	180	2,000	170	Nil	5·5	15	42	110
	9–12	8,000	8,000–24,000	800	240	80	240	2,100	480	Nil	6·0	15	58	210
Steel waste (Plot 19)[3]	0–3	2,100–7,000	2,100–7,000	7,000	210	210	210–700	39	1,300	Very High	8·5	0·9	110	—
	0–3	2,100–7,000	2,100–7,000	7,000	210	210–700	210–700	53	1,400	Very High	8·7	0·9	110	—
New Zinc Waste (Plot 17)[4]	0–3	10,000	≫10,000	3,000–10,000	10	300–1,000	10	37	3,600	Trace	9·5	320	2,600	—
„ „ (Plot 51)	0–3	9,000	2,700	9,000	90	90	9,000	110	380	Nil	5·6	11	150	630
Eroded Clay (Pentre Cawr)	0–3	900	2,700–9,000	2,700	27	27–90	90	71	280	Nil	4·2	1·3	42	Nil
	9–12	900	2,700	900	27	27–90	2·7	40	140	Nil	4·4	0·9	33	Nil
Relative abundance in normal soils	0–8	20	100	30	50	100	3	1	3	—	—	—	—	—

Classification p.p.m. 0·5 N acetic acid soluble	Very Low	Low	Medium	High	Very High
Phosphorus (P₂O₅)	0–8·6	8·7–17·2	17·3–34·4	34·5–51·6	>51·7
Potassium (K₂O)	0–50	51–100	101–150	151–200	>201

Notes: [1] Spectrographic analysis is semiquantitative only. > = greater than. ≫ = much greater than. [2] Where pH exceeds 6·5, no calcium determinations were made. [3] Steel tip was thoroughly mixed and levelled in 1957, so no 9–12 in values are given and a second 0–3 in sample from another site is included instead. [4] New zinc waste currently being tipped is homogeneous so no 9–12 in values are given and a second 0–3 in sample is included instead. [5] Interpretation of Agricultural Analyses:

produced zinc waste. Figures for soluble nitrogen extracted and analysed by the method of Mason (1952) showed that the copper tip contained four parts per million and that the nitrogen content of the zinc and steel tips and infertile clay soil was very low, being less than I p.p.m. The chemical composition of six samples of the three chosen tip materials is presented in Table 5.3 and is fairly typical of the main analytical data supplied by the National Agricultural Advisory Service (Cardiff Sub-centre).

Analyses of two samples of the new zinc waste currently being tipped are also included in Table 5.3 as well as two samples of an infertile clay soil in the valley. Levels of the various elements to be expected in normal soils are also quoted for purposes of comparison; the trace element figures are taken from Mitchell (1964), and the major nutrients from the standard N.A.A.S. nutrient interpretation table. The relatively high pH and calcium-carbonate content of the steel tip samples indicates that they are rich in calcium. By contrast, many of the other samples have little or no calcium.

Apart from the 'very high' value in one of the samples of new zinc waste, levels of phosphorus were, to use the accepted agricultural interpretation applied to plant nutrients in soils, 'very low' or 'low' in all samples. Similarly, potassium levels were either 'very low' or 'low', again with the exception of the new zinc waste ('medium' and 'very high' levels) and also with the steel waste being excepted ('medium' levels). With the new zinc waste excepted, all these materials are more or less clearly deficient in nitrogen, potassium and phosphorus and would therefore be expected to require liberal applications of general fertilizer to maintain plant growth. The new zinc waste currently being tipped by the Swansea Vale Works is of interest because some samples have a high pH, high levels of phosphorus and potassium, and low levels of soluble zinc, suggesting that this material is at present relatively innocuous, a conclusion borne out by the way in which plant colonization is rapidly proceeding on it in some places. This waste could be used to study how quickly its initial composition is altered by weathering and how quickly its colonizing vegetation reacts to this.

The analyses for the total content of individual metals in the tip materials show very high levels, particularly of zinc, copper and lead. The contrast between the tip materials is brought out by the figures for copper soluble in the chelating agent, ethylenediamine-tetra-acetate (EDTA) and for zinc soluble in acetic acid which give an indication of the amounts of these metals which can be regarded as available to plant roots. These figures support the classification of Plot 28 as a 'zinc' tip and Plot 49 as a 'copper' tip. Attention should be drawn to the relatively low figures for soluble copper and zinc for the steel waste.

It is often quite striking that ponds formed at the base of some tips support a relatively luxuriant vegetation. Analysis by the South West Wales River Authority of water from two ponds is shown in Table 5.4.

Table 5.4 Analyses of Valley pond waters
(Data supplied by South West Wales River Authority)

Pond	pH	p.p.m. of element					
		Lead	Zinc	Cadmium	Copper	Arsenic	Iron
Parkhouse pond receiving drainage from copper/zinc tip (Plot 35)	7·8	0·2	0·1	Nil	Nil	0·1	0·3
Cohen's pond receiving drainage from zinc tip (Plot 28)	7·0	0·1	20·5	10·1	Nil	0·2	<0·1

Physical chemical and
biological properties of
the tip materials

The pond on Plot 35 has a very low content of metals, with the exception of the beneficial level of iron. This pond contains roach and supports a community of aquatic and marsh plants. The pond on Plot 28, with its high content of zinc and cadmium and its low content of iron, is lacking in vegetation particularly on the side adjacent to the zinc tip.

These analyses of pond water should, perhaps, be looked at in relation to figures for water-soluble copper and zinc determined in the three tip materials by Miss C. E. R. Smith of the Botany Department (Table 5.5).

Table 5.5   Analyses for water-soluble copper and zinc in tip materials

	p.p.m. of element	
	Water-soluble copper	Water-soluble zinc
Zinc tip	0·2–0·5	72–130
Copper tip	0·8–3·0	11–16
Steel tip	0·2	0·3

Clearly, copper and zinc have a very low solubility in the steel tip, whereas the zinc tip yields a high level of water-soluble zinc and the copper tip a high level of water-soluble copper. It should also be noted that since copper and zinc may be toxic to plants at 0·25 p.p.m. and 5 p.p.m., respectively, the soluble zinc from the copper tip and copper from the zinc tip may lead to toxic levels.

(d) Biological properties

The experiments described under this heading were carried out in the glasshouses of the College Botanic Garden and involved growing plants from seeds germinated directly in the tip materials and from seedlings transplanted to tip material. Such experiments excluded the influence of such possibly unfavourable factors as atmospheric pollution, water stress and extreme temperatures which could operate at the tip sites in the valley.

Although the tip materials did not markedly inhibit the emergence of seedling roots from seeds of White Mustard (*Sinapis alba*) when used as a test plant, seedling growth was inhibited, very few seedlings breaking the surface of the copper and zinc wastes, and no plants surviving beyond the early seedling stage. The steel tip material supported a higher rate of seedling establishment but the plants grew poorly compared with growth in a good rooting medium (John Innes Potting Compost) and showed chlorosis (yellow condition of parts which are normally green). In a further experiment two-week-old plants of White Mustard were transplanted to the tip materials and their growth recorded for a month. On the copper and zinc tip materials, growth was stunted, seed-leaves (cotyledons) and normal leaves showed chlorosis and the seed-leaves were shed prematurely. Only a small number of plants survived in the zinc material. In the steel tip material, plants were healthier in appearance but slow growing compared with control plants in the John Innes Compost.

These results strongly pointed to the zinc and copper tip materials being toxic to the test plant and to a lack of nutrients in the steel tip material. This suggested that growth in the steel tip material might be improved by the use of a general inorganic fertilizer and that the toxic effects of the copper and zinc materials might be reduced by dilution or by complexing with organic matter (Lucas, 1948; Jensen and Lamm, 1961). Using three test plants—White Mustard, Red Clover (*Trifolium pratense*) and Oats (*Avena sativa*)—it was shown that, as expected, growth of plants in the steel tip material was markedly improved by addition of a general inorganic fertilizer (John Innes Base). However, growth in the presence of the steel tip material was still further improved by mixing the tip material with the full John Innes Compost. Neither addition of the inorganic fertilizer alone nor dilution of the tip material with sand (up to three parts sand to one part tip material) significantly improved the copper and zinc tip materials as media for plant growth. However, very good growth could be obtained in mixtures of these tip materials with John Innes Compost provided the amount of tip material did not exceed 25 per cent. Clearly, the addition of organic material or loam (in the form here of John Innes Compost) was beneficial in all cases and particularly with the zinc and copper tip materials.

From these preliminary greenhouse experiments it became clear that in planning planting trials on the valley tips, consideration would have to be given to incorporating, at the seeding sites, a general inorganic fertilizer, lime (this latter to apply to copper and zinc tips and not to the steel tip) and a source of organic matter. Our aim being to develop, if possible, a low cost procedure for revegetation, we had to think of readily available and cheap sources of organic material and hence of such materials as domestic refuse and sewage sludge. That both of these materials might be valuable was indicated by the demonstration that their incorporation into the copper tip material enhanced significantly percentage germination and the growth of seedlings of White Mustard.

3   Randomized block experiments

The randomized block experiments, which occupy at each tip site the wire-caged experimental areas, were laid down in May 1963 and are continuing to yield results relevant to the revegetation of the tips. These experiments were planned in the light of the results of a pilot experiment initiated in May 1962.

(a) 1962 pilot experiment

In describing the 1962 pilot experiment and the main 1963 experimental results, the phrase 'acceptable level of growth' will be used. This indicated that, in the view of the research workers, the extent of growth and the appearance of the plants at the time of observation were such as to provide a satisfactory vegetation cover. The phrase does not denote any absolute standard but, in practice, usually includes the most promising experimental treatments at any one experimental site, together with other treatments supporting only slightly inferior growth.

The pilot experiment involved experimental plots of 2×1 yd set with seed in May 1962 or with transplanted seedlings 3–5 weeks later. The trial species selected were White Mustard, Common Bent and Wild White Clover (*Trifolium repens*). The mustard plants were harvested nine weeks from sowing; the two perennial species were assessed in March 1963 following over-wintering. At the outset, the tip surface was dug over to permit of the incorporation into the surface of amending materials. The two reference or control treatments were unamended tip material and a surface layer (3 in) of good garden soil. The experimental plots were prepared by mixing into the tip surface various combinations of hydrated lime, complete inorganic fertilizer (Fisons No. 41; 10 per cent N, 10 per cent P_2O_5, 18 per cent K_2O), sodium nitrate and, as sources of organic matter, either sewage sludge (in powder form from the Llanelli and Neath Rural District Councils) or sedge peat.

This pilot experiment indicated considerable mortality during the early stages of seedling establishment from seed, particularly on the zinc and copper tips. Nevertheless, plants were successfully established from seed at each site on the more favourable experimental plots. Since sowing to seed would have a very great advantage over using transplanted seedlings when attempting to revegetate large areas it was decided that the 1963 experiment should involve only seed.

The pilot experiment also indicated clearly the value of liming on the copper tip and its possible beneficial effect on the zinc tip. A significantly beneficial effect of sodium nitrate or general fertilizer alone was only observed on the steel tip. At all sites, acceptable levels of growth were, however, only obtained where organic matter was mixed with the tip material and in this respect the sewage sludge was markedly superior to the sedge peat. The beneficial effect of the sewage sludge was in all cases enhanced by the simultaneous addition of the general fertilizer. No experimental treatment was as effective as the 3-in layer of garden soil; these soil plots still (1966) support an acceptable level of growth at each site.

(b) 1963 main experiment

For the 1963 experiment, the following seeds were used: White Mustard (3 oz/yd²); Common Bent-grass ($\frac{3}{4}$ oz/yd²) and a grass ley mixture ($1\frac{1}{2}$ oz/yd²). The grass ley mixture was that devised for the reclamation of coal-shale waste in Lancashire (Coates, 1964) and has the following composition:

		per cent
Italian Ryegrass	S22	12
Perennial Ryegrass	S23	14
Cocksfoot	S143	50
Timothy	S48	8
Creeping Red Fescue	S59	10
Early Red Clover	S151	6

At each site, 144 plots, each 1 yd square, were established; 48 for each seed type. Yields from the grass plots have been recorded for the 1963, 1964 and 1965 growing seasons. The mustard plants from the initial sowing were harvested after six weeks' growth in 1963 and a similar sowing and harvest carried out on the plots in 1964.

At each tip site and for each of the three types of seed, 24 different treatments were duplicated. The experimental treatments involved various combinations of hydrated lime (3 oz per plot), Fisons No. 41 fertilizer (3 oz per plot) and, as sources of organic matter, either sewage sludge or 3-year-old screened domestic refuse (obtained from a tip of the Swansea County Borough Corporation). Whereas in the pilot experiment a fixed addition (3-in depth as defined below) of sludge had been tested, in the present experiment both sources of organic matter were tested at several rates of application. The rates of application were determined as the depth of layer of material over the whole plot area before incorporation and were 1 inch and 2 inches for domestic refuse (referred to below as DR) and 1 inch, 2 inches and 4 inches for sewage sludge (referred to below as SS). Additions of hydrated lime were omitted in preparing the experimental plots on the steel tip which was already rich in lime, thus allowing additional rates of application of DR ($\frac{1}{4}$ in, $\frac{1}{2}$ in and 4 in) and of SS ($\frac{1}{4}$ in, $\frac{1}{2}$ in and 6 in) to be used in the range of experimental treatments. The only management necessary was a weeding of plots receiving organic matter, particularly of those into which SS was incorporated.

Mustard

The data for the 1963 harvest of mustard in this experiment have been described in an earlier publication (Weston *et al.*, 1965). Taken together with the 1964 harvest data for this test plant (see also Table 5·7), the results indicate that:

1   The zinc tip supported the poorest growth. Most treatments were failures with yellowed or bronzed plants and large bare patches in the plots. The only clearly acceptable growth was in 1963 with a 1 or 2-in application of DR plus general fertilizer, although even these had failed by 1964, when a barely acceptable growth was measured on plots having DR plus lime or DR plus lime and fertilizer. SS was obviously inferior to DR as an organic amendment on the zinc plots when mustard was the test plant.

2   The steel tip showed by far the best growth and cover, acceptable performances being obtained both on untreated plots and on plots receiving general fertilizer only. Unless general fertilizer was added at the same time, no improvement resulted from incorporating organic matter (1963 harvest) and even then, did not persist into 1964. There was a slight all-round tendency for SS to be better than DR as an organic amendment. Although by 1964 the best growth was shown by plots having 4 or 6 in of SS with or without fertilizer, all the results suggest that a performance only slightly inferior to these could have been obtained with general fertilizer only, added in that year.

3   Growth on the copper tip was intermediate between that on the zinc and steel tips. Although some plants survived on the 'lime alone' or 'lime plus fertilizer' plots, growth was only clearly acceptable on organic-matter plots, with SS again tending to be slightly more effective than DR. With a layer of organic matter present, fertilizer was markedly beneficial in the year of application (1963) but the effect was lost by 1964 when the best performance was on plots with SS plus lime or SS plus lime and fertilizer. Yellowing and bronzing symptoms and patchiness of plots were not so marked as on the zinc tip.

4   Comparison of the 1963 and 1964 results clearly indicated a loss of effect in 1964 of the 1963 application of general fertilizer and a generally poorer growth in 1964 despite no less favourable weather conditions.

Grass results

The results for Common Bent-grass and the Lancashire ley mixture are now available for three seasons. The more important quantitative results for the 1964 and 1965 harvests are summarized in Table 5.6 and largely corroborate the results obtained with Mustard as a

Table 5.6 Yields (oven-dry weight to nearest gram, of leafy shoots cut at ground level, per $\frac{1}{4}$ yd^2) of Common Bent-grass and grass ley mixture grown under various soil treatments on the steel, copper and zinc tips

		Plot	Nil 1964	Nil 1965	Lime 1964	Lime 1965	Fertilizer 1964	Fertilizer 1965	Lime plus fertilizer 1964	Lime plus fertilizer 1965	Organic matter only 1″ 1964	1″ 1965	2″ 1964	2″ 1965	Organic matter plus lime 1″ 1964	1″ 1965	2″ 1964	2″ 1965	Organic matter plus fertilizer 1″ 1964	1″ 1965	2″ 1964	2″ 1965	Organic matter plus lime and fertilizer 1″ 1964	1″ 1965	2″ 1964	2″ 1965	L.S.D. 5% 1964	1965
GRASS LEY	Steel slag (Duffryn Tip)	DR	19	24	—	—	84	26	—	—	87	50	91	47	—	—	—	—	99	49	83	39	—	—	—	—	32	18
		SS			—	—			—	—	60	36	94	45	—	—	—	—	122	39	94	53	—	—	—	—		
	Copper slag (I.C.I. Tip)	DR	0	0	0	1	1	0	1	—	17	15	22	13	14	5	31	23	30	10	48	16	39	13	95	29	18	8
		SS	0	0							16	11	31	21	23	17	38	28	29	13	46	23	35	17	45	26		
	Zinc slag (Cohen's Tip)	DR	0	0	0	0	3	0	2	—	4	3	8	4	1	2	11	1	7	—	18	5	11	2	28	3	13	4
		SS	0	0			0	2			6	2	4	1	7	4	8	9	1	—	36	7	14	4	55	21		
AGROSTIS	Steel slag (Duffryn Tip)	DR	0	1	—	—	3	3	—	—	2	1	4	3	—	—	—	—	5	2	7	4	—	—	—	—	17	5
		SS			—	—			—	—	51	14	91	19	—	—	—	—	74	14	120	30	—	—	—	—		
	Copper slag (I.C.I. Tip)	DR	0	0	0	0	0	0	1	—	3	2	8	5	5	4	8	6	5	4	9	6	4	4	8	4	17	5
		SS	0	0							17	12	27	24	29	12	38	18	12	9	76	30	30	12	37	19		
	Zinc slag (Cohen's Tip)	DR	0	0	0	0	0	0	0	—	1	1	6	2	1	1	2	1	2	0	6	2	2	1	2	2	17	5
		SS	0	0							3	2	3	1	11	2	6	4	0	0	2	1	21	5	36	13		

L.S.D.: Least significant difference at P < 0·05.

Table 5.7 Summary of dry weight yields in terms of 'acceptable growth' of Mustard (1963 and 1964 harvests), Common Bent-grass (1964 and 1965 harvests) and grass ley (1964 and 1965 harvests), grown under various soil treatments on the steel, copper and zinc tips

Tip type	Test plant		Nil	Lime	Fertilizer	Lime plus fertilizer		Organic matter 1"	Organic matter 2"	Organic matter plus lime 1"	Organic matter plus lime 2"	Organic matter plus fertilizer 1"	Organic matter plus fertilizer 2"	Organic matter plus lime and fertilizer 1"	Organic matter plus lime and fertilizer 2"
Steel tip (Duffryn)	Mustard	DR	*	—	*	—		†	†	—	—	*	*	—	—
		SS						†	*	—	—	*	*	—	—
	Grass ley	DR	§	—	*	—		*	*	—	—	‡	‡	—	—
		SS						*	*	—	—	‡	*	—	—
	Common Bent	DR	§	—	§	—		§	§	—	—	§	§	—	—
		SS						‡	*	—	—	‡	*	—	—
Copper tip (I.C.I.)	Mustard	DR	§	†	§	†		†	†	†	+	†	‡	§	†
		SS						*	*	†	*	*	§	‡	‡
	Grass ley	DR	§	§	§	§		*	*	§	*	‡	§	§	§
		SS						‡	‡	*	*	‡	§	‡	*
	Common Bent	DR	§	§	§	§		§	§	§	§	§	§	§	§
		SS						‡	*	‡	*	§	*	‡	‡
Zinc tip (Cohen's)	Mustard	DR	§	§	§	§		§	†	§	§	‡	§	‡	†
		SS						§	§	§	§	§	§	‡	‡
	Grass ley	DR	§	§	§	§		§	§	§	§	§	§	‡	†
		SS						§	§	§	§	§	§	§	‡
	Common Bent	DR	§	§	§	§		§	§	§	§	§	§	§	§
		SS						§	§	§	§	§	§	‡	‡

* Acceptable growth in 1st and 2nd harvests.
† Acceptable growth in 2nd harvest only.
‡ Acceptable growth in 1st harvest only.
§ No acceptable growth either in 1st or 2nd harvests.

Acceptable growth for grass ley on steel waste taken as 25 g D.M./¼ yd²
Acceptable growth for all other grass trials taken as 15 g D.M./¼ yd²
Acceptable growth for mustard in 1963 taken as 20 mg D.M./plant
Acceptable growth for mustard in 1964 taken as 1·8 g D.M./¼ yd²

test plant. The results of the grass plots have also been assessed on the basis of an acceptable level of growth performance in their third year. Table 5.7 indicates, for both mustard and the grasses, which treatments support acceptable levels of growth.

It is perhaps of interest to point out in relation to Table 5.6 that if the figures for grams of oven-dry grass/$\frac{1}{4}$ yd^2 are divided by two, then the numerical values give an indication of yields in cwt air-dry grass per acre. For farms in South West Wales, the average yield of a grass field cut once for hay is about 50 cwt/acre (figure supplied by the Ministry of Agriculture).

The data in Table 5.6 show, as previously noted, that, in general, growth was worst on the zinc tip, best on the steel tip and intermediate on the copper tip. It is also clear that without organic matter added, the lime and the fertilizer treatments were failures on the zinc and copper tips with both types of sward whereas on the steel tip the fertilizer alone was sufficient treatment to produce good growth of the grass ley mixture. The necessity of SS in order to produce an acceptable growth of the Bent-grass on each tip; the effectiveness of DR for the Mustard and grass ley mixture and the general decline in growth of all test plants from 1964 to 1965 are evident from the data in Tables 5.6 and 5.7. On the zinc and copper tips, the Clover and, to a lesser extent, the Cocksfoot tended to become dominant in the grass ley mixture except where SS was incorporated. This suggests nitrogen shortage in the absence of the SS addition. The Common Bent-grass plots on the copper and zinc tips commonly showed a patchiness and a browning of the leaf tips; the Cocksfoot in the grass ley plots often showed yellowing and death of leaves. Except where Clover became dominant, all the grass plots were less green in 1965 than in 1964, this being particularly marked on the zinc tip.

One important feature of this randomized block experiment as envisaged at the time of its initiation was that the experimental treatments should be 'once for all'. This was done in the hope that grass cover could be maintained in the absence of costly fertilizer reapplication. In consequence, no top dressings of general fertilizer, lime or organic matter have been added to the plots since they were sown to seed in 1963. The fall off in growth of the grass plots in 1965, together with visual symptoms (spread of the nitrogen-fixing clover, reduction in green colour of the grasses), particularly as developed at the relatively non-toxic steel tip, suggest that one factor now limiting growth may be lack of mineral nutrients (particularly nitrogen, phosphorus and potassium). This has been tested by applications of top dressings at all three sites in the spring of 1966. Although visually, there has been a strong growth and greening-up response to the fertilizer on the copper and zinc tips, until the harvest results of the autumn of 1966 are available it is difficult to estimate whether permanently acceptable grass swards can be established on these tips.

4 Large-scale seed trials, 1965

It was decided to set up at each experimental site large demonstration plots using those treatments which had shown greatest promise (1964 harvest) in the Randomized Block Experiment (Sect. 3b). Only by this means could the suitability of the grass cover obtainable be easily appreciated and some provisional estimate be made of the physical problems and costs which would be encountered in large-scale revegetation of the tips along these lines.

The laying out of these large-scale trials was also made the occasion to test the value of a surface layer of pulverized fuel ash (PFA) as a seed bed and of an additional grass species, Red Fescue (*Festuca rubra*). The PFA was made available by the Superintendent of the Tir John Power Station, Port Tennant, Swansea. This power station uses anthracite duff and the resulting ash being relatively low in boron is non-toxic and, following application of a suitable general fertilizer, has been sown successfully with a grass-clover mixture (Tir John Ley Mixture), devised by the Department of Botany, Birmingham University, and having the following composition:

		per cent
Perennial Ryegrass	S23	40
Creeping Red Fescue	S59	30
White Clover	S100	30 (inoculated with *Rhizobium trifolii*)

The choice of Red Fescue as an additional species for sowing arose out of a test (1964–5), conducted at each site on plots amended only by application of general fertilizer or of general fertilizer plus hydrated lime, of the growth of six selected grass species: *Poa annua* (Annual Meadow-grass); *Poa pratensis* (Meadow-grass); *Festuca longifolia*; *Festuca ovina* (Sheep's Fescue); *Festuca rubra* ssp. *rubra* (Red Fescue); *Cynosurus cristatus* (Crested Dog's-tail). The Red Fescue alone, of those tested, showed ability to establish itself from seed at all three sites.

The Large-Scale Seed Trials involved the seeding at each site of four plots, each of $\frac{1}{4}$ acre with a layout and treatment régime as shown in the following diagram (Table 5.8). Seeding to this plan (Table 5.8) took place in May 1965. By September 1965, these plots, with the exception of 'general fertilizer only' on the zinc tip and 'general fertilizer plus lime' on the copper tip, all showed very vigorous growth. By the summer of 1966, however, they appeared to support (quantitative yields not yet harvested) a poorer growth except where fertilizer had been added to selected strips. In view of the decline in yields in the Randomized Block Experiment in its third year, the future of these large-scale trials must be regarded as uncertain and a management plan has been devised so that they will continue to yield valuable information.

It is doubtful whether the cost of laying out these large-scale trials is a close guide to the costs which would be involved in attempts at more extensive revegetation. To establish to experimental standards, $12 \times \frac{1}{12}$th acre areas using a number of different amendments and four types of seed is inevitably an expensive operation relative to a single treatment and single seeding over a similar total area. The cost of cultivation (ploughing, stone-picking, harrowing, spreading and fencing) were high, at about £120 per acre. Although the DR, SS and PFA were available free, their transport to the separate sites was very expensive. The purchase and spreading of lime, fertilizer and seed on an acre of tip already fenced, cultivated and stone-picked was roughly £35 (£10–£15 higher than large-scale agricultural re-seeding operations) but to this must be added another £150 or so if a 3-in layer of PFA or a 2-in layer of organic material is transported and spread. The transport of soil amendments in bulk is by far the costliest item in reseeding operations and emphasizes the need to determine beforehand, by field trials, the minimal amounts required. If some source of organic matter proves essential for successful grass establishment, then the controlled

Table 5.8 Layout of large-scale seed trial plots (A–D)

Ground preparation	Amendment added to tip:	Fertilizer added:	Seeds mixture
1 acre of level tip: (a) ploughed with scarifier[1] (b) raked with heavy spike harrow (c) stone picked (d) divided into 4 plots each ¼ acre (A–D) (e) each plot A–D divided into 3 sub-plots each 1/12th acre (1–3)	A: SS spread 2 in thick/yd² by earth-moving machinery and harrowing to mix SS with tip material[2]	A: 2 cwt Fisons 41 and 2 cwt ground limestone spread over A[4]	Sub-plot 1: 5 lb Lancashire ley mixture sown and harrowed in. Sub-plot 2: 5 lb Agrostis tenuis sown and harrowed in. Sub-plot 3: 5 lb Festuca rubra sown and harrowed in.
	B: DR spread 2 in thick/yd², as above[3]	B: 2 cwt Fisons 41 spread over B	Sub-plot 1 / Sub-plot 2 / Sub-plot 3 } Seeding treatments as above
	C: No organic material added	C: 2 cwt Fisons 41 and 2 cwt hydrated lime spread over C[5]	Sub-plot 1 / Sub-plot 2 / Sub-plot 3 } Seedling treatments as above
	D: PFA spread, but not mixed with tip material, as follows: Sub-plot 1: 3 in thick/yd² Sub-plot 2: 6 in thick/yd² Sub-plot 3: 9 in thick/yd²	D: 1 cwt Fisons 41 spread over D[6]	Sub-plot 1 / Sub-plot 2 / Sub-plot 3 } Each sown with 5 lb Tir John ley mixture

Notes: [1] (a) omitted on copper tip. [2] SS ½ in thick/yd² on copper tip. [3] DR ½ in thick on steel plot. [4] 2 cwt hydrated lime substituted on copper plot. All lime treatments omitted on steel plot. [5] Half of C received 2 cwt hydrated lime and half, 1 cwt only, on copper plot. [6] 1 cwt Fisons 52 substituted on copper and steel plots (Fisons 41: N 10%; P_2O_5 10%; K_2O 18%. Fisons 52: N 20%; P_2O_5 10%; K_2O 10%).

Seeds mixtures:

Lancashire Ley mixture
12 per cent S22, Italian Ryegrass
14 per cent S23, Perennial Ryegrass
50 per cent S143, Cocksfoot
8 per cent S48, Timothy
10 per cent S59, Creeping Red Fescue
6 per cent English Broad Red Clover (instead of S151)

Tir John Ley mixture
40 per cent S23 Perennial Ryegrass
30 per cent S59 Creeping Red Fescue
30 per cent S100 Wild White Clover (inoculated)

Agrostis tenuis
American Highland Bent

tipping of domestic refuse in the valley may be an effective way of reducing this component in the overall cost.

5 Trials of selected transplants and seeds

Experimental trials initiated in the spring of 1963 involved the planting of trees, shrubs and non-woody species, some of them capable of fixing atmospheric nitrogen, at seven tip sites. The plants had well-developed root systems when transplanted or, in the case of the two non-woody species normally raised from seed, were sown directly in the tips at each of the sites. There were two amendments which were applied to the tips in various ways as indicated in Table 5.9 to give eleven treatment types, each 3×3 yd. Some seventeen selected species were tested in these experiments (six trees, nine shrubs and two herbaceous species, as shown below), but reference here will be confined to those which have become most successfully established or failed conspicuously:

Table 5.9   Layout of treatments for species trials

Cultivation	Amendment used	Amendment applied
	A Nil	1 None
Tip surface dug over	B { SS spread 2 in thick plus 3 oz/yd² Fisons 41 fertilizer plus 3 oz/yd² hydrated lime	2 to tip surface / 3 in shallow trenches / 4 in small pits
	C { DR spread 2 in thick plus 3 oz/yd² Fisons 41 fertilizer plus 3 oz/yd² hydrated lime	5 to tip surface / 6 in shallow trenches / 7 in small pits
Tip surface left undug	D—As B above	8 to tip surface / 9 worked into surface
	E—As C above	10 to tip surface / 11 worked into surface

Trees
Alnus glutinosa (Common Alder)
A. incana (Grey Alder)
Betula spp. (chiefly verrucosa) (Birch)
Robinia pseudoacacia (Black Locust)
Sorbus aucuparia (Rowan)
Thelycrania sanguinea (Dogwood)

Shrubs—contd.
Hippophae rhamnoides (Sea Buckthorn)
Ligustrum vulgare (Privet)
Lupinus arboreus (Tree Lupin)
Rhododendron ponticum (Rhododendron)
Salix repens (Creeping Willow)
Sarothamnus scoparius (Broom)
Ulex europaeus (Gorse)

Shrubs
Buddlejia davidii (Buddleia)
Clematis vitalba (Traveller's Joy)

Herbaceous Species
Medicago sativa (Lucerne)
Tagetes minuta (Tagetes)

As would be expected from previously described experiments, the highest number of successful species and the most vigorous growth occurred on the steel tip sites; the zinc tip sites were least successful and the copper tip sites intermediate in performance. Results, expressed as records of growth in 1964 (1963 growth for Tagetes which is an annual) and survival up to 1965, can be summarized as follows:

1   In general, none of the cultivation treatments shown in Table 5.9 stood out as being clearly better than the others. Of the species planted, Privet showed the greatest survival, closely followed by Buddleia and Gorse. Clematis, Sea Buckthorn and Creeping Willow showed only half to a third of the survival of these first three, with Rhododendron faring very badly.

2   There was a distinct tendency for Sea Buckthorn, Creeping Willow, Lucerne and Tagetes to survive and grow better in the DR treatments than in the SS plots, whilst Buddleia grew slightly better in the SS treatments. However, in the case of Creeping Willow, the best survival and growth was recorded in unamended materials.

3   On the steel tips, the most successful species were Privet, Buddleia, Gorse, Sea Buckthorn, Grey Alder and Locust, the last four being nitrogen fixers. They grew well when planted directly into the untreated tip material, but the best growth was generally found when DR or SS plus general fertilizer were applied. Clematis was successful with SS.

4   On the copper tips, good growth was obtained only when organic matter was used, and growth in general was below that obtained on the steel tips. The best treatment was DR plus general fertilizer; this supported relatively good growth of Privet, Buddleia, Birch and particularly Alder and Tagetes. Gorse performed well in SS but Sea Buckthorn survived badly and grew poorly.

5   On the zinc tips, growth was inferior to that on the copper tips, Lucerne failing completely. Relatively good growth was, however, again recorded with Privet, Buddleia, Gorse and Tagetes, especially in the presence of organic matter. Sea Buckthorn survived poorly on SS.

These results taken as a whole suggest that domestic refuse is a suitable organic amendment for the majority of successful species and since it was quite satisfactory when spread over the tip surface, there is no need to incur the heavy costs of cultivation prior to planting.

6   Grasses collected from old mining spoil areas

The experiments described in this section tested the growth performance of twenty-three grass strains collected from eighteen sites of old copper, or lead–zinc mines in North Wales, Cornwall, Devon, Staffordshire and the Republic of Ireland, where they were found growing naturally on heaps of old mining spoil. The work of Jowett (1958) and Gregory and Bradshaw (1965) has shown that, during the course of their evolutionary history, grasses found growing on old mining spoils have frequently become specially adapted to exhibit an inherited tolerance to the high concentrations of metals found at their home sites; they will root and grow in soils containing sufficient poisonous metal to kill a normal grass, and moreover their tolerance is quite specific to the metal contaminating their site of origin. From twelve of these sites, samples of Common Bent-grass were obtained. The other species collected were: Creeping Bent-grass, Red Fescue, Sheep's Fescue (Festuca ovina), Wavy Hair-grass, and Sweet Vernal Grass (Anthoxanthum odoratum). To this collection was added a sample of Creeping Bent and a sample of Common Bent, both found colonizing the copper tip (Plot 49) in the valley; a sample of Creeping Bent obtained from Cohen's Pond at the foot of the Cohen's zinc tip and another from the newly tipped zinc waste in the valley.

Most of the above grasses were suspected to be tolerant of higher than normal concentrations of zinc/lead or copper, depending on their origin, and for purposes of comparison a normal strain of Common Bent was collected from Penrice Woods in Gower, where the soil had never been contaminated with copper, lead or zinc.

All these strains were multiplied vegetatively in normal soil, and when sufficient material was ready two sets of shoots of each grass strain were transplanted out, either in the zinc or the copper tip, depending on whether their home site had been zinc or copper-contaminated. For each strain, shoots of one set were planted in the untreated surface of the appropriate tip type while the shoots of the other set were planted in tip material which had been dressed with Fisons No. 41 general fertilizer (3 oz/yd²) and hydrated lime (3 oz/yd²). The plantings were carried out in 1963 and growth of the plants was assessed in 1964 and 1965 by measuring the increase in girth of each from May to August 1964 and again in 1965.

In 1964 a second experiment with these grasses was initiated using the vacant White Mustard plots of the Randomized Block Experiment (see Section 3b). The plots which had originally been treated with DR or SS, lime and/or fertilizer received, immediately prior to planting, a new dressing of Fisons No. 41 general fertilizer, and hydrated lime where appropriate, at the standard rate. The plots were then planted with the Penrice Woods Common Bent, a grass naturally colonizing the tip (Common Bent in the case of the copper tip and Creeping Bent in the case of the zinc tip) and seven strains from the grass collection chosen from their first-year performance in the 1963 experiment. Growth measurements were made during 1965 in each of the organic matter plots and the average growth performance for each strain calculated.

On each tip type and under each soil treatment régime (i.e. fertilizer plus lime, organic amendment, untreated, etc.) the grass strains used, all grew at different rates and could be arranged in a hierarchy of increasing growth rate, starting with the value for the non-tolerant Penrice Woods strain which showed virtually no growth or even a gradual dieback. One important feature was that the order of merit of any particular strain in the hierarchy varied depending on whether it was growing in the untreated tip or receiving 'fertilizer plus lime' or 'organic amendments'.

Position in the hierarchy as revealed in these tip plantings may be governed by many factors apart from tolerance to zinc or copper, e.g. tolerance of low mineral nutrient supply, or of the unfavourable water or temperature régimes normally associated with mine dumps or tips. In order to obtain an assessment of each grass strain's tolerance of copper or zinc uncomplicated by the other factors, a laboratory culture solution technique was used. Wilkins (1957, 1960) developed a method for testing the tolerance of a grass to a solution of poisonous metal and this technique, suitably modified, has been used to test the tolerance either to zinc (using a solution of 10 and 20 parts per million) or to copper (using a solution of 0·5 p.p.m.) of all the grass strains used in the present experiments. The test is based on the observation that metal ions at concentrations toxic to plant growth are strongly and rapidly inhibitory to the growth of young roots. It involves the preparation, under standard conditions, of replicate tillers (a rooted side shoot) each with a single root, their growth by a drip culture technique and the measurement over successive two-day periods of the growth in length of the root in the absence and then in the presence of the test concentration of the metal ion. From these measurements, an Index of Tolerance is calculated using the formula:

$$\text{Index} = 1 + \log \frac{A}{B}$$

where A is the mean value for root growth in absence of the test metal, and B in its presence. A low Index, therefore, indicates high tolerance, a high Index low tolerance (e.g. an Index of 2·0 indicates that growth is 90 per cent inhibited by the test metal).

How far is the relative tolerance of a strain to high zinc or copper (as measured by the Index of Tolerance) correlated with its position in the hierarchical lists obtained from the 1963 and 1964 planting trials described above? There was a strong statistical agreement between the Index of Tolerance of each strain to zinc and its relative growth on the zinc tip, both when lime and fertilizer had been added and when the tip material had been left untreated. However, for the grass strains grown in the organically amended plots, there was no correlation between their growth and the solution test. This result suggests that tolerance of high levels of zinc was the principal factor controlling growth on the zinc tip in the absence of organic matter, but that when this was present, zinc tolerance no longer conferred any special growth advantage on the strains. There was a strong statistical correlation between the Index of Tolerance to copper and growth on the copper tip with added lime and fertilizer, but no special correlation between the solution test results and the unfertilized treatment data or the organically amended results. This indicates that strains grown on the unfertilized copper tip were being controlled more by the absence of fertilizer and lime than by high copper and that only when the mineral nutrient régime on the tips was improved did they react primarily to high copper. Like the zinc tip, possession of copper tolerance conferred no special advantage in the presence of organic matter. The results indicate that an important aspect of the beneficial effect of organic matter is that it neutralizes the effects of high levels of copper or zinc. This suggests that inherited tolerance to copper and zinc could be of importance when the plant roots penetrate below the organic matter layer or if organic matter added becomes, with the passage of time, less effective in antagonizing metal toxicity. These experiments should now be extended to test for tolerance to other metals such as lead and nickel. These elements are present in high amounts in the tips and it is possible that they are more important than zinc in inhibiting growth. It is known that the strains of grass that grew best on the zinc tip are also tolerant of lead but no assessment has been made of how far lead tolerance can be correlated with growth at the tip sites.

7 Microbiological studies

When considering the problem of how to grow plants on the valley tips, the question of their persistence is clearly of great importance. The nitrogen, phosphorus and potassium added in fertilizer during revegetation operations is taken up into the leaves and stems of the growing plants and these nutrients are eventually returned to the soil as dead plant remains which fall to the ground each winter. Until these nutrients are released from this organic debris by the activities of soil bacteria, fungi and soil animals (springtails, mites, fly larvae, worms, etc.) which normally feed off organic matter, the nutrients remain unavailable to roots of the growing plant. Thus, succeeding generations of plants would eventually suffer mineral nutrient starvation if, for some reason the nature of the soil inhibited the activity of micro-organisms. It was therefore important to discover whether the toxic metals in the tips inhibit the development of a normal active micro-organism complement, thus preventing continuous regeneration.

Fertile soils have a rich flora of micro-organisms (bacteria and fungi) which are particularly abundant and actively growing within the outermost regions of the roots, on root surfaces and in the soil close to the roots. The harmless micro-organisms thus closely associated with growing roots constitute what is termed the rhizosphere microflora and the dominant organisms in this flora are often characteristic of particular species of flowering plants. It was, therefore, considered important to find out what micro-organisms occur naturally in the valley tips; how far this microflora differed appreciably in size from that of normal soil; to what extent it would be modified by additions to the tips of organic materials; how far micro-organisms would actively decompose organic matter at the tip sites and how far normal rhizosphere microflora would develop in association with experimentally planted species of flowering plants. The microbiological studies undertaken have provided information on these aspects of the plant trials described in earlier sections of this chapter.

(a)   Microflora of the tips

Microbial colonization of buried cellulose film was followed using the technique of Tribe (1961). The cellulose film (cellophane film, PT 300) was attached to microscope slides and these were buried in the unamended experimental plots (Randomized Block Experiment, 1963) at all three tip sites and in samples of material brought into the laboratory from these plots and incubated at 25° C and 60 per cent moisture-holding capacity, either unamended, or mixed with DR or SS (9 per cent by weight, i.e. roughly equivalent to a 2-in layer of organic matter). At intervals, the slides were dug up and organisms colonizing the films were studied microscopically after appropriate staining. Colonization of the cellulose film buried in untreated zinc tip material was extremely slow in the laboratory and even after ten weeks' incubation the film was invaded only by a few straggling hyphae. Film buried in untreated copper and steel tip material slowly became well colonized. Fungi of seven well-known soil genera were identified in the films. Primarily colonization by fungi was followed by bacteria and still later by amoebal colonization. When the tip materials were amended by the addition of DR or SS in the laboratory, colonization and the succession of fungi, bacteria and amoeba occurred rapidly in all three types. In addition, nematodes and nematode-trapping fungi were observed. Films were disintegrated in the presence of SS, apparently as a result of the activity of mites. The unamended tip materials in the field became colonized in patches only, even after as long as thirty weeks, and there was no sign of animal activity.

Bacteria were isolated from the zinc (23 isolates) and copper (25 isolates) tip materials by standard bacteriological methods. The tolerance of these bacteria to zinc and copper was tested by a technique used routinely in testing antibiotics. Sterile flat dishes (Petri dishes) containing suspensions of the separate bacterial isolates in a rich culture solution solidified to a jelly with agar were used. Holes (0·275 in diam.) were made in the jelly by removing a circular disc of jelly with a sterile cork-borer. Into such holes was placed a neutral solution containing a pure zinc or copper salt at known concentration. The dishes were then incubated when, unless inhibited, the bacteria multiply rapidly and turn the originally clear jelly opaque. If the metal solution as it diffuses into the jelly is inhibitory to bacterial growth, a clear zone appears around the hole containing the metal solution, and the more sensitive to inhibition are the bacteria the greater is the diameter of this clear zone. By this technique the tolerance of the bacteria isolated from the zinc tip was tested against zinc and those from the copper tip tested against copper. For comparison, bacteria isolated from garden soil (10 isolates) were tested for their tolerance to both metals. The bacteria from the zinc tip only showed inhibitory (clear) zones when the test solution contained 100 parts per million (p.p.m.) or more zinc; all the garden soil bacteria were inhibited by 10 p.p.m., but not at 5 p.p.m. zinc. The bacteria from the copper tip were inhibited by 50 p.p.m. and strongly by 100 p.p.m. copper; the garden soil bacteria were all inhibited by 4 p.p.m. but not by 1 p.p.m. copper.

Nitrogen-fixing bacteria (*Azotobacter*) could not be detected in the tip materials. The survival of such bacteria (e.g. *Rhizobium* spp.) introduced with clover into the experimental plots has yet to be tested.

(b) Rhizosphere microflora

As indicated earlier, the rhizosphere microflora includes bacteria and fungi. It is related to the species of plant whose roots are examined and is markedly influenced by the general soil conditions. In the studies now reported, attention was confined: to fungi actually adherent to the roots as vegetative filaments (mycelium) or growing within the superficial root tissues; to the roots of the single grass, Common Bent-grass; and to plants growing in the tip materials amended only by inorganic fertilizers (Fisons No. 41 general fertilizer only on the steel tip; this fertilizer plus hydrated lime on the copper and zinc tips).

Bacteria and fungal spores were removed from the root pieces by a washing technique (Harley and Waid, 1955). The washed root pieces were either submitted to direct microscopic examination after appropriate staining or were placed on the surface of a nutrient-rich agar jelly and the fungal hyphae, growing out from the root, isolated and examined (bacteria which might otherwise have competitively colonized the agar jelly from the root pieces were inhibited by the bacteriostatic agent, streptomycin).

The fungal population found on the roots was similar when plants from all three sites were examined. Fungi belonging to fifteen genera were recognized; they were all amongst those commonly reported in rhizosphere studies (Waid, 1957; Chesters and Parkinson, 1959; Parkinson and Clarke, 1961; Gadgil, 1965b). One species, *Fusarium solani*, was particularly abundant on young roots at all sites but especially on the zinc tip where it was also dominant on older roots. This was in contrast to the old roots of Bent-grass from the copper and steel tips which yielded a large proportion of dark fungal mycelium and few *Fusarium solani*. The abundance of this species and also of other fungi was apparently subject to considerable seasonal fluctuation at all sites. Commonly encountered were species of *Penicillium* and, within the root tissues, a mycelium closely resembling the 'bead system' of Nicolson (1959) and identical with that previously reported from grass roots (Gadgil, 1965b). As expected, mycelial isolates, both 'thin and translucent' and 'dark', which remained vegetative in culture and could, therefore, not be identified, were frequently encountered. A proportion of the root segments (at certain times as many as 30 per cent) did not yield any fungi although they did carry a bacterial population. These segments were often from near the growing root apices. The patchiness of distribution of fungi over the root revealed here supports the view that these organisms do not spread rapidly in a longitudinal direction over the root but reach the surface by lateral spread in the rooting medium (Taylor and Parkinson, 1961; Parkinson et al., 1963). The patchiness of invasion would then reflect the relatively low density of micro-organisms and other roots at the tip sites. Although the roots clearly had a rhizosphere microflora, this differed from that typical of the roots of Common Bent-grass growing in soil. The most marked difference was the complete absence of a definite root-fungus association (mycorrhiza) of the type described as 'endotrophic vesicular-arbuscular' and extremely common in many grasses including Common Bent-grass growing in normal soil (Nicolson, 1959; Mosse, 1963). The other was the total absence of any nematodes (Linford, 1942; Gadgil, 1965b).

(c) **Activity of the microflora of the tip materials in decomposing organic matter**

The rate of respiration, as measured by the rate of release of the gas, carbon dioxide, is a useful index of the activity of living organisms. Hence, it is possible to assess the activity of the living population of micro-organisms in the tip materials by determining the rate at which these materials released this gas. The bodies of the micro-organisms are rich in proteins and since these are nitrogen-containing compounds there is retention of nitrogen in any material where such organisms are increasing in number. However, micro-organisms can also decompose organic manures containing nitrogen, leading to the production of soluble ammonium salts or nitrates or a mixture of both these inorganic forms of nitrogen, according to the conditions and organisms present. Since green plants need an adequate supply of inorganic nitrogen, the activities of the microflora in releasing nitrogen from soil organic matter and in retaining nitrogen in their own bodies are of importance in relation to plant growth. Studies have therefore been made of the activities of the microfloras of the tips in releasing inorganic nitrogen from such organic amendments as SS, DR and dead grass leaves and of the extent to which nitrate becomes incorporated into microflora proteins and hence is made unavailable for plant growth.

As might have been anticipated from the results of the cellophane colonization experiment, the micro-organisms' activity in all three types of untreated tip material, as assessed by its carbon dioxide release, was at an extremely low level and no nitrate nitrogen was liberated. This low activity of the microflora may be due, not so much to the poisonous nature of the tip materials, as to the shortage of naturally occurring organic matter to act as a food source for the bacteria and fungi; all three tip materials are known to be extremely poor in organic matter. When, however, an *insoluble* source of organic matter in the form of pure powdered cellulose was added to the copper and zinc wastes, the rate of carbon dioxide evolution was barely increased. In order to exploit the added cellulose effectively, it would be necessary for the small natural population of soil micro-organisms to increase greatly in size and, in so doing, their demand for nitrogen to incorporate into their body proteins would be high, perhaps much higher than the relatively nitrogen-free tips could supply. The further addition of a soluble nitrogen source, in the form of nitrate, trebled the carbon dioxide production in the zinc–cellulose mixture but barely affected the copper–cellulose mixture. A similar result was once again obtained in the case of the zinc waste, where nitrate plus a *soluble* organic source (glucose) caused carbon dioxide output to rise by a hundredfold or more, after a period during which the population of micro-organisms increased very greatly. It is clear that microbial activity in the zinc tip material is limited far more by lack of organic matter and nitrogen, than by any other factor such as zinc toxicity. This fits in with the results of the zinc tolerance tests using bacteria isolated from the zinc tip. The result with the copper tip material indicates that some other factor, as yet unknown, is limiting microbial activity. The high degree of tolerance to copper solutions shown by the copper tip bacteria suggests that copper toxicity is not involved, and other evidence, not now reported, points to a deficiency of some nutrient other than nitrogen limiting bacterial growth, a hypothesis which must remain tentative until tested by further experiments.

Addition of SS (9 per cent by weight and equivalent to a 2-in layer incorporated at the tip surface) enhanced carbon dioxide evolution about ten times with each tip material, but in all cases there was very little release of nitrate. DR had a much smaller stimulatory effect on carbon dioxide evolution, but in presence of this amendment there was more nitrate release (although it was still far below that which occurs from a fertile soil). In an attempt to assess how far the microflora of the tips would decompose organic matter added by leaf fall, a powder prepared from dried leafy shoots of Common Bent-grass was incorporated with the tip material both in the presence and absence of added nitrate and carbon dioxide output measured. Since plants of Common Bent-grass grown at the tip sites contain relatively high concentrations of zinc and copper (Table 5.10), dried powders from leafy shoots of this species grown in soil and on the tips were tested separately.

Table 5.10 Zinc and Copper content of Common Bent-grass (*Agrostis tenuis*) **grown in garden soil and on tips**

Determined by Miss C. E. R. Smith, Botany Department, Swansea

Grown in:	Copper p.p.m.	Zinc p.p.m.
Normal rich soil	20	8
Zinc tip (Plot 28)	40	3,000
Copper tip (Plot 49)	120	350

Incorporation of the plant powder enhanced carbon dioxide output of the tip materials; powder of tip-grown plants was less active in this respect than that from soil-grown plants. Whether this was due to lower contents of nutrients or higher contents of heavy metals in the tip-grown grasses was not determined.

The above results indicate that regular dressings with inorganic fertilizer rich in nitrogen will be necessary whenever organic amendments are added to the tip materials in the revegetation procedures. Unless such regular dressings are made, the activity of the microflora will be restricted and inorganic nitrogen will not be released in the amounts necessary for good plant growth.

8 Tree planting

Quite large areas of the valley are covered with a very sparse growth of grass and weeds overlying an infertile clay soil or a tip of some fairly innocuous industrial waste material. In such places, the problem of establishing vegetation was judged to be no more difficult than those already successfully overcome elsewhere in Britain and Europe (Knabe, 1965). For reasons explained in Chapter 10, on 'Visual Improvement', it was decided to establish large demonstration plots of grass and trees on such sites in the valley. Since these areas of clay soils or innocuous wastes are, at certain points, near roads or active industrial centres, these were chosen so that at one and the same time we would: (a) learn which were the most successful tree or grass species, fertilizer and cultivation régimes; (b) estimate what were the costs of large-scale planting; (c) capture public interest and demonstrate the feasibility and visual effect of revegetation.

In 1962 a ground survey was made to locate these sites and the following empirical 'soils' classification was arrived at for all the ground in the Lower Valley:

I Natural soils

These may have been modified by subsequent industrial activity:

(a) *Glacial clay*. Locally derived sandy clay-loams with Pennant Grit boulders; present in the valley as a recessional moraine (Plots 36, 37, 38) and as lateral morainic material (Plots 31, 53, 54). These had lost their topsoil layers in the nineteenth century as a result of smelter-smoke pollution and were now very infertile, rather acid (pH 4·5–5·5) and with some zinc or copper contamination from the smelter smoke (see Section 9 below).

(b) *Alluvium*. A freshwater deposit of a silty or gravelly nature; sometimes peaty. These are found bordering the river Tawe, Nant-y-Fendrod and other smaller streams, as well as around pool margins. They include the natural soil of the valley floor, frequently contain the topsoil washed from the surrounding glacial clays and often tend to become waterlogged (Traversing plots 16, 18, 20).

II Artificial deposits of tipped industrial waste

(a) *Non-ferrous metal waste* derived, in the main, from zinc smelting (Plots 17, 20, 21, 28, 52) or copper smelting (Plots 21, 22, 40, 49, 50, 52, 54, 57).

(b) *Coal shale* from old mine workings (there are several small areas in plots 18, 31, 42).

(c) *Furnace ash*. This material is usually mixed with coal-shale, clinker, etc. (Plots 16, 24, 51, 66).

(d) *Ferrous metal waste*, e.g. furnace slag constituting the 'steel' tips (Plots 3, 7, 15, 19, 24, 26, 27).

(e) *Sand*—either calcareous sea-ballast (Plot 17) or acid foundry sand (Plot 40).

(f) *'Rubble'*. This is a rather variable material, mainly brick, mortar, plaster, etc., but may contain industrial waste such as iron-scale or broken porcelain.

(g) *Domestic refuse*. In the past, household rubbish has been tipped in parts of the valley (Plots 16, 18 and on part of Plot 19).

In each of the two main categories (I and II above) the 'soils' are arranged in order of decreasing physical and chemical unsuitability for plant growth. Categories II(a) and II(d) have already been dealt with in the previous sections (Sections 1–7). Trees of various species have been planted on all other categories in the above classification, as shown in Table 5.11.

Table 5.11 Species and numbers of trees planted on different soil categories in the Lower Swansea Valley

No.	Scientific name	English name	I (a) Glacial clay 5, 31, 36, 37, 38, 53, 54	I (b) Alluvium 16, 18, 20	II (b) Coal shale 17, 18, 31, 42	II (c) Furnace ash 16, 24, 51, 66	II (e) Sand 17, 40	II (f) Rubble 15, 24, 62	II (g) Domestic refuse 16, 18, 19	Species Totals	Remarks on performance (5=excellent; 4=good; 3=satisfactory; 2=poor; 1=very poor)
1	Larix leptolepis	Japanese Larch	22,700	—	1,350	3,300	450	400	700	28,900	No growth 1st season, but 4–5 afterwards
2	Pinus contorta	Lodgepole Pine	16,400	—	1,100	2,500	200	200	1,500	21,900	5 if 2+1 stock used; 2+2 give more failures
3	Betula spp.	Birch species	7,950	—	450	3,820	1,250	250	2,700	16,420	4 from robust 1+1 stock on II sites; 1–2 on I sites
4	Pinus nigra ssp. laricio (calabrica)	Corsican Pine	7,050	—	950	500	450	500	—	9,450	Very poor rooting (10%) but 4 when established
5	Alnus glutinosa	Common Alder	2,800	—	200	450	2,500	—	—	5,950	4 on all sites
6	Alnus incana	Grey Alder	—	1,400	300	650	2,550	—	—	4,900	4 on all sites. May not survive exposure so well as A. glutinosa
7	Picea abies	Norway Spruce	4,500	—	—	—	—	—	—	4,500	1
8	Pinus sylvestris	Scots Pine	4,000	—	—	—	—	—	—	4,000	4 but slow starter
9	Robinia pseudoacacia	Black Locust	1,170	—	750	250	800	100	2	3,072	5 on II sites, but 1 on I sites
10	Abies grandis	Silver Fir	3,000	—	—	—	—	—	—	3,000	1
11	Alnus spp. (5 and 6 mixed)	Alder species (5 and 6 mixed)	—	—	—	—	250	—	950	1,200	—
12	Picea sitchensis	Sitka Spruce	200	—	—	130	—	100	600	1,030	3–4
13	Larix decidua	European Larch	—	—	—	500	500	—	—	1,000	4
14	Quercus borealis	Red Oak	420	—	—	—	400	—	—	820	3–2; failed on II (e)
15	Platanus × hybrida (acerifolia)	London Plane	390	—	—	—	350	—	—	740	1, largely failed
16	Chamaecyparis lawsoniana	Lawson's Cypress	—	—	100	200	—	—	—	300	3–2
17	Salix spp.	Willow species	—	100	—	8	—	—	100	208	—
18	Salix alba var. coerulea	Cricket-bat Willow	—	100	—	—	—	—	100	200	4 from cuttings; suffers frost damage
19	Salix daphnoides		—	100	—	—	—	—	100	200	4–5 from cuttings; quite hardy
20	Populus spp.	Poplar species	15	100	—	—	3	12	3	133	2
21	Castanea sativa	Sweet Chestnut	100	—	—	—	—	—	—	100	2–3
22	Fagus sylvatica	Beech	100	—	—	—	—	—	—	100	Failed
23	Ulmus glabra	Wych Elm	50	—	—	—	50	—	—	100	1–2
24	Carpinus betulus	Hornbeam	—	—	—	—	—	—	50	50	1–2
25	Populus robusta		—	—	—	—	12	—	—	12	1–2
26	Populus tremula	Aspen	10	—	—	—	—	—	—	10	
	Site totals		70,855	1,800	5,200	12,308	9,765	1,562	6,805	108,295	

From the table it may be seen that considerable use has been made of various coniferous species. Knowledge of the extent of atmospheric pollution available in 1962 and subsequent data collected during the project period (Oliver and Gadgil) all supported the view that this would not be deleterious to the growth of the selected conifer species. The species selected were frost-hardy and it is now clear that this is important since the climatographic studies (Oliver and Gadgil) show that the valley is subjected to inversion frosts as initially envisaged.

The tree plantings are of two kinds: (1) large blocks, planted by the Forestry Commission on an agency basis; (2) many smaller scattered sites planted by the Project's Conservator. All tree planting took place during the winters of 1962/3 and 1963/4. The first winter, the Forestry Commission planted 20 acres on plots 36 and 37, after ploughing the sites with furrows at 4–5-ft intervals. The principal species used were Japanese Larch; Birch; Lodge-pole Pine; Corsican Pine; Norway Spruce; Scots Pine and Silver Fir (see Table 5.11). In the spring of 1963 it was seen that only about 10 per cent of the Corsican Pine planted had taken root. This failure has been attributed partly to the exceptionally severe winter of 1962/3 and the well-known tendency for this species to transplant badly, particularly if the root system is not well formed. During the 1963 growing season, each tree received 1½ oz ground mineral phosphate and some of the larches had a further dressing of ½ oz nitrochalk each. During the winter of 1963/4, the Forestry Commission completed their planting commitment in the valley by afforesting 4 acres on plot 38 and 14 acres on plot 31 using, in the main, the same species as before except that Corsican Pine was omitted and where it had failed on plots 36 and 37 it was replaced chiefly by Lodgepole Pine and Larch. These trees in turn received a dressing of 1½ oz ground mineral phosphate the following spring. All these areas were covered by infertile glacial clay soils where the topography of the sites lent itself to ploughing and large-scale methods.

The remaining sites had much more variable ground conditions and were often quite small, which made ploughing and mass planting methods impossible. These areas were planted by the Project's Conservator, either by mattock planting into small pits or by notch and slit planting, using Mansfield and Schlick spades. No survival advantage of the trees planted in pits over those which were notch or slit planted is apparent, so that the latter methods are to be recommended on grounds of speed and cost. During the 1963 growing season, all the trees put in the previous winter by the Conservator received ½–1 oz of a general fertilizer (Gregor's MG4B) or Fisons 'Topgro' 8. However, the nitrogen contained in these fertilizers stimulated a luxuriant growth of weeds and therefore nitrogen was omitted from the fertilizer (per tree: 3 oz of a mixture of ground mineral phosphate, 30 per cent and granite dust, 70 per cent by volume) applied in the 1964 growing season.

A general indication of success in establishment and of growth is given in Table 5.11 although it should be emphasized that the growth assessment is based upon only 2 or 3 seasons. The overall impression to date is that the plantings are slightly below average forestry performance expectations which, considering the nature of the sites planted, is regarded as very encouraging. Total losses to date are estimated at about 10,000 (10 per cent of the total planted). Many of the species have been slow to establish. Severe chlorosis (leaves yellow and brown at the tip) has been widespread in Larch, Lodgepole Pine and Norway Spruce during their first, and often during their second growing seasons. This often led to complete dieback and casting of the needles, but only in severe cases to death of the

Tree planting

tree. A fertilizer trial with these species yielded no evidence that establishment was limited by a nutrient deficiency. The most important factor making for successful establishment and good initial growth of a species seems to be the development of the root system at the time of planting; many failures can be traced to poorly rooted nursery stocks. Trees which have been transplanted after one or two years' initial growth in the nursery and then grown on for a further year before planting in the valley (1+1 or 2+1), develop a good root-ball and have always established well.

Other difficulties encountered in the tree plantings were: (1) *Weeds*: Ploughing has often caused such a luxuriant weed growth, particularly on domestic refuse or on sandy soils, that trees have suffered. Hand weeding has proved impracticable but careful spraying with 'Paraquat' using a tree guard has given very promising results; (2) *Vermin*: Rabbits and hares have damaged trees quite seriously. These are difficult to control as they live among the piles of slag boulders and cannot be reduced by snares, dogs or ferrets. Considerable damage has been caused by voles 'ring barking' Lodgepole Pine and Alder on plots where there is a dense cover of weeds. Transplants have been protected by dipping in 'Thiram' which acts as a vole repellant; (3) *Fire*: About 1,000 trees have been destroyed by fires starting in dead weed growth; (4) *Exposure*: The prevailing south-westerly wind and the absence of local cover has tended to retard growth on southerly slopes; (5) *Vandalism*: See Chapter 10.

9 Grass trials of infertile clays

National Agricultural Advisory Service trials

In the autumn of 1962 the National Agricultural Advisory Service (Cardiff Sub-section) set up, using normal agricultural methods, two fenced experimental areas, each $\frac{1}{6}$ acre, one on completely bare soil at the northern end of plot 31 near the Imperial Smelting Corporation's Swansea Vale Works and the other, less than half a mile to the south, on ground sparsely covered with Wavy Hair-grass, Creeping Bent-grass and Common Bent-grass (Hooper, 1965). Preliminary soil analyses showed that, in general, the potassium and phosphorus status of the ground was 'low' or 'very low' and that available copper (EDTA soluble) was very high (70–180 p.p.m.). The acidity of the soil varied from around pH 4·5 on the bare ground, which usually had a ground limestone requirement of about 5 tons/acre, up to above pH 5·5 on the sparsely vegetated ground which required anything up to 1·5 tons/acre ground limestone. It was felt that limestone and phosphate applications would have the dual effect of correcting deficiencies and at the same time reducing the availability of copper and other metals potentially toxic.

Each experimental area of 20 × 40 yards was divided into twenty-four equal subplots on a split-plot layout as shown in Table 5.12 in which the bracketed figures at the end of the table indicate the number of plots under each grass seeds mixture. One of the two Red Fescue dominant plots received seed which was inoculated with a culture of the nitrogen-fixing bacterium, *Rhizobium trifolii*, shortly before sowing, in the hope that, because of the slower development of the dominant grass, a clover dominant sward would form in the early stages. The grass seed on the ploughed portion was cultivated in, but only scarified in with a light harrow on the unploughed part.

99

Table 5.12 Layout of two experimental grass trial areas sown on plot 31 in autumn 1962

Original surface ploughed	High limestone[1]	High phosphate[3]	Red Fescue dominant[5] (2)
			Ryegrass dominant (1)
		Low phosphate[4]	Red Fescue dominant (2)
			Ryegrass dominant (1)
	Low limestone[2]	High phosphate	Red Fescue dominant (2)
			Ryegrass dominant (1)
		Low phosphate	Red Fescue dominant (2)
			Ryegrass dominant (1)
Original surface unploughed	High limestone	High phosphate	Red Fescue dominant (2)
			Ryegrass dominant (1)
		Low phosphate	Red Fescue dominant (2)
			Ryegrass dominant (1)
	Low limestone	High phosphate	Red Fescue dominant (2)
			Ryegrass dominant (1)
		Low phosphate	Red Fescue dominant (2)
			Ryegrass dominant (1)

Notes:
[1] 5 tons ground limestone/acre
[2] 2 tons ground limestone/acre
[3] 5 cwt superphosphate/acre
[4] 2 cwt superphosphate/acre
[5] Grass seeds–mixtures as follows:

		'Red Fescue dominant' lb/acre	'Ryegrass dominant' lb/acre
Festuca rubra	Red Fescue S.59	15	3
Lolium perenne	Perennial Ryegrass S.23	3	15
Phleum pratense	Timothy S.48	3	
Trifolium repens	White Clover S.100	1	
„ „	„ „ S.184	1	
T. hybridum	Canadian Alsike Clover	2	
T. pratense	Red Clover S.123	2	
Medicago lupulina	Black Medick	1	
Achillea millefolium	Yarrow	0·3	
*Poa pratensis**	Smooth-stalked Meadow-grass	2	
*Trifolium subterraneum**	Subterranean Clover, Mt Barker	3	
*T. fragiferum**	Strawberry Clover, Palestine	2	

* Omitted in South plot

Germination and establishment were quite satisfactory. During the 1963 growing season (in April and again in July) all plots were top dressed with nitrochalk and muriate of potash at the rate of $\frac{1}{2}$ cwt potassium and $\frac{1}{2}$ cwt nitrogen/acre. These two fertilizer applications were repeated during the 1964 growing season and one dressing given in 1965. All the clover on the northern plot disappeared suddenly and completely during the early months of 1963 with necrotic symptoms suggestive of atmospheric pollution. During 1963 Ryegrass began to die out at both sites, probably suffering from a lack of nitrogen and from an inadequate number of cuttings to which it is unsuited. Red Fescue and Timothy grew better. particularly the latter, which came to cover as much ground as the Ryegrass and Red Fescue put together. The higher rate of liming caused a slight increase in productivity; there was no noticeable difference between the two phosphate treatments. Despite the fact that there was a deeper penetration of roots on the ploughed subplots, in all cases the unploughed subplots grew with almost the same vigour. By 1965, Timothy had become the dominant grass in the Ryegrass dominant mixture, but in the other mixture Red Fescue

had reasserted its dominance. By this time the high limestone dosages had affected the soil acidity in all subplots down to a depth of 6 inches but much more efficiently in the ploughed subplots. The phosphate was showing a similar pattern of penetration as revealed by soil analysis. Contrary to expectation, available copper showed no change from the original high levels irrespective of treatment. Available zinc (soluble in 0·5 N acetic acid) measured annually from 1963 to 1965 was very high on the north site (100–200 p.p.m.) and high on the south site (10–30 p.p.m.). By 1965 there was a striking increase in available zinc in the top inch of soil, anything up to a factor of six, both on ploughed and unploughed plots, possibly caused by root action.

The results taken as a whole suggest that although all treatments gave quite satisfactory swards, the high rates of lime and phosphate coupled with ploughing would probably give the most reliable grass cover. However, a longer follow-up period is necessary to determine whether ploughing is necessary to establish a satisfactory permanent sward.

Large-scale demonstration plots

The results obtained from the two N.A.A.S. experimental enclosures described above were sufficiently encouraging for the Project to consider the establishment of larger areas of grass. In the autumn of 1963 two areas, each of 2 acres and adjacent to each N.A.A.S. enclosure, were seeded with a mixture closely similar to the Red Fescue dominant grass mixture used in the N.A.A.S. experiments. The southerly area, at Cwm, was already covered with a poor growth of Wavy Hair-grass, Creeping Bent-grass and Common Bent-grass; the northerly area, at Pentre Cawr, was on a completely bare, heavily eroded sandy loam. Surface cultivation was carried out by disc harrow and dressings of basic slag, ground limestone and muriate of potash were applied at the rates of 10 cwt per acre, 3 tons per acre and 2·5 cwt per acre respectively. Seeding was carried out in October, rather late for good seedling development before the winter. However, both areas grew well in the spring of 1964. Nitrochalk was applied at the rate of ½ cwt nitrogen per acre in the early summer. It was observed that the clovers on the northerly plot (Pentre Cawr) had completely disappeared by midsummer, except in two or three narrow strips which had missed the nitrochalk application. This suppression of the clover growth may be caused by a combination of increased grass competition following nitrogen application with other factors adverse to clover growth such as atmospheric pollution and/or heavy metal toxicity. On the southerly plot (Cwm), the clover survived to produce a luxuriant sward of Wild White Clover by 1965. Lack of adequate resources prevented the cutting of the grass at sufficiently regular intervals but both swards were cut once in mid-1964 and the southerly sward was grazed by horses. The northern sward carried a heavy grass cover in 1964 after the cutting and this died back in the usual way during the ensuing winter but was burned off early in 1965 by children. Both plots received potassic slag (1 ton/acre) in April 1965 and 2 cwt/acre Fisons 44 in May 1966. The burning seriously impaired the survival of several species at this northern site but the fertilizer application in 1966 will stimulate a vigorous growth once more. The southerly plot, at the time of writing (1966), is a striking illustration of the possibilities of producing good growth following the correction of nutrient deficiencies.

As an exercise in the complete range of operations required to reclaim derelict land, a sloping 4-acre site (Plot 33) was cleared of its ruined buildings (see Chapter 10) and graded.

The area was formerly occupied by an arsenic works and the ground was also heavily contaminated with copper (free copper carbonate occurred in quantity among the slags on the site). In an attempt to immobilize the toxic metals, ground limestone at the rate of 5 tons/acre was spread over the old soil and rubble left after the clearance of buildings. This was then covered by a layer of 6–12 in of a poor, acid, sandy loam subsoil of very low nutrient status in the autumn of 1964 and left to settle over the winter. In April 1965 the soil was dressed with 3 tons ground-limestone per acre, 1 ton of potassic slag per acre and sown to a grass/Red Clover mixture. Growth was very luxuriant in the summer of 1965, but by autumn the grass component was suffering severe competition from the Red Clover whose luxuriant vivid growth completely dominated the sward. Both grass and clover have survived the winter and after suitable nitrogenous fertilizer application in May 1966 a more reasonable grass/clover balance was restored to give a luxuriant sward.

10 The practical problem of revegetating the Lower Swansea Valley

Experimental plantings have been made on every type of soil and industrial waste in the valley so that whatever land-use plan is adopted the findings of the botanical enquiry should be relevant to the resulting revegetation programme. It is, however, anticipated that those concerned with evolving land use proposals will bear in mind that sites in the valley vary from those where good permanent vegetation cover could be easily established to those where this may be very difficult.

Limitations of the botanical study

The botanical work of the Project has, to date, been limited in both duration and scope. The recommendations now to be made regarding techniques of revegetation, particularly as they apply to the tip areas, must therefore be regarded as based on very limited knowledge. The declines in plant growth recorded in 1965 in some of the plant trials clearly demonstrate the uncertainty of the long-term fate of such experimental plantings. To determine whether the newly established vegetation is likely to become a self-perpetuating system, it is important not only to continue the management of the plantings but to initiate a long-term study of the rate at which soil micro-organisms release nutrients from the dead leaves of the vegetation established on the various soils and tips.

Although the balance of evidence seems to point to chemical factors such as lack of nutrient salts and presence of abnormally high levels of poisonous metals rather than to physical factors (such as impaction, low water-holding capacity, temperature fluctuation) as being most inhibitory to plant establishment and growth, the relative importance of these different factors and their interactions has yet to be worked out. Further, although it may be postulated that such metals as zinc, copper and lead are probably present in the tip materials in forms and amounts which render them toxic to plants, this has not been demonstrated unequivocally, nor has the relative importance of the separate metals been established. In this context, an investigation into the cycling of toxic metals through the plant and back to the soil, in parallel with the study on the cycling of nutrients already referred to, should be initiated. The need for such work is clearly indicated by the striking increase in soil-available zinc following plant growth in the grass trials established by the National

The practical problem
of revegetating the
Lower Swansea Valley

Agricultural Advisory Service (Section 9). The work undertaken could not responsibly have been directed primarily towards answering such fundamental questions as these, but clearly, until answers to them are available, proposals regarding revegetation must rest on an inadequate scientific foundation. Further, until we have such knowledge the relevance of the botanical work of the Project to revegetating other areas of industrial dereliction cannot be assessed.

The plant trials described in this chapter are capable of furnishing additional valuable data if they can be supervised and their yields recorded for a further period. It would clearly now be desirable, in the light of present knowledge, to make additional experimental plantings on the tip sites and record their performances relative to experimental tip amendments already under test. The most promising possible colonizers of the tip areas have been found from the grass collections brought to Swansea from old mining spoil areas in other parts of the United Kingdom and in Ireland. The possibility of their use in any extensive programme of revegetation calls, however, for an immediate start to a programme for their multiplication.

In the light of all these considerations, it is of considerable significance to the possibility of a successful revegetation programme for the valley that the National Environmental Research Council has now made a research grant to our Department to continue work along precisely some of the lines proposed. To this end a trained plant ecologist, working in collaboration with one of us (G.T.G.) will devote his full time for at least two and probably for up to five years from now (1966). If, as now seems possible, the work of the Project's Conservator can also be extended until 1968 there will continue to be a nucleus to assist in the preparatory work for and detailed planning of a revegetation programme.

Recommended revegetation procedures

It seemed necessary at the beginning of this section of the report to stress the reservations which must be borne in mind in considering any programme of revegetation based on our present limited knowledge. This should, however, not obscure the very positive findings which have followed from the plant trials and microbiological studies.

Although localized discharges of pollution and frosts (Oliver and Gadgil) may somewhat restrict the choice of species to be planted, it is clear that these climatic factors are not responsible for the present poverty of vegetation in the valley. The excellent condition of the Sports Centre of Richard Thomas and Baldwins (Plot no. 40) is further evidence of this. The problem of revegetating the valley is that of improving the tip materials and the infertile areas as rooting media and the planting of suitable strains and species.

The experimental grass planting reported in Section 9, and the tree planting report in Section 8, indicate that revegetation of the 300 acres which can be classed as 'infertile clays' is not only possible but could be achieved without greatly exceeding normal agricultural or forestry costs per acre (say £35 per acre, exclusive of any earth moving required, e.g. filling up of erosion channels and of fencing). Notch or slit planting of selected tree species would be an inexpensive method of revegetating banks and uneven ground wherever the substratum is infertile but innocuous. In dealing with steep slopes at the edges of tips it may be necessary to create terraces which could be planted with suitable shrubs as was successfully undertaken on the sides of the Beaufort zinc tip (Plot no. 20) in one of our transplant trials (Section 5).

Revegetation of the tip areas will be more difficult and expensive. Whilst initial emphasis should be given to the establishment of grass cover this could be followed by group planting of suitable shrubs and herbaceous plants, particularly on the steel tips and possibly also on the copper tips (See Section 5). The steel tips present the least difficulty and will demand least in the way of seed-bed preparation. These tips will not require organic amendment, although a light dressing with organic matter would be advantageous. The old zinc tips are most difficult areas and the copper tips occupy an intermediate position. The method which seems most likely to yield satisfactory results on the copper tips is a 1 inch organic matter layer (such as 135 yd^3 per acre of DR or SS) plus lime and fertilizer, planted to a selected grass-ley mixture. The only satisfactory growth of standard grass-seed mixtures on the zinc tips has been with a 2–4-in layer of organic matter plus lime and fertilizer. We must not lose sight of the fact that on both these tip types there was a regression of grass growth during the third growing season of our trials and that this was particularly so at the zinc tip site. How far this regression is the beginning of a progressive decline will only be clear when the quantitative results from fertilizer applications in the 1966 growing season are known.

In view of the present doubts regarding the long-term persistence of swards established on the zinc and copper tips from standard grass-seed mixtures, consideration should be given to two alternative approaches. One of these would be to use strains selected from the collection of metal-tolerant grass clones already used in experimental plantings in the valley (Section 6). As already indicated this would require a multiplication programme which would occupy at least three growing seasons. The scale of this multiplication programme could be greatly reduced if successful establishment of a tolerant sward could be achieved by sowing the metal-tolerant seed along with a high proportion of commercially available seed of the same species as a 'nurse' crop. This seeding would be done with a minimum amendment of the tip material with organic matter under the assumption that the plants derived from the commercial seed would be dominant in the population for the first two seasons and that subsequently non-tolerant plants would progressively die out. Studies by Bradshaw and his co-workers (Bradshaw et al., 1965) indicate that in such a situation the plants from the commercial seed would act as a pollen and ovule source hybridizing with the tolerant strain and producing a heavy seeding, much of which would inherit characters from the tolerant strain. Natural selection would act on the next generation, leading to preferential establishment of tolerant progeny and ultimately to a fully tolerant sward. If this approach were successful the multiplication of tolerant plants would have been speeded up and would have occurred at the vegetated tip surface.

The second alternative approach which might have special relevance to vegetating the old zinc tips would be to cover them with at least 9 in of steel slag. Where the two tip types are adjacent this could be an economic proposition, particularly in view of the high cost of transporting and spreading organic amendments like SS.

The kind of revegetation of the tip sites which we have envisaged would not, in the near future, be capable of standing up to hard wear and tear, although regular clay marling might help considerably. Actual play areas at the tip sites could either be as islands free of vegetation or, if required as grass pitches, would have to be dealt with in a different way from the main revegetation. Pathways to such recreational sites would be very desirable.

In setting up the large-scale seed trials in 1965 (Section 4) it became clear that cultivation of the tip surfaces was a major item of expense. A similar difficulty would be presented by

The practical problem
of revegetating the
Lower Swansea Valley

newly exposed level tip surfaces created as a consequence of hardcore removal or land-scaping. This argues that where a seed-bed is required this should be obtained by spreading a suitable material directly on the tip surfaces. Although we have never contemplated re-vegetation by covering the tips with a thick layer of soil (because of the cost of this opera-tion) consideration should be given to the spreading directly on the unbroken tip surfaces of a thin layer (2–3 in) of foundry sand (of which considerable quantities have been tipped on plots 27 and 40 by Richard Thomas and Baldwins Foundry), PFA or soil as a seed-bed, into which amendments could be incorporated or, as already suggested, of thicker layers of steel slag, PFA and foundry sand which would not require organic amendments.

As an organic amendment to the tip materials, SS when available as a fine dry powder is easy to handle and to incorporate, although it is not suitable for stockpiling and should be spread and incorporated as soon after delivery as possible. The profuse weed flora which develops from sludge is not a serious deterrent to its use. DR as an organic amendment has the serious disadvantage that it contains bulky indestructible material (tins, bottles, etc.) which have to be sieved out before the DR can be used in experimental trials. This is a costly labour-consuming process and leaves much residue to be disposed of. When considering large-scale revegetation it seems that DR should, at appropriate low, accessible and drained sites, be deposited fresh *in situ* in a layer several feet in thickness, allowed to mature and then covered with a thin seed-bed of foundry sand, soil or PFA before planting. With a thicker soil layer, this method might be the most effective way of establishing sports pitches on certain areas at present covered with tip materials but in the process of being reduced to a convenient low level following hardcore removal. With the steady removal of hardcore from the valley floor other areas of this kind will continue to be created. Since this technique may involve a period of five or six years from commencement of DR tipping to revegetation, the preparation of selected areas by this method should be started at the earliest opportunity and the depth of the DR layer kept to an agreed minimum to ensure most rapid coverage.

In suggesting treatments for the revegetation of the tip areas, consideration must be given to the availability of the amendments and the costs involved in their use. Table 5.13 below gives estimates for the existing stocks and annual production of potentially useful amend-ment materials available near the valley, estimates of the acreage which these could be used to treat and costs of their transportation (with additional purchase costs where appropri-ate).

The amendments can be regarded as falling into two classes depending on whether they would be used as a 9-in layer to effectively bury the copper or zinc tip material (steel slag, foundry sand, PFA), or alternatively used (as in the experimental trials) as a 3-in layer on zinc tips, or a 1-in layer on copper tips to improve the physical and chemical characteristics of the tip surface (DR, SS). Since the costs of lime, fertilizer and seed and their incorporation by harrowing, etc., would be constant for all reclaimed areas (approx. £35 per acre) this figure is not included in Table 5.13.

Enough PFA, domestic refuse and steel slag could be found to treat all the valley tips but supplies of foundry sand and SS would allow fewer acres to be treated. About 8 per cent of the steel slag is easily available, the rest could only be dug out with difficulty. Moreover, since the removal of any steel slag would have to take place over a large area of steel tip, thus affecting its development, it would be essential to synchronize the levelling of the

Table 5.13 Estimated supplies, transport and purchase costs of potential amendments

Amendment		Existing stock and annual production (cubic yards)	No. of acres capable of treatment if amendment is spread to stated thickness (in inches)			Cost of amend-ment per cubic yard	Cost per acre of removing, loading, transporting amendment to stated depth (in inches)		
			9	3	1		9	3	1
Steel slag	Stock	500,000[1]	370 and 30[2]	—	—	0	£720 or £360[3]	—	—
	Production	0	0	0	0				
Foundry sand	Stock	50,000	40	—	—	0	£120	—	—
	Production	3,500	3	—	—				
Domestic refuse	Stock	0	—	0	0	0	—	£250[6]	£85[6]
	Production	130,000[4]	—	110[5]	325[5]				
Sewage sludge	Stock	500	—	1	4	0	—	£200	£70
	Production	2,000	—	5	15				
Pulverized fuel ash	Stock	1,000,000	800	—	—	2s 6d	£360 plus £153[7]	—	—
	Production	20,000	16	—	—				

Notes: [1] Comprises 40,000 yd³ easily removable material, the remainder being much more difficult to dig and load; [2] 370 acres using less available, and 30 acres using readily available, steel slag; [3] £720 using less available, and £360 using readily available, steel slag; [4] Figure refers to compressed DR; [5] DR contains two-thirds unusable material, e.g. metal, glass, etc. 110 and 325 acres are calculated on the basis of the usable one-third, i.e. after screening out the useless material; [6] DR costs include removal of the whole material together with costs of screening it to obtain the useful material; [7] £153 is cost of purchase.

steel tips with use of steel slag in revegetation work which would have to wait until the levelling operations could be undertaken. Foundry sand can make a useful contribution as a covering amendment but it is clear that SS, which is in short supply, would treat three times more acreage of copper tips than zinc tips.

Turning to costs of material and its transportation, it has been assumed that all except PFA are available free. SS is cheaper to use than DR but it is in short supply and would probably be most economically used on copper tips where light dressings would be effective. Unless a cheaper method of transporting PFA is found, it is doubtful if it will ever compete with the readily available steel slag or the foundry sand as a covering amendment, both of which could be fairly easily transported to any tip site in the valley although, as mentioned earlier, problems of timing may complicate the use of steel slag. It must be emphasized that although a 9-in cover of PFA, steel slag or foundry sand would be effective for grass establishment, it might not be quite as useful in shrub planting where the longer roots of woody species are likely to penetrate to the underlying copper or zinc wastes. Nor would it be recommended for areas which are to be temporarily revegetated and put to later alternative use. An instance of this situation would be where old zinc tips were kept intact for a number of years as a deposit of low-grade zinc ore. The zinc content of certain of the tips is currently being seriously considered in this light, and in such a case the tip would not be flattened but some grassing over would be required to prevent its being an eyesore. Tips of this kind could be inexpensively vegetated by using a 1-in layer of DR or SS plus lime and fertilizer, sown to a zinc-tolerant grass.

The practical problem
of revegetating the
Lower Swansea Valley

Some consideration should be given to the overall cost of revegetation per acre. As already mentioned, costs for the purchase and spread of lime and fertilizer and attendant harrowing-in of seed should not be more than £35 per acre. To this must be added about £150 where it is necessary to use a 2-in layer of organic amendment or foundry sand, or £360 for a 9-in cover of 'available' steel waste. Cultivation, stone picking and fencing could, in some cases, add as much as another £100, making a ceiling total of up to approximately £285, or £495 per acre depending on the type of waste used. This does not include salaries of scientific or gardening staff associated with the scheme or the costs of land purchase and grading. Annual maintenance, i.e. fertilizer application, cutting, weeding, etc., would probably cost not more than £15 per acre. As a comparison with these figures, the 'Countryside in 1970' Conference's Study Group on 'Reclamation and Clearance of Derelict Land' (1966) finally adopted a figure for revegetation of £500 per acre as a realistic estimate. This figure did not include land purchase but did, unlike our calculations, include a figure for grading to desired levels and contours.

Organization of a large-scale revegetation scheme

Planning authorities, experienced in the treatment of derelict land in other parts of Britain, have found that one of the most important factors inhibiting re-use of derelict land is its ugliness. It has been noted that as soon as an area is revegetated, it tends to attract developers. It is, of course, also possible to use the land as parkland, play areas, or open space. Revegetation therefore introduces flexibility of use and promotes redevelopment.

The mounting of a comprehensive programme of revegetation proceeding at a rapid tempo would be a complex operation. Given an effective organization, the tempo would be determined by the availability of money, appropriate manpower, machinery, materials (such as appropriate seed and transplants, seed-bed materials and organic amendments) and accessible sites conforming to the levels specified in the Land Use Plan. The planting programme would have to be integrated with a controlled programme of hardcore removal and a landscaping programme designed to establish agreed levels (where these would not arise from the hardcore removal programme). If these two aspects of the land use programme were not accorded high priority in a redevelopment scheme then the revegetation work would either be seriously delayed or wasteful of effort. Our findings suggest that in working out a phased programme of hardcore extraction priority should be given to the removal of old zinc tip material since this is the most difficult to revegetate with any certainty.

If a measure of uncertainty is involved in our recommendations regarding techniques of revegetation this is even more so if one attempts to estimate the finance required and the availability of materials for a major programme of revegetation. It is therefore strongly recommended that the tentative proposals which will now be put forward should be the subject of immediate further study.

The Land Use Plan which is developed in Chapter 11 envisages that ultimately at least 120 acres of woodland and 20 acres of playing fields will be required on the valley floor. If the floor and the sides of the valley are to be redeveloped in the comprehensive way suggested by the Plan, the acreage of amenity land will be even more extensive than this. The revegetation of the valley floor alone, as this chapter has tried to show, presents a complex of problems and it is clear that any programme for achieving this will require to be carefully planned and integrated with the development of roads, services, industry and housing.

In the early stages of the plan it might for example be desirable to revegetate large areas which in the later stages will be developed primarily for building.

This suggests that some organization is needed to plan the revegetation programme and to guide its execution within the overall plan for the whole Lower Swansea Valley area. What we have in mind is a small advisory committee to include representatives of the local authority (particularly a representative from the Borough Engineer's Department and the Parks Department), the Forestry Commission, the National Agricultural Advisory Service and the Department of Botany of the University College of Swansea.

We have confined our discussion to the strict boundaries of the Lower Swansea Valley Project area. It seems important, however, to mention Kilvey Hill in view of its dominating position in regard to the valley. Its afforestation would not be basically more difficult than the afforestation of the infertile clay areas of the valley already discussed. Further, we would recommend that if such afforestation should be undertaken then conservation of the Kilvey Forest should be closely linked with the conservation of the revegetated sites within the Project area. The enhanced area of responsibility would make it easier and relatively less expensive to organize an effective conservation service.

Bibliography

Atkinson, J. R. (1964) 'Afforestation of pit heaps' (typescript), Durham County Council.

Barber, E. G. (1963) 'Win back the acres—ash and agriculture.' Central Electricity Generating Board, London.

Bates, A. (1957) 'The rehabilitation of mine and industrial waste heaps', *Planning Outlook* **4**, 59–64.

Bradshaw, A. D., *et al.* (1965) 'Industrialization, evolution and the development of heavy metal tolerance in plants', in *Ecology and Industrial Society, Symposium 5*, British Ecological Society, ed. G. T. Goodman *et al.*, Blackwell, Oxford.

Bridges, E. M. (1965) *The Soils of the Lower Swansea Valley* (Study Report No. 9).

Chesters, C. G. C., and Parkinson, D. (1959) 'On the distribution of fungi in the rhizosphere of oats', *Plant and Soil* **11**, 145–56.

Coates, U. A. (1964) 'Experiment in grassland establishment on colliery shale. Bickershaw Reservoir site Abram, 1954–60' (typescript), Lancashire County Council County Planning Department.

'Countryside in 1970' (1965) Study Group Report No. 12, *The Reclamation and Clearance of Derelict Land*, Proceedings of the Second Conference (November 1965).

Evans, H. E. (1962) Private communication.

Gadgil, P. D. (1965a) *The Soil Biology of the Lower Swansea Valley* (Study Report No. 10).

Gadgil, P. D. (1965b) 'Distribution of fungi on the living roots of certain Gramineae and the effect of root decomposition on soil structure', *Plant and Soil* **22**, 239–59.

Gadgil, P. D., and Gadgil, R. L. (1965) *The Plant Ecology and Soil Biology of the Lower Swansea Valley* (Study Reports Nos. 9 and 10).

Gregory, R. P. G., and Bradshaw, A. D. (1965) 'Heavy metal tolerance in populations of *Agrostis tenuis* Sibth. and other grasses', *New Phytol.* **64**, 131–43.

Harley, J. L., and Waid, J. S. (1955) 'A method of studying active mycelia on living roots and other surfaces in the soil', *Trans. Brit. mycol. Soc.* **38**, 104–18.

Holliday, R., *et al.* (1958) 'Plant growth on fly ash', *Nature (Lond.)* **181**, 1079–80.

Hooper, J. L. (1965) *N.A.A.S. Large Scale Grass Trials* (Study Report No. 9 (b)).

Jensen, H. L., and Lamm, C. G. (1961) 'On the zinc content of Danish soils', *Acta Agricultura Scandinavica* **11**, 63–81.

Jowett, D. (1958) 'Populations of *Agrostis* spp. tolerant of heavy metals', *Nature (Lond.)* **182**, 816–17.

Knabe, W. (1965) 'Observations on world-wide efforts to reclaim industrial waste land', *Ecology and the Industrial Society, Symposium 5*, British Ecological Society, ed. G. T. Goodman *et al.*, Blackwell, Oxford.

Bibliography

Linford, M. B. (1942) 'Methods of observing soil flora and fauna associated with roots', *Soil Sci.* **53**, 93–103.

Lucas, R. E. (1948) 'Chemical and physical behaviour of copper in organic soils', *Soil Sci.* **66**, 119–29.

Lyon, T. L., *et al.* (1952) *The Nature and Properties of Soils.* Macmillan Co., New York.

Mason, A. C. (1952) 'Note on the determination of nitrate in culture solutions', East Malling Research Station Annual Report.

Mitchell, R. L. (1964) 'Trace elements' in *Chemistry of the Soil*, ed. F. E. Bear. 2nd edn. Reinhold, New York.

Mosse, B. (1963) 'Vesicular arbuscular mycorrhiza: an extreme form of fungal adaptation', *Symbiotic Associations*. 13th Symposium of the Society for General Microbiology, eds. P. S. Nutman and B. Mosse, Cambridge University Press.

Nicolson, T. H. (1959) 'Mycorrhiza in the Gramineae. I. Vesicular arbuscular endophytes, with special reference to the external phase', *Trans. Brit. mycol. Soc.* **42**, 421–38.

Oliver, J., Gadgil, P. D., and McDermott, M. 'The climatology and air pollution of the Lower Swansea Valley', Appendix, page 292.

Parkinson, D., and Clarke, J. H. (1961) 'Fungi associated with the seedling roots of *Allium porrum*, L', *Plant and Soil* **13**, 384–90.

Parkinson, D., *et al.* (1963) 'Studies on fungi in the root region. I. The development of fungi on young roots', *Plant and Soil* **19**, 332–49.

Piper, C. S. (1950) *Soil and Plant Analysis.* Interscience Pub. Inc., New York.

Richardson, J. A. (1957) 'Derelict pit heaps and their vegetation', *Planning Outlook* **4**, 59–64.

Slater, B. R. (1965) *Afforestation of the Lower Swansea Valley* (Study Report No. 11).

Taylor, G. S., and Parkinson, D. (1961) 'Growth of saprophytic fungi on root surfaces', *Plant and Soil* **15**, 261–7.

Tribe, H. T. (1961) 'Microbiology of cellulose decomposition in soil,' *Soil Sci.* **92**, 61–77.

Waid, J. S. (1957) 'Distribution of fungi within the decomposing tissues of ryegrass roots', *Trans. Brit. mycol. Soc.* **40**, 391–406.

Weston, R. L. *et al.* (1965) 'Problems of revegetation in the Lower Swansea Valley, an area of extensive industrial dereliction', *Ecology and the Industrial Society, Symposium 5*, British Ecological Society, ed. G. T. Goodman *et al.*, Blackwell, Oxford.

Wilkins, D. A. (1957) 'A technique for the measurement of lead tolerance in plants', *Nature (Lond.)* **180**, 37–8.

Wilkins, D. A. (1960) 'The measurement and genetical analysis of lead tolerance in *Festuca ovina*', Scottish Plant Breeding Station Report 1960, 85–98.

Authorship

This chapter was written by Professor H. E. Street and G. T. Goodman. It is based upon biological studies carried out in the Botany Department of the University College of Swansea by the permanent staff of the Project, as follows:

Dr R. L. Gadgil (née Weston), botanical study; Dr P. D. Gadgil, microbiological study; S. Casson and subsequently B. R. Salter, afforestation study. These received field assistance from B. Roberts and laboratory help from Miss J. Short and subsequently Miss R. Demarco and Mrs A. Nelson-Smith. The studies were coordinated by G. T. Goodman, Senior Lecturer in the Department of Botany and K. J. Hilton, Director of the Project.

Detailed planning of the studies was carried out by the botanist, microbiologist, forester and G. T. Goodman as a group, meeting under the chairmanship of Professor Street who was responsible for the biological work as a whole.

Acknowledgements

The botanical and microbiological studies were made possible by a grant of £11,438 from the Department of Scientific and Industrial Research, to Professor H. E. Street in the Botany Department of University College, Swansea. The work of the forester and the establishment of experimental areas was supported by a grant of £12,089 from the general fund of the Lower Swansea Valley Project (contributed by the Nuffield Foundation, Swansea Borough Council and the Ministry of Housing and Local Government). We also wish to thank those owners of land in the Lower Valley who provided a total of £1,776 for the purchase of trees, fertilizer, etc., for the establishment of woodland plantations on their properties.

We are indebted to the Forestry Commission for help and advice with the tree-planting work and to the National Agricultural Advisory Service, particularly L. J. Hooper and R. Garrett-Jones of the Cardiff Sub-centre, for their continued help and advice with all the grass trials and with soil analyses.

We are also indebted to the following for their kindness in providing experimental material, or for assistance in other ways: Llanelli Rural District Council (R. C. Jones, Engineer), Neath Rural District Council (A. Mandeville, Engineer), for sewage sludge; Swansea Borough Council (W. J. Ward, Engineer), for domestic refuse; Central Electricity Generating Board, South Western Division and A. Cadman, Tir John Station Superintendent, for pulverized fuel ash; Steel Company of Wales, for potassic slag; 53rd Div. Royal Engineers (T.A.), for ground preparation of the large-scale grass trials; Richard Thomas and Baldwins, Duffryn and Landore Works, for help with the erection of wire enclosures; Professor S. H. Beaver, University of North Staffordshire, Dr A. D. Bradshaw, University College, Bangor, Dr D. A. Wilkins, University of Birmingham, and the Camborne School of Metalliferous Mining, for helpful discussions concerning heavy-metal-tolerant grass strains.

6   The River Tawe

The river Tawe is a major physical feature of the Lower Swansea Valley and must therefore be included in any plan for the redevelopment of the area. The exact role to be played by the river, however, can only be determined after consideration of its hydrological characteristics. It is the purpose of this chapter to analyse these and to show their relevance to the project as a whole.

The flood problem

The area included within the Lower Swansea Valley Project lies almost entirely within the flood plain of the river Tawe. Although a large part of the valley floor has been raised above flood level by large-scale tipping, several low-lying tracts remain. These are marshy and are frequently flooded. As the Tawe within the project area is confined by tips and buildings to a fairly straight and narrow channel on the western side of the valley floor, these low-lying areas are drained by a small tributary stream—the Nant-y-Fendrod—flowing across the flood plain in a south-west direction. It is apparent, therefore, that flooding may result either from high flows originating from within the Fendrod system or from water overflowing into that system from the Tawe. It is possible that a severe localized storm over the Lower Swansea Valley could produce a flood in the Fendrod (Figure 6.1) but an analysis of past conditions clearly shows that major floods have always been caused by the overflow of water from the Tawe firstly into Llansamlet Marsh and thence over the Morriston-Llansamlet road into the Project area (see Figure 6.1). Any discussion of flood control in the area must therefore be based on a full understanding of flow conditions in the river Tawe.

Before examining the hydrology of the Tawe it is perhaps relevant at this point to consider exactly what is meant by the term 'flood'. The line of distinction between ordinary high flows and a flood is indefinite, being in part determined by the height of the banks and in part by the economic use to which the flood plain is put. It is commonly assumed that a river attains flood level when it overflows its banks, but the height of the banks, and consequently the capacity of the channel, varies considerably within relatively short distances. The definition of 'flood' is therefore arbitrary, and in the context of the present study is used to denote the level at which water finds its way from the Tawe into the Fendrod, a level corresponding to a gauge height of 9·5 ft and a discharge of approximately 7,500 cubic feet per second at the South West Wales River Authority's hydrometric station at Ynys Tanglws levels, which is a short distance upstream of the Project area.

Figure 6.2 shows the profiles of the Tawe river and the relevant normal, flood and bank levels.

All floods are primarily due to surface runoff resulting from a period of intense rainfall, or

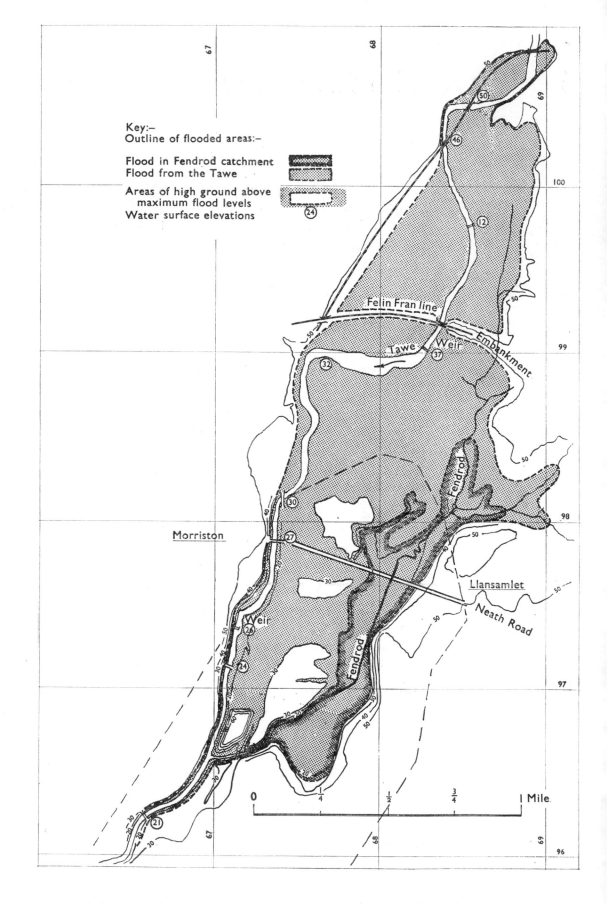

Key:–
Outline of flooded areas:–

Flood in Fendrod catchment
Flood from the Tawe

Areas of high ground above
maximum flood levels
Water surface elevations

Felin Fran line

Tawe Weir

Embankment

Fendrod

Morriston

Llansamlet

Neath Road

Weir

Fendrod

0   ¼   ½   ¾   I Mile.

Figure 6.1 Areas flooded by the River Tawe and the Nant-y-Fendrod

the melting of accumulated snow, or a combination of these factors. In the Tawe basin, an analysis of past floods shows that they have been caused by heavy rainstorms usually in the autumn months. With sufficient rainfall a flood will occur on any stream, but the amount necessary to cause flooding varies greatly according to the interaction of factors such as the type of drainage area, the season of the year and the intensity and duration of the rainfall.

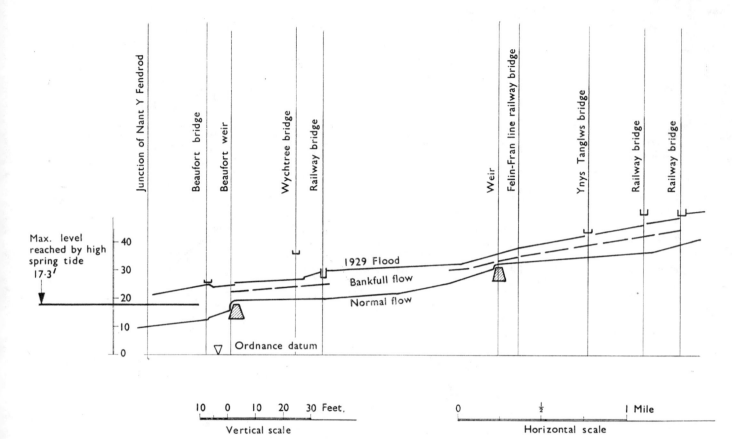

Figure 6.2 River Tawe profiles

The river Tawe drains an area of about 90 square miles upstream of the Project area. In its upper reaches the river, which originates in a boggy depression below the Black Mountain escarpment at an altitude of 1,960 feet, is little more than a mountain torrent. But after falling some 1,200 feet in its first four miles, the valley widens and stream gradient decreases rapidly so that for most of its course the Tawe flows through a wide, flat-bottomed valley floored with alluvial deposits. In its middle reaches the Tawe is characterized by a wide, shallow channel, particularly in the section between Ystradgynlais and Clydach. In this section, too, it receives a number of tributaries which descend sharply to the main stream from the mountains above. The drainage system as a whole is markedly asymmetric with all the main tributaries entering from the west (Figure 6.3). The absence of any major east bank tributaries partly accounts for the long, narrow shape of the catchment area. Geologically the Tawe basin covers a region in which the dominant rocks are the sandstones, grits, shales and limestones of the Old Red Sandstone and Carboniferous series. For the most part these rocks are hard and fairly impermeable. The limestone outcrops over only a small area and has little effect on the runoff characteristics of the catchment as a whole

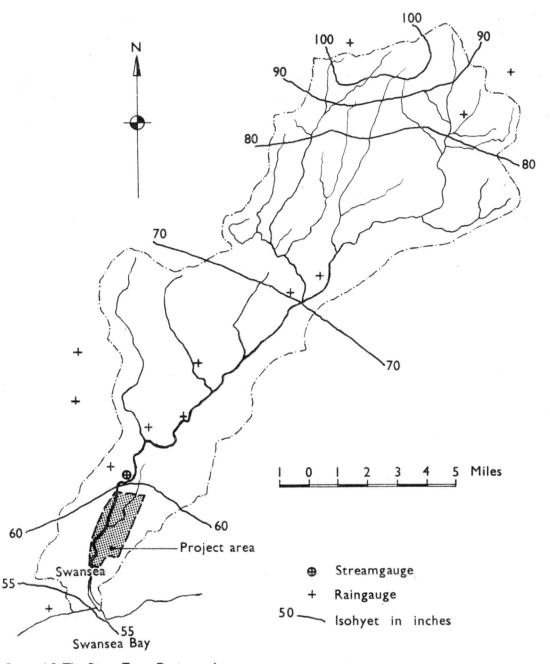

Figure 6.3 The River Tawe Drainage Area

except at low flows when a number of springs from this formation contribute significantly to the flow of the river.

Because of its mountainous character the Tawe basin receives a heavy annual rainfall, averaging 72·5 inches for the period 1916 to 1950. The distribution of this rainfall is very uneven, reflecting the great difference in relief and exposure from one part of the catchment to another. Thus while the average rainfall at Swansea is 42·99 inches, it exceeds 80 inches in the upper Tawe basin. Fig. 6.3 shows the contours of annual rainfall (isohyets). The seasonal rainfall pattern over the catchment is shown in the following table:

	Jan.	Feb.	Mar.	Apr.	May	June	July	Aug.	Sept.	Oct.	Nov.	Dec.
Inches rainfall	8·6	5·6	4·5	4·1	4·3	4·1	5·7	6·1	5·8	7·7	7·8	8·2

It can be seen that no part of the year is dry, but that the period October to January is significantly wetter than the rest of the year. In a catchment as small as that of the Tawe, rainfall intensity is a factor of major importance. Large falls of great intensity are rare in South Wales, but the records show a surprisingly large number of daily falls in excess of 2·5 inches, almost all of them occurring as prolonged spells of heavy rain. There is a fairly close relationship between the amount of rainfall and storm duration. Smaller falls of greater intensity frequently occur, but these are localized, affecting only part of the catchment area, and do not result in floods although they may cause the river to rise sharply in flow.

In the Tawe basin, therefore, both climatic and physiographic factors favour a high and rapid rate of runoff. The low evaporation and high rainfall, much of which is concentrated in fairly considerable falls over a period of hours, promote a high and irregular rate of runoff and the small size, steep slopes, impermeable rocks, dense drainage network and long narrow shape of the Tawe basin result in the rapid concentration of surface runoff into the main stream. If the rainfall is sufficiently heavy the river floods because the amount of water carried by it exceeds the channel capacity. Past records suggest that such flooding occurs on average once a year, but it must be stressed that this is an average figure and that in fact some years will experience no floods and others several. Fig. 6.4 provides a useful illustration of the hydrological characteristics of the Tawe. From this it can be seen that it is essentially a 'flashy' river, showing a rapid alternation of high and low flows ranging from 4,900 cusecs in November 1959 to 16 cusecs in October 1959. It should be stressed that the values plotted in Fig. 6.4 represent computed and not actual discharges, and that on any day the flow in the river may vary considerably above and below the mean value. Thus, for example, on 26 November 1959 the flow varied from 7,500 cusecs at 3 a.m. to 1,200 cusecs at 9 p.m., the mean flow for the twenty-four-hour period being 2,150 cusecs. In other words, the Tawe is even more erratic than Figure 6.4 suggests.

An essential part of any flood analysis is the prediction of the maximum flood likely to occur within a given period of time—for example, once in 100 or 1,000 years—for without such information it is more difficult for the engineer to design flood control schemes. Such predictions are usually based on the statistical analysis of a streamflow record covering a considerable period of time, preferably at least twenty years. Unfortunately the systematic collection of streamflow records on the Tawe did not begin until 1957, so the period of record is too short for such an analysis, particularly since there is information on only a few floods before this date. Fortunately there are reasonable records of the heights—though not the discharges—attained by the floods of November 1929 and October 1933, which were the largest in living memory, and of the rainfall conditions causing them. By using the unit hydrograph method to establish a relationship between river flow and rainfall from the records available from 1957 onwards, and knowing the rainfall conditions in 1929 and 1933, it has been possible to make a reasonably accurate estimate of the peak flows of these floods. The larger—that of 1933—is believed to have reached a peak of some 12,500 cusecs, a value in accordance with the findings of the Interim Report of the Institution of Civil Engineers on Floods in Relation to Reservoir Practice which suggests a maximum probable flood of approximately 14,000 cusecs for a catchment area of 90 square miles in highland Britain.

Although the rainfall records show clearly that the 1933 storm was the greatest over this catchment during the present century, this does not imply that greater storms are not

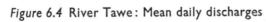

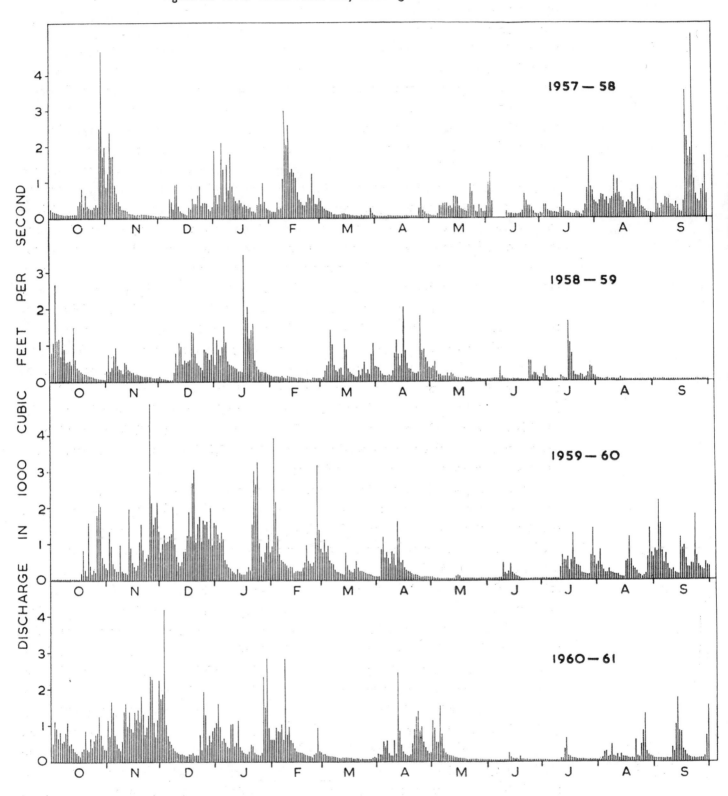

Figure 6.4 River Tawe: Mean daily discharges

possible. Other parts of Wales have experienced heavier rainfalls than any recorded in the Tawe basin. Indeed, investigations by a sub-committee of the Institution of Civil Engineers suggest that a maximum flood far in excess of the 14,000 cusecs 'normal maximum flood', is possible from a catchment of this size. However, it should be pointed out that the long narrow shape of the Tawe basin, coupled with the fact that most large storms move up rather than down the valley, mitigates against the propagation of 'maximum' floods.

While rainfall is the prime cause of flooding in the Tawe valley as a whole, the extent of flooding within the Lower Swansea Valley is affected by other factors. The water level of the Tawe is artificially raised at a number of points, especially at high discharges, by the presence of weirs and bridges in or across the river, as can be seen from Figure 6.2. The presence of these obstructions means that the river overflows its banks at lower discharges than if they did not exist. In its lower reaches the Tawe is affected by tidal influences which, in certain circumstances, contribute to the flood problem. In the first place, the coincidence of high flows and high tides tends to produce higher flood levels than would occur with similar flows at low tides. Secondly, it is suggested that once the Tawe has overflowed its banks, a near coincidence of peak flow and high tide tends to prolong the duration of flooding by preventing the rapid discharge of water through the lower reaches of the river to the sea.

Once floodwater has overflowed from the Tawe into the Fendrod system, a number of other factors must be considered. Like the Tawe, the Fendrod is obstructed by bridges at high discharges, especially near its confluence with the Tawe, where a narrow culvert causes extensive ponding such that the lower part of Llansamlet marsh is drowned to depths of 10 ft or more during severe floods, and also limits the rate at which the marsh drains when water levels are falling. The lower Fendrod is also affected by tidal influences which cause localized flooding even at low flows.

In view of the situation in the lower Fendrod, the storage capacity of the lower part of Llansamlet marsh plays a crucial role in determining the severity of flooding resulting from a given flow condition in the Tawe. For, as in any flood the water enters the lower Fendrod more quickly than it can get out, the depth to which the area is flooded is determined in part by the area over which the water can spread. There is considerable evidence to suggest that average flood levels in the lower valley have increased over the past fifty years as a result of extensive tipping, which has much reduced the available storage. It is possible, therefore, that a peak flow equal to that experienced during the 1933 flood might give appreciably higher flood levels if it occurred again. Hence, because the conditions affecting flood levels are not constant, it is necessary to think in terms of discharge when comparing one flood with another.

Flood control

A solution of the flood problem in the Lower Swansea Valley will involve engineering works on a considerable scale. Undoubtedly the most effective way of solving the problem would be by the construction of levées along the Tawe to prevent it from spilling into the Fendrod. This course of action has the one disadvantage that in so far as the flood plain acts at present as a natural storage reservoir, the construction of levées to prevent overbank flow causes an increase in the levels attained by a given flood discharge. The extent of this increase depends on the proximity of the levées to the banks of the river and can be determined by using standard flood routing procedures once the alignment of the levées is decided upon.

The degree of protection afforded by the construction of levées depends, of course, upon their height, which is decided upon after a consideration of the economic and hydrologic factors involved in the particular flood problem. Complete protection against all floods is usually uneconomic, and frequently it is not economic to offer protection against the maximum recorded flood which is usually much lower than the maximum flood likely to occur in a given catchment. The normal practice is to design works which will control floods up to a given frequency of occurrence. Thus, for example, if the 100-year flood was adopted as the design criterion, it would be expected that the levées would be overtopped on average once in a hundred years. The choice of a design flood is, therefore, largely a question of economics.

A fairly complete scheme of protection is presented in Figure 6.5. With a suitable height of levées, not only the main project area but the area north of the A48 road would be protected from all but catastrophic floods. The scheme involves the construction of a levée along the eastern bank of the Tawe from the high fill land about one mile south of Wychtree Bridge to the railway embankment just south of Ynys Tanglws Bridge. The railway embankment itself would prevent water entering the flood plain from the north except through the culvert by which the upper Fendrod passes beneath the railway. A floodgate at this culvert is therefore necessary. A better solution would be to divert the upper reaches of the Fendrod directly into the Tawe, thus eliminating the culvert altogether. In addition, to prevent flooding in the area bordering the Fendrod to the south of the A48 from high tides, or floods in the Fendrod itself, it is suggested that the Fendrod be carried from the A48 to the Tawe in an open-ended culvert of about 80 sq ft in cross-sectional area. After heavy rain it is possible that localized flooding north of the A48 might still occur. This would have to be borne in mind when developing this area. It is estimated that the cost of this scheme, including all works but excluding the cost of land acquisition and the cost of the culverting of the Fendrod, which would only be carried out after completion of all development in the valley, would be near £105,000 at current prices.

A more limited scheme could be envisaged in which the A48 forms the upper part of the levée protecting the development area. The need to provide special gates at the Fendrod culvert to avoid ingress of main floodwater as well as the necessity of raising the road level in places to deal with sizeable floods would probably make its initial lower capital cost less attractive.

The Tawe as a water resource

Although it has a high mean annual discharge averaging 414 cusecs for the period 1958 to 1963, the river Tawe frequently experiences appreciable periods of low flow. The available records cover too short a period to allow for an accurate statistical analysis of low flow conditions in the Tawe, but a descriptive analysis of existing data is of considerable value in that it gives some indication of the conditions which might be expected over a longer period. Data for the water years 1957–8 to 1961–2 have been analysed to produce a flow duration curve for the five-year period (Figure 6.6), from which it is possible to see the

Figure 6.5 Flood Control Scheme

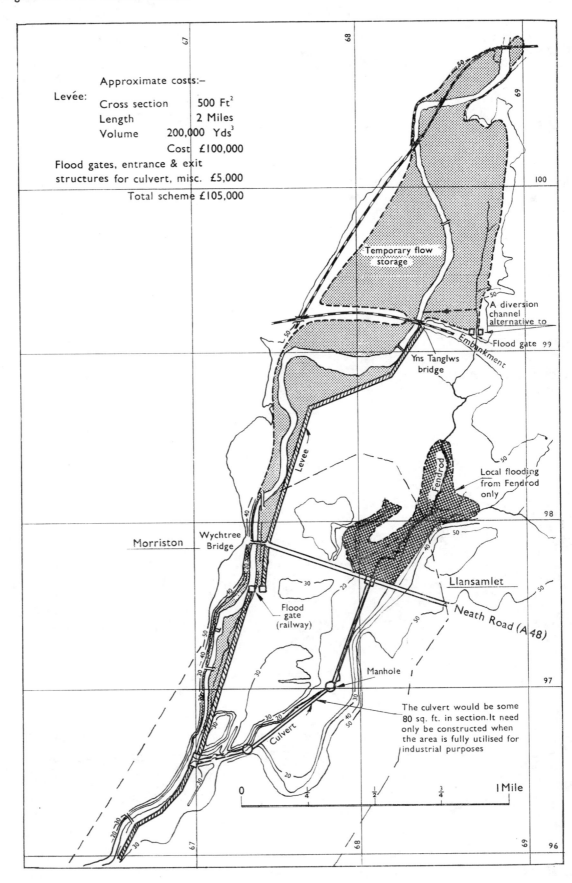

Approximate costs:—

Levée:

Cross section		500 Ft²
Length		2 Miles
Volume		200,000 Yds³
	Cost	£100,000

Flood gates, entrance & exit
structures for culvert, misc. £5,000

Total scheme £105,000

Temporary flow storage

A diversion channel alternative to

Embankment

Flood gate

Yns Tanglws bridge

Fendrod

Local flooding from Fendrod only

Morriston

Wychtree Bridge

Levee

Llansamlet

Neath Road (A 48)

Flood gate (railway)

Manhole

The culvert would be some 80 sq. ft. in section. It need only be constructed when the area is fully utilised for industrial purposes

Culvert

0   ¼   ½   ¾   1 Mile

frequencies with which flows of given magnitude might be expected to occur. Thus 5 per cent of all the mean daily flows were below 20 million gallons per day (m.g.d.), 10 per cent were below 26 m.g.d. and 30 per cent were below 70 m.g.d. (For the conversion of units:

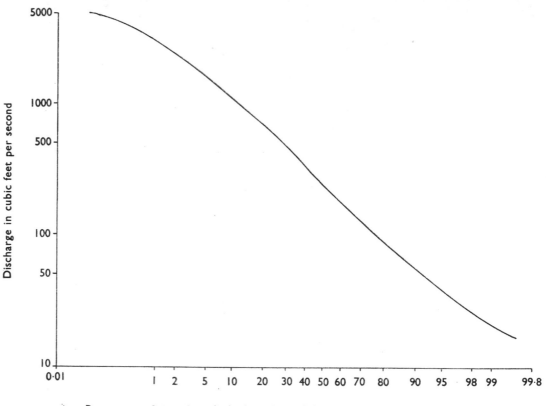

Figure 6.6 Duration curve of mean daily flow

1·8 cubic feet per second over a twenty-four-hour period is equivalent to 1 million gallons per day.) Conditions vary considerably from year to year as can be seen from the following table:

Year	Number of days on which the flow was less than 25 m.g.d.
1957–8	7
1958–9	71
1959–60	50
1960–1	37
1961–2	22

The use of the water year is a little misleading when dealing with low flows, since it runs from 1 October to 30 September, whereas the period of lowest flows frequently extends until late October. Thus in 1959, for example, the drought resulted in flows of less than 25 m.g.d. for the whole of the period 16 August to 16 October; and of less than 10 m.g.d. from 11 to 21 September, and 27 September to 15 October. The minimum recorded flow for the same year was approximately 8 m.g.d. As far as can be gathered from a rapid survey of rainfall statistics, it is most unlikely that lower flows than this would have occurred this century, although they may have been approached during the dry spell in the summer of 1933.

In the absence of any form of water storage and on the assumption that those interested in using water from the Tawe would require a guaranteed minimum supply at all times, it is apparent that the Tawe has very little future as a source of water because of its low summer discharges. Moreover, it is almost certain that the South West Wales River Authority would use the powers vested in it by the 1963 Water Resources Act to place stringent controls on the use of water during periods of low flow, in order to prevent aggravation of the pollution problem. The Tawe has a long history of pollution by industrial wastes, and despite the closure of many of the tinplate works in the valley, the river is still heavily contaminated in its lower reaches. A number of works still discharge large volumes of effluent into the Tawe, amounting in all to between 1 and 2 m.g.d. While every effort is being made to improve the quality of these effluents, they are still a source of pollution. Since the degree of pollution depends on the volume of water available for dilution of the offending effluents, it is unlikely that the River Authority would allow unrestricted abstraction of water from the river unless all that water was returned, with its quality unimpaired, at a point immediately downstream of the point of abstraction. This would, in effect, tend to limit the use of water to cooling purposes only, for which, without recycling of water, the minimum flows of the Tawe would be generally inadequate.

It is extremely unlikely, therefore, in view of the limited water available and the possible restrictions on its use, that any major water user would be attracted to the area because of its water resources. Most other industries have relatively small water requirements and adjust their processes and plant to suit the particular water situation.

The interrelationships between flow conditions and water quality are also important when considering the possibility of developing the lower Tawe as an amenity. A combination of low flows and the presence of readily oxidizable wastes means that the concentration of dissolved oxygen in the lower Tawe is often very low during the summer months. A survey made at Landore on 4 September 1964, for example, indicated that the river water contained only 0·3 parts per million of dissolved oxygen: a level inimical to any form of fish life. Furthermore, between the Wychtree and New Cut bridges, water discharges into the river at several points after passing through tips of non-ferrous waste. This water has been found to contain quantities of zinc, cadmium, lead and copper in solution, and while its volume has not been measured as it fluctuates with rainfall, it is obvious that it contributes to the pollution of the river. It is to be expected that with the removal of the tips or with their colonization this source of pollution will be reduced. The quality of the water in the Tawe generally should improve considerably in the future as pollution control measures, taken under the powers contained in the Rivers (Prevention of Pollution) Act, 1961, are applied.

The present unaesthetic appearance of the lower Tawe is due in large part to tidal influences which not only bring in polluted water from Swansea Bay but are also responsible for the unsightly mud banks exposed at low tide. A considerable improvement could be effected here by the construction of some form of movable weir near the New Cut Bridge. The function of such a weir would be to maintain the Tawe at a level some 20 feet above mean low tide level so that the lower river could be developed as an amenity area with boating and other facilities.

The weir would have to be capable of automatic operation for level adjustment so as to be able to discharge the full flood flows without raising the water to a dangerous level. Its

The River Tawe   periodic opening would prevent silting and accumulation of debris. Many forms of suitable construction are available, varying from 'drum gates' to 'bear trap' weirs. In all of these the movable parts are of steel and rest on a suitable concrete base. A recently developed form of weir in which the movable part is simply an inflated rubber tube is available. The low maintenance costs of such a structure coupled with a limited amount of concrete foundation needed would make a structure of this type very suitable for the purpose (Plate 7). This idea is developed in Chapter 11.

Finally, the Tawe must be considered as a means of access into the Project area. In the past the river was used extensively for navigational purposes in its tidal reaches. A survey carried out by the British Transport Docks Board in July 1964 shows that the river could still be used by shallow-draught barges, for there is a minimum depth of 6 ft in the centre of the river for two hours either side of high tide as far upstream as Landore Quay. The Swansea Harbour Act of 1836 permits the British Transport Docks Board to deal with the gradient of the river so that navigational facilities could be improved if it was economic to do so. At the present time, however, navigation is limited to vessels of not more than 6 ft freeboard due to the limited clearance under bridges at high water.

Summary and conclusions

The river is an important feature of the Project area. Future industrial development north of the A48 requires the construction of a levée system to contain overspill from the river and to prevent flooding. Such a system of levées and flood gates could be provided for £105,000. The river is not suitable as a source of industrial water other than for cooling, where the water could be returned to the river close to the point of abstraction with its quality unimpaired. The river is navigable at high tide for shallow-draught vessels as far as the Landore Quay, but it seems unlikely that advantage will be taken of this to any considerable extent as freight movements are more expeditiously made by road. The river, however, has considerable amenity potential and as pollution will tend to be reduced in the future, the development of this by means of a movable weir is suggested.

Bibliography

R. K. Linsley, M. A. Kohler, and J. L. H. Paulhus, *Applied Hydrology*, McGraw-Hill, 1949, chapter 17.
L. K. Sherman, 'Stream Flow from Rainfall by the Unit Graph Method', *Eng. News Record*, **108**, 1932, pp. 501–5.
P. O. Wolf, J. Glasspoole, and W. Allard, 'Floods in the British Isles', *Proc. Inst. Civil Eng.* V of **15**, Feb. 1960, pp. 119–29.

Authorship

This chapter was written by D. C. Ledger, Lecturer in Hydrology, Department of Forestry and Natural Resources, University of Edinburgh, with the cooperation of Dr Paul G. Mayer, Georgia Institute of Technology, Atlanta, U.S.A., who proposed and costed the various flood control works mentioned in this chapter.

Authorship

The author wishes to acknowledge the help given to him and Dr Mayer by C. C. Evans, the Chief Engineer of the South West Wales River Authority, and his staff; Dr W. Roscoe Howells, the Chief Fisheries Officer, South West Wales River Authority; E. A. C. Howells and A. D. Morgan, Managers of Swansea Docks, and C. C. Fenner, hydrographer, South Wales Docks.

7   Highway and transportation planning

This chapter of the report is concerned with the highway and transportation planning aspects of the redevelopment of the Lower Swansea Valley. It is based on a series of studies carried out by the Civil Engineering Department of the University College, during the period October 1962–October 1963, and it forms part of that department's contribution to the Project's overall research programme.[1]

The need for a transportation study

At the present time, as Figure 7.1 illustrates, the valley floor is almost totally devoid of road access. Existing M.O.T. classified traffic routes border the valley on three sides, but the floor itself is served only by short lengths of badly surfaced, unconnected works access roads. Several large tracts of land in the centre of the area are completely inaccessible except on foot.

In contrast to the lack of road access, the valley floor is crisscrossed by a complex network of railway lines, canals, and natural waterways. The effect of this network, much of which dates from the mid-nineteenth century, has been to divide the area up into a series of small, awkwardly shaped, isolated zones, each one cut off from its neighbour by the barrier of a railway embankment or stretch of open water. (Perhaps the most significant of these barriers is the river Tawe itself. No road bridge adequate to meet the demands of modern traffic crosses the river for a distance of over three miles, between the northern and southern ends of the Project area.)

In addition to dividing the valley floor into a series of isolated zones, too small for large-scale development, this existing transportation network appears to have had three major effects on the valley and its hinterland. In the first place it has hampered the efficient working of existing works on the valley floor, in the second it has very seriously inhibited the prospects of future redevelopment, and thirdly, through the absence of a central cross-river link, it has resulted in the isolation of the residential areas lying to the east of the valley from the main body of the County Borough lying to the east.

Clearly, any redevelopment proposals for the valley floor must incorporate a considerable amount of road construction, coupled, if possible, with the removal of one or more of the 'barrier' railway lines or waterways mentioned above.

In somewhat wider terms, it is also apparent that the redevelopment of the valley will have considerable implications for the Borough as a whole. Two of the five major approaches to the town centre pass along the borders of the Project area, so that any improvements to the system of access roads leading onto the valley floor must involve a consideration of the

Figure 7.1 **Existing transportation facilities within the Project Area**

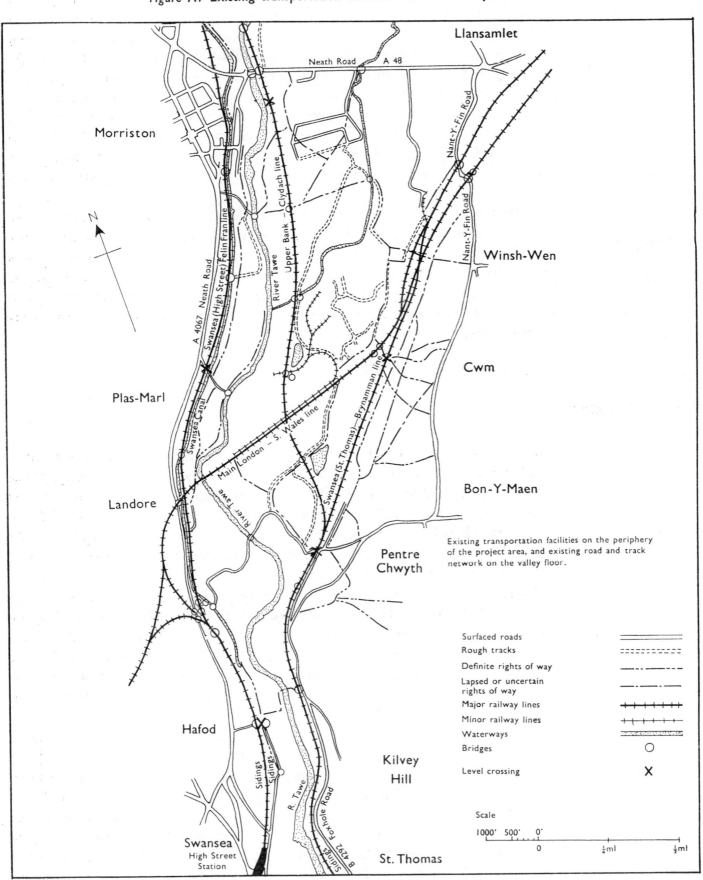

Existing transportation facilities on the periphery of the project area, and existing road and track network on the valley floor.

Surfaced roads	
Rough tracks	
Definite rights of way	
Lapsed or uncertain rights of way	
Major railway lines	
Minor railway lines	
Waterways	
Bridges	O
Level crossing	X

Scale

1000' 500' 0'

0   ¼ml   ½ml

need for improvements to these peripheral facilities. In fact, owing to the central position which the valley occupies within the County Borough, it is impossible to consider the development of a system of roads on the valley floor without at the same time considering the future road requirements of the whole of the eastern section of the town (Figure 7.2).

Finally, in even more general terms, the efficiency of the interregional transportation facilities—roads, railways, docks and air services—serving the Swansea area is likely to have a considerable effect on the redevelopment potential of the Lower Swansea Valley, particularly in comparison with competing areas in South-East Wales. Unless these facilities permit the fast, unhampered movement of goods and raw materials to and from the Swansea area, the prospects for achieving effective development in the valley are extremely remote.

There are, therefore, three major areas of interest to the transportation planner concerned with the redevelopment of the Lower Swansea Valley: the provision of an improved system of access onto the valley floor, the improvement of the major arterial road network in the vicinity of the valley and the efficiency of the interregional transportation system. These three areas are dealt with, in reverse order, in the following sections of this chapter. The reversal of their order is purely a matter of convenience; it in no way affects the validity of the results.

Regional analyses

As previously mentioned the Lower Swansea Valley is bounded on three sides by classified traffic routes. These routes connect the valley area directly with the main interregional road network, which in turn is linked, at Newport and Ross-on-Wye, to the proposed national motorway system. They also link the valley with the town centre and with Swansea Docks, which lie some three-quarters of a mile to the south of the Project area. All three of the routes are either scheduled for future improvement, or else have recently been made up to improved standards.

Swansea Docks, mentioned above, constitute the largest single port in South Wales. They include both general cargo and specialized oil and coal handling facilities. They are connected with the valley by road and also by direct rail links. Three separate railway lines, including the main London–South Wales route, traverse the valley floor. (The Swansea High Street–Felin Fran line has recently been closed.) These three lines feed into a number of sidings distributed across the valley floor and also into two major marshalling yards immediately to the south and east of the Project area.

Swansea airport, which carries a relatively light volume of traffic, is located on Fairwood Common, eight miles west of the town on the A4118.

It is apparent from the above remarks that the Lower Swansea Valley enjoys a number of locational advantages with respect to the existing regional transportation network (Figure 7.2). This does not mean, however, that this network is 100 per cent adequate to meet either the needs of existing traffic movements nor those to be expected in twenty to twenty-five years time. The following paragraphs discuss some of the more important deficiencies of each element of the network, and formulate proposals for their future improvement. In interpreting this discussion it should be borne in mind that, whilst the requirements of the Swansea area were given paramount attention, a number of the conclusions are based on the overall requirements of the South-West Wales region as a whole.

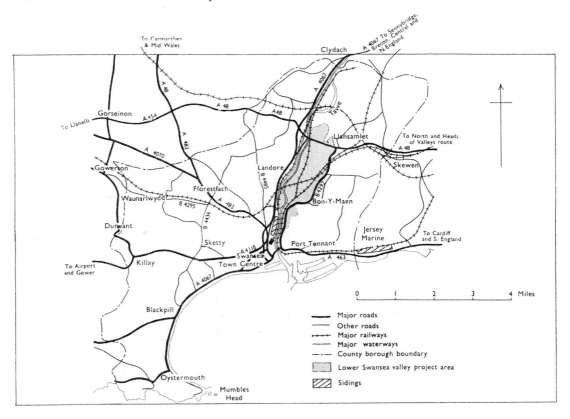

Figure 7.2 **Existing Local and Regional transportation facilities**

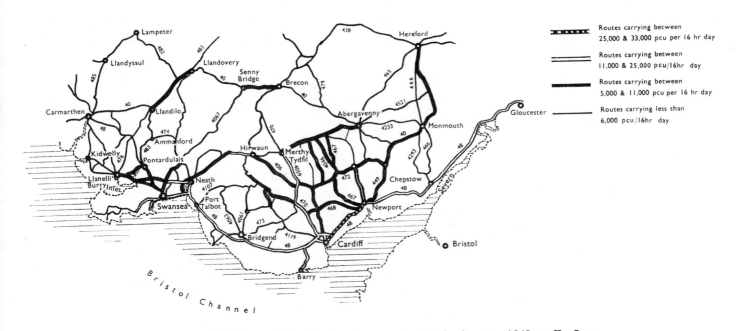

Figure 7.3 **Existing Regional road network (1963), showing 1963 traffic flows**

Road transportation

The existing regional road network is illustrated in Figure 7.3, together with the average daily traffic flows carried by its major links during the year 1963. The relation that this network bears to the current Ministry of Transport road improvement programme for South Wales and to the proposed national motorway system is shown in Figure 7.4. These two figures are based on an accumulation of data derived from a number of sources, including local authority traffic counts, information supplied by the Divisional Road Engineer (Wales and Monmouth Division), MOT, and an earlier general report on highway needs prepared by the Industrial Association of South Wales and Monmouthshire.[2] This external data was supplemented by a series of traffic counts and roadside interview surveys conducted during 1963 by the Project staff.

From Figure 7.3 it is immediately apparent that the major traffic flows affecting the Swansea area are concentrated along the coastal corridor (A48) and the 'Heads of the Valleys' route (A465). This pattern of movement is borne out by the average daily interregional road traffic flows summarized in Table 7.1. These latter data are based solely on studies carried out by the Lower Swansea Valley Project during 1963.

Table 7.1   Regional transportation study—average 1963 daily road traffic movements between Swansea area and major regions of United Kingdom (excluding Wales and Northern Ireland)

Region	S.E. England	S.W. England	Midlands	N. England and Scotland
Average daily traffic flow (pcu)	1,650	450	1,200	600

An analysis of future regional road traffic movements, based on an assumed annual growth rate of 5 per cent compound per annum modified to take account of the peculiar characteristics of particular routes, indicated that the concentration of traffic along the coastal corridor is likely to be accentuated in the future (see Figure 7.5). [An annual growth rate of 5 per cent is probably somewhat conservative when compared with statistical analysis of

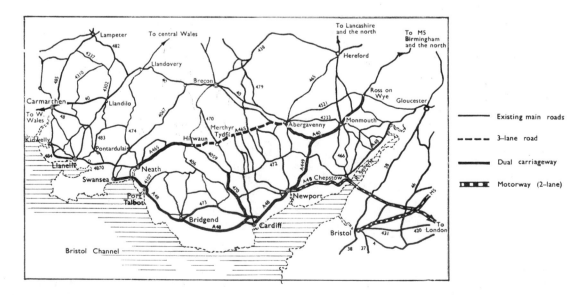

Figure 7.4 (a) Proposed Ministry of Transport road improvement schemes for South Wales

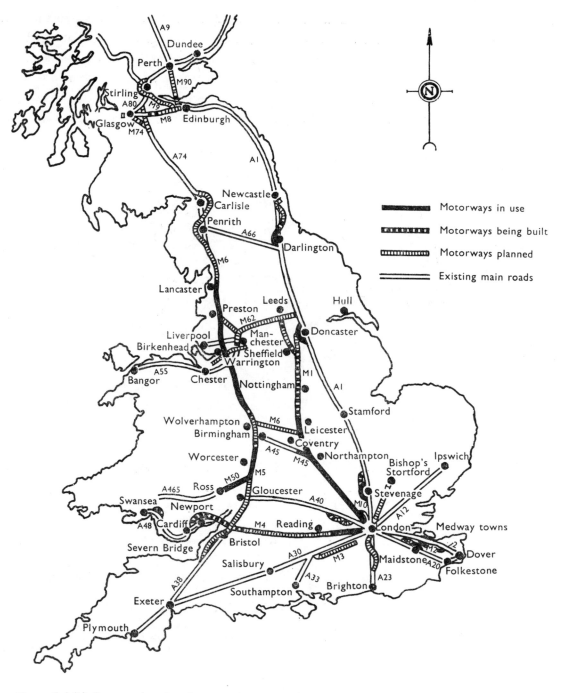

Figure 7.4 (b) Proposed national motorway network

recent growth trends in South Wales.[5, 7] The modifications of growth rates for particular routes were based on predictions of the probable effects of proposed road improvement schemes, the distribution of future industrial developments and the results of a series of industrial and residential traffic surveys conducted by the Project in the Swansea area (see reference 5 for details of techniques employed).] In particular, it may be expected that by 1985 the section of the A48 route between Cardiff and Swansea will carry average sixteen-hour daily volumes of approximately 40,000 pcu/sixteen-hour day and the A465 'Heads of the Valley' route volumes in excess of 20,000 pcu/sixteen-hour day.

These data indicate that the current Ministry of Transport proposal to terminate the M4, 'South Wales Motorway', at a point immediately west of Newport is inadequate. It would appear essential that this motorway be extended westward at least as far as Swansea and preferably as far as Llanelli, and that it be constructed to limited-access, three-lane dual carriageway standards. It is of interest here to note that an earlier report[2] utilizing totally different forecasting techniques arrived at much the same conclusions in 1961.

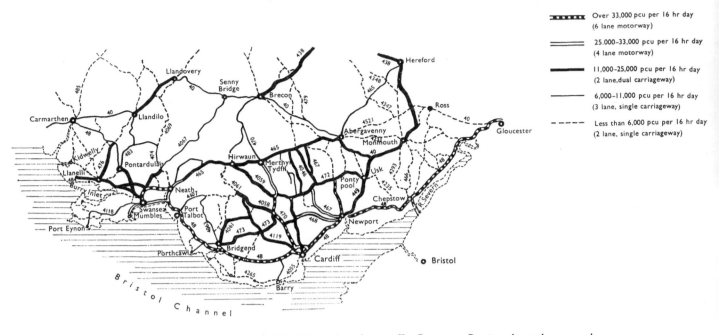

Figure 7.5 Predicted 1985/86 16-hr. day traffic flows on Regional road network

The upper limits of the volume ranges illustrated correspond to the design capacities of the following types of facility:[6]

Two-lane single carriageway	6,000 pcu/16-hour day
Three-lane single carriageway	11,000 pcu/16-hour day
Dual two-lane carriageways	25,000 pcu/16-hour day
Dual three-lane carriageways	25,000 pcu/16-hour day

In addition to these M.O.T. standards the following approximate design capacities are also adopted for the purposes of this report:

Motorway, dual two-lane carriageways	33,000 pcu/16-hour day
Motorway, dual three-lane carriageways	33,000 pcu/16-hour day

pcu = passenger car unit

For rural conditions the following equivalent values hold:

1 passenger car, motorcycle or light goods vehicle	= 1 pcu
1 heavy goods vehicle, bus or coach	= 3 pcu
1 pedal cycle	= 0·5 pcu

A brief economic analysis of the feasibility of such a motorway indicated that it might be expected to yield a rate of return on its capital investment of over 20 per cent. This figure is well in excess of the minimum generally required to justify construction. Other desirable but less important road improvements within the South-West Wales region are illustrated in Figure 7.5.

An analysis of existing bus passenger and commercial road haulage services in the Swansea area indicated that these are generally adequate. As in other parts of the country, however, the former is in a process of steady decline. There also appears to be a small but significant unsatisfied demand on the part of a number of small to medium-sized firms for an improvement in 'part load' haulage facilities between Swansea and other parts of the country.

Rail transportation

Most of the necessary improvements in rail transportation services have already been discussed in the Beeching Report.[3] Figures 7.6a and 7.6b illustrate the current pattern of rail traffic movements within the South Wales region. (These figures are based directly on Maps 1 and 2 of the Beeching Report.) Again a concentration of traffic, both freight and passenger, along the coastal corridor is immediately apparent.

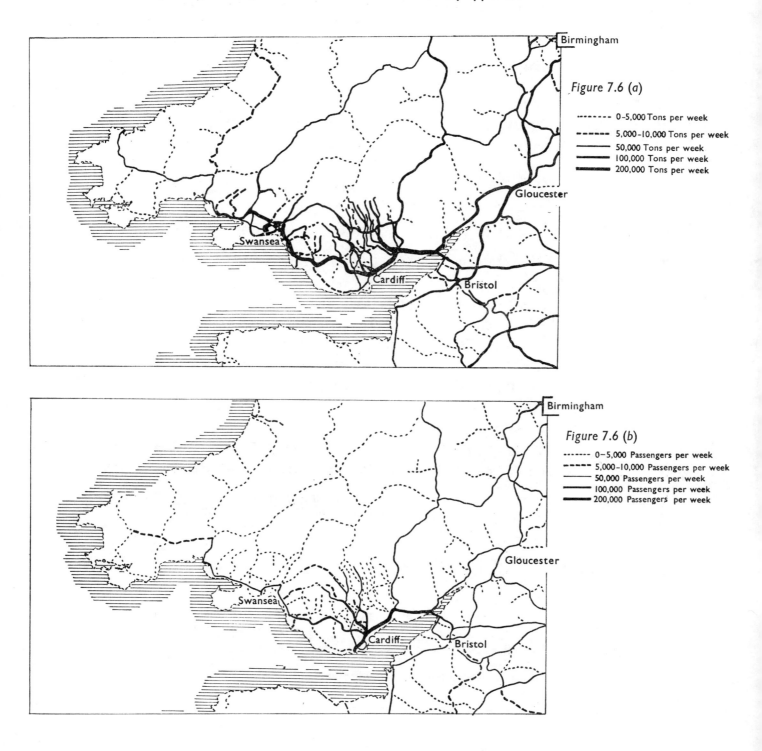

Figures 7.6 (a) and (b) Existing patterns of rail traffic movements (1961) within South Wales

The proposals of the Beeching Report to concentrate freight sundries traffic in a central depot in Swansea and at the same time to create a Swansea terminal for the proposed nationwide 'liner train' services both appear to offer considerable improvement over existing services. If accompanied by effective road development in the vicinity of the new terminals, they would both certainly result in an increase in the proportion of total freight traffic carried by rail. [This conclusion is based on a survey of firms in the Swansea area questioning their reaction to possible improvements in regional transportation facilities.] A detailed analysis of the probable effects of terminating existing passenger services, particularly along the Central Wales line between Swansea and Shrewsbury, was considered outside the scope of this report. It may be noted, however, that the effects of this particular closure are certain to be far less severe in the Swansea area than in central Wales. They are likely to have no measurable effect on the redevelopment of the Lower Swansea Valley.

No additional major improvements in regional rail services over and above those proposed in the Beeching Report appear necessary in the light of the studies conducted by the Project. Several minor improvements in local services, particularly in the handling of coal shipments, however, appear desirable, though once again these are of little importance to the Valley's redevelopment.

Waterways and docks

Swansea Docks, lying three-quarters of a mile south of the Project area, constitute the largest single element of the Welsh divisional dock system (see Table 7.2). They encompass both general cargo and also extensive oil handling facilities. They are, however, severely under-utilized. A large amount of potential traffic even from the Swansea area itself is currently diverted to the ports of Bristol, London and Liverpool. The reasons for this appear primarily to be lack of regular sailings and consolidation of overseas shipments by firms operating branches in South Wales.

Table 7.2 Regional transportation study—existing capacity of South Wales ports (general dry cargo) in comparison with selected English ports

Port	Number of dry cargo berths of specified draught					
	15'–20'	20'–25'	25'–30'	30'–35'	35'–40'	Over 40'
South Wales ports						
Swansea	—	28	—	18	—	—
Cardiff/Barry	1	4	25	—	—	—
Newport	—	—	9	13	—	—
Other ports						
Bristol	22	18	6	10	7	—
London	25	32	71	60	15	4
Southampton	12	6	3	10	13	—
Liverpool	16	56	54	71	13	—
Manchester	17	2	59	—	—	—

Source: Ref. 4 and Port Authority Reports

The Rochdale Commission, reporting in 1962,[4] proposed a consolidation of existing port facilities in South Wales with a concentration of general cargo handling for the South-West Wales area at Swansea, and the creation of a new single authority to operate jointly the ports of Newport and Bristol. These proposals if implemented would make efficient modernized port facilities, adjacent to the Project area, connected with it by means of direct road and rail links, and capable of handling a considerable increase in traffic.

There are no canals or rivers now open to navigation in the Swansea area. The Swansea Canal, operated by the British Waterways Board, is used solely as a source of industrial water supply. There is no prospect of any future demand for inland waterway transportation in the area.

Air transport

Swansea Airport, located eight miles west of the town, carries very little regular traffic. The prospects of its future development into a full-scale regional airport are extremely remote, as this function is already served by Rhoose Airport located close to the city of Cardiff. It is not considered likely that the absence of a regional airport in the Swansea area will in any significant way affect the future development of the valley.

Conclusions

1 The Lower Swansea Valley is advantageously situated relative to all major elements of the existing regional transportation network. A number of improvements in this network, are, however, indicated in the light of studies of future traffic growth.
2 The 'South Wales Motorway' (M4), currently under construction, should be extended westwards as far as Llanelli. Other desirable road improvements are shown in Figure 7.5.
3 The Beeching proposals[3] for improvements in rail freight services and the Rochdale Committee's proposal for South Wales ports[4] would, if implemented, enhance the development potential of the valley. No major improvements in rail and port facilities, other than those indicated in these reports, are considered necessary.

Local analyses

A series of 'roadside interview' studies and classified volume counts were performed during 1963 on the major roads fringing the valley sides. These studies were supplemented by a further series of traffic generation analyses conducted as a sample of industrial and residential land uses in the Swansea area. From the data so obtained, coupled with information on probable land use developments in the Borough and future population distributions, estimates were then made of the future demand for transportation in the vicinity of the Lower Swansea Valley. These estimates in turn formed the basis for the design of a series of road and rail improvement schemes in the area.

Presentday road traffic movements

Figure 7.7 illustrates the current distribution of traffic over the major road network flanking the valley sides, whilst Figure 7.8 illustrates a typical 'desire line' diagram for traffic using the A4067 (Neath Road). Similar 'desire line' diagrams were prepared for all of the other major routes in the vicinity of the valley and also for the survey areas as a whole. Table 7.3 summarizes the distribution of 'trip purposes' for the three peripheral routes according to the time when the trip was made.

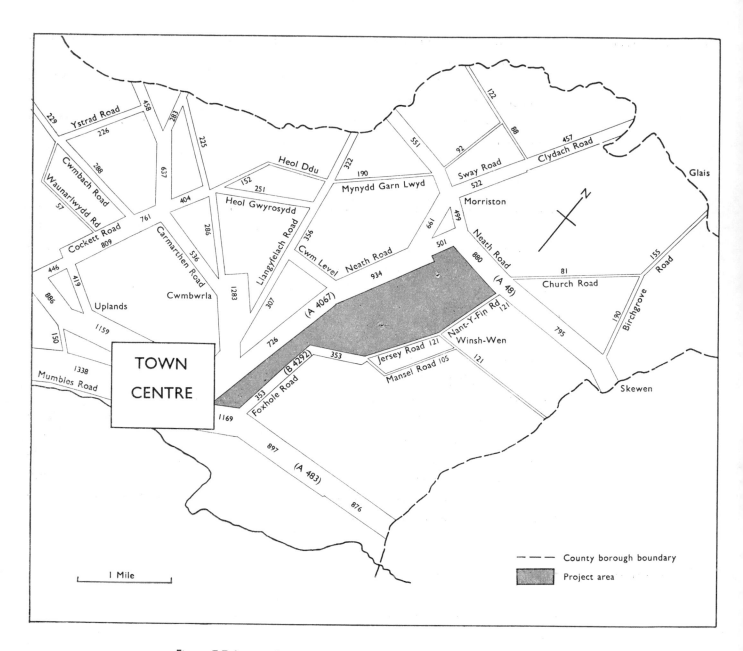

Figure 7.7 Lower Swansea Valley: 1962 traffic flows on existing peripheral routes—road widths proportional to traffic flows

On the basis of these studies of existing movements it would appear that:

1   Both the A4067 and A48 routes carry consistently heavy volumes of traffic. The existing roundabout at their point of intersection is already operating close to its maximum capacity.

2   The A48 route carries a heavy volume of through traffic at all times of the day, including the morning and evening peak periods. The volume of through traffic provides ample justification for the construction of a bypass route to the north of Llansamlet and Morriston, as proposed by the Swansea Borough Engineer.[8] It would be of considerable benefit, both to the redevelopment of the valley and also to the area as a whole if this route could be constructed as part of an extension of the M4 'South Wales Motorway' as discussed above. If, furthermore, such a bypass could be located as close as possible to the

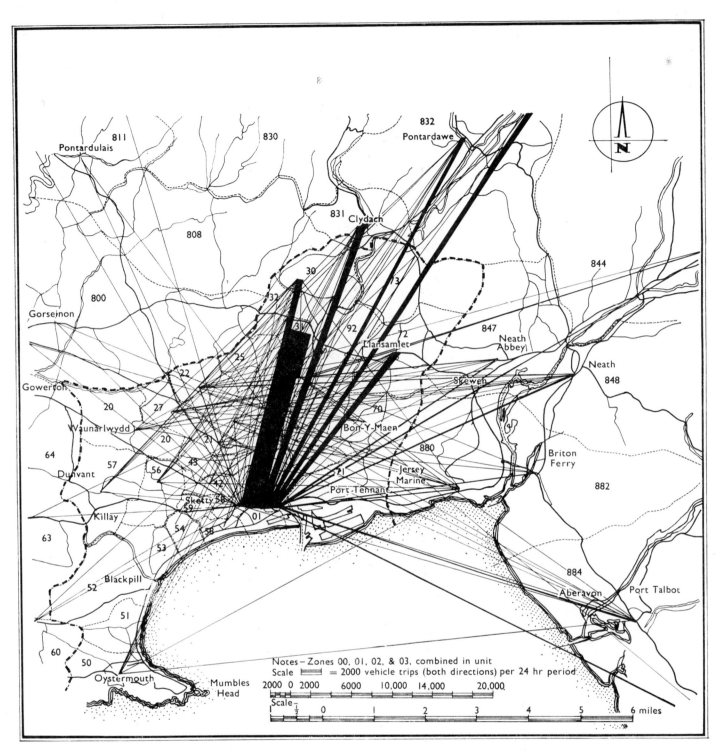

Figure 7.8 1963 desire lines for vehicles passing the A4067, Neath Road survey point

present line of the A48 it would greatly reduce the commuter traffic load on the existing road during peak periods, and at the same time provide an increased level of service to traffic destined for Morriston and Llansamlet.

3   The A4067 carries a high proportion of commuter and industrial–commercial traffic, that is directly related to the land uses in the immediate vicinity of the road. It also serves as a major approach to the town centre for traffic originating in central Wales and northern-central England.

Table 7.3 Lower Swansea Valley roadside interview traffic survey classification of person trips by trip purpose

Survey point	Neath road (A48)			Neath road (A4067)			Pentrechwyth road (B4292)		
Period of day	A.M. peak	P.M. peak	All day	A.M. peak	P.M. peak	All day	A.M. peak	P.M. peak	All day
Trip purpose category				Percentage of persons trips observed in each category					
'Go to Work'	64%	4%	29%	70%	4%	34%	69%	2%	35%
'Business'	22%	12%	26%	16%	10%	20%	17%	14%	18%
'Shopping'	1%	3%	5%	3%	1%	6%	0%	4%	4%
'Social/recreational'	0%	4%	4%	1%	8%	7%	2%	5%	4%
'Go to school'	1%	0%	1%	2%	0%	1%	3%	0%	1%
'Go home'	9%	76%	33%	5%	75%	30%	3%	73%	38%
'Miscellaneous'	3%	1%	2%	3%	2%	2%	6%	1%	0%

Note: This table omits public service vehicle trips.

4 The B4292 route serves predominantly as a feeder road for the residential areas on the eastern side of the Borough. It does not currently carry sufficient traffic to justify the construction of a new cross-river link in the centre of the Project area.

Future road traffic movements

Figures 7.9–7.12 and Tables 7.4 and 7.5 summarize some of the data obtained from studies of residential and industrial traffic generation. The results of these studies, together with those of the origin and destination studies described above, were used to predict a probable pattern of traffic movements for the year 1985.

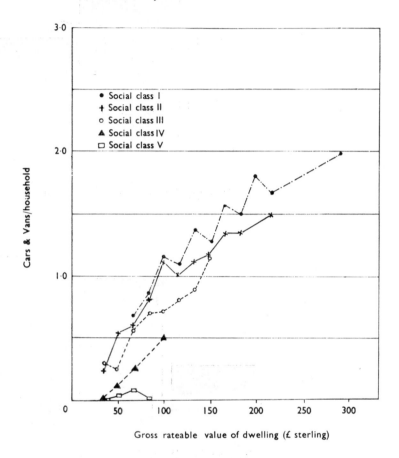

Figure 7.9 Residential traffic generation studies: Car ownership and social class of household versus gross rateable value of dwelling

All future traffic movements were first divided into four major categories:

1 Residential-based traffic (i.e. traffic that either originates or terminates in 'the home'). Approximately 79 per cent of all current journeys recorded in the origin and destination surveys fell into this category.

2 Industrial-based traffic (i.e. traffic that originates or terminates at a commercial or industrial land use, excluding journey to work or other traffic which falls under category 1). Approximately 12 per cent of all current journeys fell into this category.

3 External traffic (i.e. traffic originating or terminating over ten miles from Swansea town centre).

Figure 7.10 Residential Trip Generation Analyses—Mode of travel to work by social class of
household and car ownership

a) Mode of travel versus social class of individual households

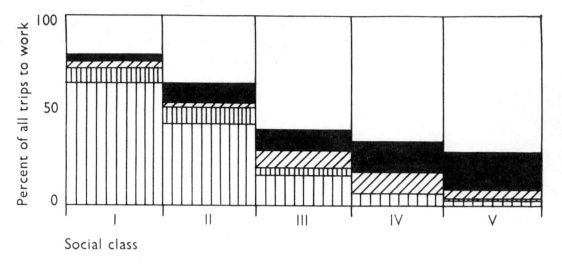

Social class

b) Mode of travel versus car ownership of individual households

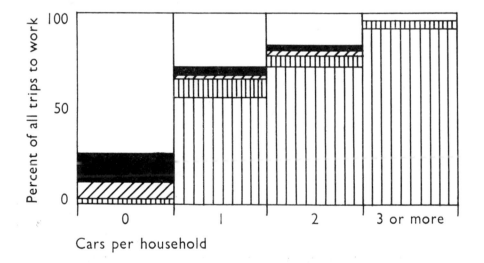

Cars per household

Notation:

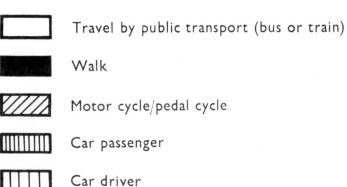

Travel by public transport (bus or train)

Walk

Motor cycle/pedal cycle

Car passenger

Car driver

4 Other or miscellaneous traffic (i.e. traffic not falling into any of the categories listed above). Approximately 8 per cent of all traffic observed in the origin and destination studies fell into this category.

The probable intensity of each of these movements was then analysed in turn, the results being amalgamated to provide a forecast of probable 1985 traffic volumes.

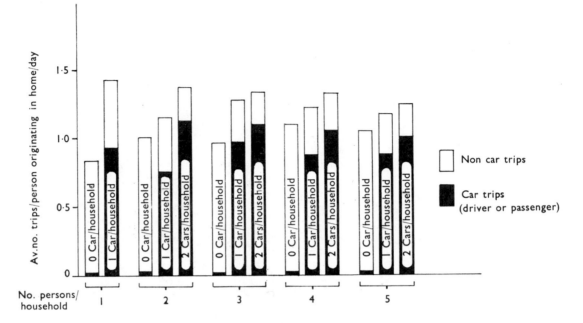

Figure 7.11 Residential traffic generation studies: Intensity of trip making versus car ownership

1 Residential-based traffic

This traffic was further subdivided by detailed trip purpose ('travel to work', 'shopping and formal recreational', and 'other'), and by travel mode (private car, public transport, and other). Estimates were then made of probable changes in population, population structure and car ownership for each residential neighbourhood as defined in the Borough Development Plan,[8] over the period 1963–85. The results of these analyses were in turn utilised to compute 'growth factors' for each neighbourhood for each subcategory of residential-based traffic. These growth factors, when applied to 1963 data on the observed number of 'person-journeys'/household, yielded estimates of 1985 'person-trip-ends' (i.e. the average number of trips per person of a given type originating or terminating in a household). These trips were then distributed, by means of a 'gravity model' technique, between the major areas of 'industrial' or 'commercial' and 'shopping/formal recreational' land use within the Borough and its immediate hinterland. Trips greater than ten miles in length were excluded from the analyses.

2 Industrial-based Traffic

The estimation of the probable growth and change in character of industrial-based traffic is somewhat more complex than for the case of residential-based traffic. The future industrial use of road transport will, for example, be highly dependent on such factors as future goods handling techniques and the attractiveness of competing rail facilities, as well

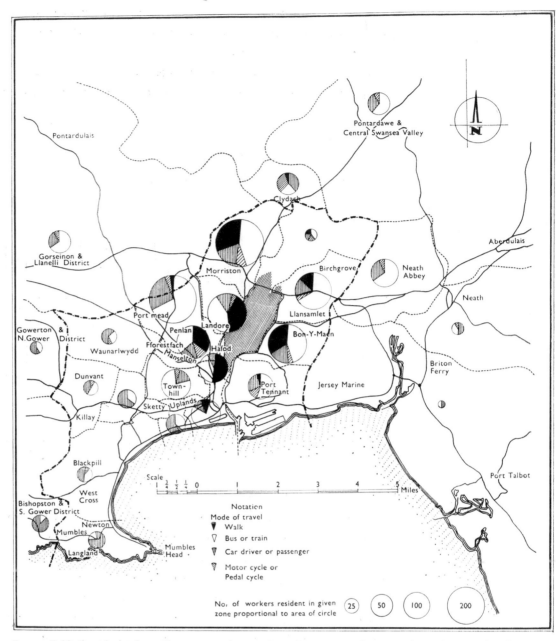

Figure 7.12 Residential traffic generation studies—Location of place of residence of valley area workers, 1963

as on the type of goods to be transported and the location of origins and destinations, all factors which are likely to vary considerably between different firms. It was, therefore, decided in this case to rely mainly on simple trend analyses, coupled with the results of the industrial generation studies summarized in Table 7.5. The average annual increase in commercial vehicle registrations in the Swansea area, over the past five years, has been approximately 2 per cent compound per annum. This rate has remained relatively uniform during this time. As it can be shown[7] that the average mileage travelled per vehicle is approximately constant with time, this growth in registrations also implies a general increase in commercial traffic of 2 per cent compound per annum. In the absence of more complete data, this single figure was applied to the current intensities of 'industrial-based' traffic

Table 7.4 Residential traffic generation studies—summary of data for twenty-three residential neighbourhoods

	Neighbourhood[1]	Estimated[2] population 1960	Planned household increase to 1971 (No. houses)	Current socio-economic grouping[3] (% workers in each socio-economic class)					Gross rateable value[4] distribution (% households in each rateable value group)				Estimated current[5] car ownership (car/house)	Predicted[6] ultimate car ownership (car/house)	Average traffic generation growth factor (averaged over all trip purposes and travel modes)
				A	B	C	D	E	A	B	C	D			
1	Oystermouth	} 7,209	129	10	30	45	10	5	20	20	30	30	0·32	0·80	2·25
2	Newton/Langland		415	15	30	45	5	5	10	15	30	45	0·71	1·15	2·00
3	West Cross	5,469	1,097	10	20	55	5	10	20	30	30	20	0·29	0·75	3·50
4	Town Centre	10,375	} 974	0	20	50	15	15	15	55	25	5	0·21	0·55	2·50
5	Uplands	3,646		20	30	40	5	5	5	25	40	30	0·43	1·00	2·25
6	Brynmill	15,161	1,638	10	25	50	10	5	25	5	50	20	0·30	0·90	2·50
7	Sketty	11,269	1,303	15	30	40	10	5	10	10	35	45	0·44	0·95	2·00
8	Killay	1,740	779	10	30	40	15	5	5	20	40	35	0·46	0·95	3·25
9	Waunarlwydd	1,077	51	5	10	55	20	10	15	30	50	5	0·21	0·55	3·50
10	Townhill	15,494	356	0	10	50	25	15	10	70	20	0	0·20	0·50	2·75
11	Cadle	12,843	846	} 0	10	60	15	} 15	} 0	85	15	0	0·12	0·50	3·75
12	Penlan	11,103	661										0·11	0·50	3·75
13	Clase	2,817	927	10	10	55	15	15	10	55	15	10	0·10	0·50	3·75
14	Birchgrove	1,906	380	5	10	55	15	15	10	80	10	0	0·17	0·65	4·50
15	Landore/Hafod	13,009	134	0	10	60	10	20	10	90	0	0	0·08	0·40	4·75
16	Brynhyfryd	13,340	333	5	10	55	20	10	10	70	15	5	0·09	0·50	3·50
17	Morriston	} 13,837	583	0	15	55	15	15	10	55	25	} 20	0·27	0·75	3·00
18	Cwmrhydyceirw		} 340	} 0	15	55	15	15	10	55	25		0·14	0·75	3·25
19	Bwllfa Ynystawe												0·15	0·60	2·75
20	Llansamlet	5,717	948	5	10	20	45	20	10	70	15	} 5	0·12	0·55	3·25
21	Pentrechwyth	3,894	633	0	15	50	20	15	10	80	10	0	0·08	0·45	4·00
22	Glais	746	136	0	15	50	20	15	0	65	35	0	0·11	0·45	3·75
23	St Thomas	11,931	150	0	10	55	20	15					0·09	0·50	2·50
	Total Co. Borough		12,813												

[1] Based on residential neighbourhoods defined in Development Plan.
[2] Rosser and Harris, *The Family and Social Change*, Routledge, 1965.
[3] A=Professional; B=Semi-professional, managerial and higher clerical; C=General clerical and skilled manual; D=Semi-skilled manual; E=Unskilled (Registrar-General's classification).

[4] A=less than £50; B=£50–£100; C=£100–£150; D=more than £150.
[5] Current car ownership as measured in survey.
[6] Predicted car ownership based on probable increase in real income (2½ per cent p.a.) and reduction in proportional car running costs.

Table 7.5 Industrial traffic generation studies—average traffic generation rates by type of industry

Category of firm (Number in brackets refers to Standard Industrial Classification)	No. of firms in sample	Average trip generation for each category of firm			Per cent workers travelling to work by public transport or walking
		Total person trip ends per worker per day	'Non-travel to work' vehicle trip ends per worker per day[1]	Total vehicle trip ends per worker per day	
(3) Food and drink manufacture	7	2·63	0·63 (45%)	1·32	61
(4) Chemical and allied industry	3	2·27	0·27 (60%)	0·81	60
(5) Metal manufacture	4	2·26	0·36 (65%)	0·90	59
(6) General and light engineering (large firm)[2]	8	2·30	0·30 (65%)	0·98	61
(6a) General and light engineering (small firm)[2]	16	2·42	0·42 (60%)	1·30	50
(12) Clothing manufacture	8	2·18	0·18 (75%)	0·42	76
(14) Timber, carpentry and furniture making	6	2·31	0·31 (70%)	0·85	69
(16) Other manufacturing industries	12	2·23	0·23 (60%)	0·49	78
(18) Gas, electricity distribution	6	3·03	1·03 (45%)	1·83	51
(19) General distribution depots	13	5·05	3·05 (80%)	3·95	80
Total sample	83				

[1] Figures in brackets indicate percentage of trips made by medium/heavy commercial vehicles.
[2] Small firm employs less than 200 workers; large firm employs more than 200 workers.

movements, as measured on the origin and destination surveys, to provide an estimate of 1985 flows. Industrial traffic originating from redevelopment sites on the valley floor was estimated by assuming that these sites would in general attract industries of the type to be found on the Fforestfach trading estate (i.e. industries with similar employment floor area characteristics). The results of the industrial traffic generation studies summarized in Table 7.5 were and can be applied to determine the number of trips likely to be generated in the valley area allowing for a similar 2 per cent growth ratio. These trips were finally distributed between different destinations in proportion to the presentday pattern illustrated on Figure 7.13.

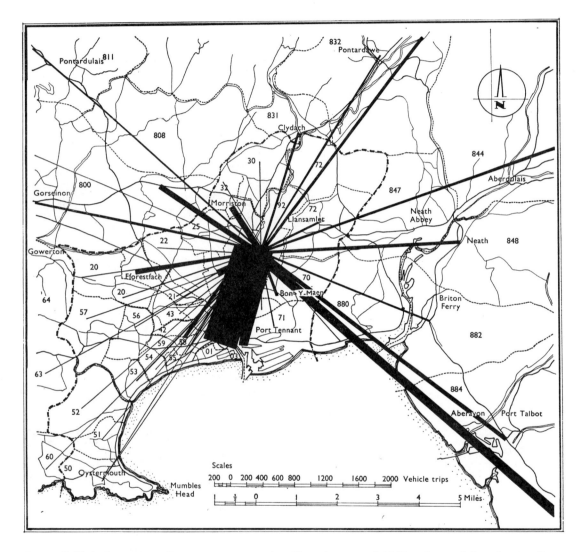

Figure 7.13 Industrial traffic generation study—Distribution of 1963 industrial based trips from Valley area industries

3 External traffic

The approximate volume of external traffic was estimated directly from the data collected in the regional studies described previously.

4 Miscellaneous traffic

Miscellaneous future trips were estimated by simply applying average growth rates of 5 per cent compound to each pair of current miscellaneous interzonal transfers.

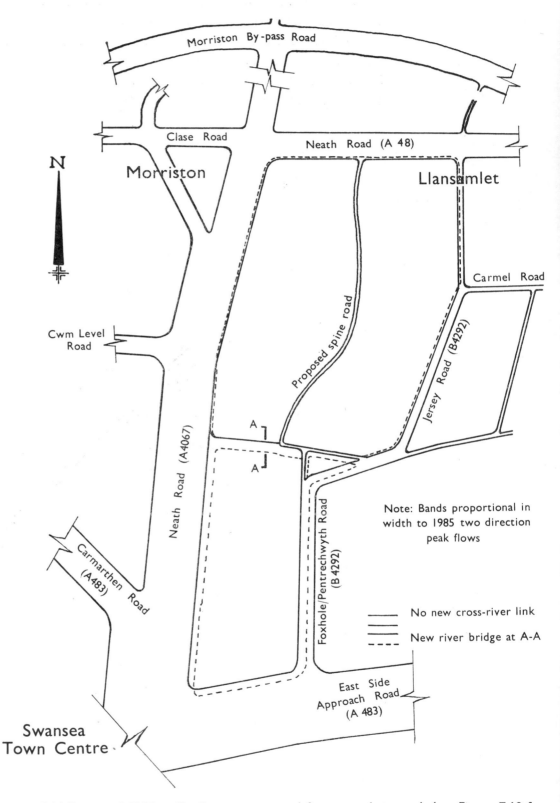

Figure 7.14 Estimated 1985 traffic flows on proposed future road network (see Figure 7.18 for details of network)

The estimates obtained from these separate studies were then combined to provide a general estimate of future 'desire line' movements. These 'desire line' movements in turn were then assigned to alternative, elementary networks of major roads, on the basis of a simple 'quickest route' principle. Figure 7.14 illustrates the distribution of traffic that results from the network ultimately adopted as the most satisfactory.

On the basis of these studies of future traffic movements, it was concluded that the following improvements to existing roads are required.

(a) The A4067 (Neath Road) should be replaced by dual, two-lane carriageways, having maximum possible control of access, along the western fringe of the Project area and connecting directly with the proposed extension of the 'South Wales Motorway'.

(b) A grade separated junction should replace the existing Wychtree roundabout at the junction of the A4067 and A48 (Neath Road). If this improvement is not effected the existing roundabout will rapidly become overloaded, resulting in a considerable diversion of through-traffic, both on to any new roads constructed on the Valley floor and also on to the B4292 (Nant-y-Ffin/Foxhole Road). Both of these possibilities are highly undesirable.

(c) The B4292 (Nant-y-Ffin/Foxhole Road) should be improved to a consistent three-lane standard and be realigned to pass to the west of Pentrechwyth village. The existing railway bridges spanning the road immediately south of Llansamlet should be reconstructed and fully channelled; signalled intersections should be provided at the intersections of the B4292 with the A483 (East Side approach road) and the A48 (Neath Road). Under no circumstances should this road be regarded as an alternative route for through traffic.

(d) There is no justification, in terms of traffic demand, for the construction of a new river bridge and cross-valley route in the centre of the Project area. Such a project, however, remains highly desirable in terms of the general development of the Borough.

(e) The existing A48 should be supplemented by a bypass/motorway route passing to the north of Morriston. The existing carriageway in the vicinity of Morriston Cross should be widened.

(f) Provided that the above improvements are completed, no significant volumes of traffic should be diverted from the peripheral routes on to any new roads constructed on the Valley floor.

(g) Attention should be paid as soon as possible to the development of a comprehensive road improvement programme for the Swansea area. The current road planning proposals are thoroughly inadequate to meet future needs.

Rail traffic

An analysis of rail traffic movements along the three lines traversing the valley floor indicated that it would be impracticable to propose closure or consolidation of any of these routes. As well as the main London to South Wales line (see Figure 7.1), traversing the valley floor from north to south, the Swansea (St Thomas) to Brynamman line also forms an important link in the regional railway network. The latter line connects a number of collieries and major industrial plants with Swansea Docks. It carries shipments of bulk materials of approximately 5,000 'wagon movements' per month. The third railway route, between Swansea (Upper Bank) and Clydach, is of only single track. It has some nine different users, including the Richard Thomas and Baldwins plant on the valley floor, and the Rees and Kirby Steelworks at Clydach. Both of these works are entirely dependent on the line for the transport of bulk and heavy materials, there being no alternative rail route available. It is highly undesirable that this traffic be diverted on to the roads, which are already over-loaded. It would, however, greatly reduce the costs of operation of the line if 'one engine in steam' working could be introduced between its terminal points.

Waterways traffic

None of the waterways lying within the boundaries of the Project area is now open to navigation. The Smith's canal is totally derelict and the Swansea Canal, operated by British Waterways, is used solely as a source of industrial water supply. This use of the canal greatly reduces the load placed on the Borough's existing water supply system. It is unde-sirable that it be terminated until the planned expansion of municipal water resources has been completed in five to seven years' time.

Both the river Tawe and the Nant-y-Fendrod fall under the jurisdiction of the South-West Wales River Authority. Both are used as discharge points for industrial effluent, and the Fendrod also serves as a source of water supply for the National Smelting Company Works. The problems of flooding have been discussed in Chapter 6.

Conclusions

On the basis of the studies described in the foregoing paragraphs, the following conclusions and recommendations are made:

1   A bypass, preferably forming part of an extension of the 'South Wales Motorway', should be provided for the existing A48 route passing to the north of Llansamlet and Morris-ton.

2   The A4067 Neath Road should be replaced by a two-lane dual carriageway, connecting the town centre with the bypass proposed above. A graded separated intersection should be provided at the intersection of this new road with the existing A48.

3   The B4292 Foxhole/Nant-y-Ffin Road should be widened to a uniform three-lane stand-ard with a realigned section passing west of Pentrechwyth village and reconstruction of two existing railway bridges immediately south of Llansamlet.

4   There is no significant traffic demand for a new cross-river link in the centre of the valley. Such a link is desirable, however, in terms of the general development of the Borough.

5   The three existing railway lines crossing the Valley floor are likely to remain.

6   The Swansea Canal, though closed to navigation, serves as a useful source of industrial water supply and should not be filled in for at least five to seven years.

Valley floor analyses

As previously pointed out, any extensive redevelopment of the valley floor is likely to necessitate an extensive programme of road construction. This programme should be such that it meets four general requirements:

1   Any new road network should provide access to all areas of the valley floor. It should link the various 'zones' of the valley into a single unit, and it should be fully coordinated with any schemes to improve the existing peripheral road system.

2   The network should be capable of adequately meeting the transportation requirements of any future redevelopment plan. It should be flexible and be capable of staged construction.

3   Full cognizance should be paid in the design of the network to existing rights of way, ownership boundaries and the requirements of established works and factories.

4   The total construction cost should be kept to a minimum.

The final section of this chapter discusses the development of such a network, the relationship between future land use and future road planning, and the estimated costs of construction.

The existing situation

As has been previously noted, the valley floor today is almost totally devoid of road access (see Figure 7.1). There are less than five miles of discontinuous poorly surfaced roads, less than six miles of rough tracks currently serving over 1,200 acres of land on the valley floor. Considerable tracts in the centre of the valley are virtually inaccessible except on foot. The network of railway lines and canals that crisscross the valley floor are crossed by a total of forty bridges and underpasses. Almost without exception these roads, tracks and bridges are inadequate to meet the requirements of modern traffic.

In contrast again to the absence of roads, a complex and confused system of pedestrian rights of way and wayleaves traverses the valley floor. As the local authority opted not to prepare a statutory rights of way map under the provisions of the National Park and Access to the Countryside Act, 1949, many of these rights of way are of dubious validity. The pattern illustrated on Figure 7.1, although it represents, to the author's best knowledge, an accurate description of existing rights of way, should not be considered as having any legal or statutory significance.

Future land use plans

To provide a working basis for the development of a detailed road plan, it was first necessary to consider what general form the future land use development of the valley floor might take. A detailed discussion of this latter subject is given in Chapter 11 of the report. It is sufficient to note at this stage that three outline development plans were prepared, one representing 'minimal formal development' (consisting primarily of visual rehabilitation schemes, tree planting, clearance of derelict buildings and a limited amount of industrial and formal open space development); a second representing 'maximal industrial development', in which every area in which industrial development was at all feasible was so designated; and finally a third 'compromise plan', in which a balance was attempted between the requirements of industrial development, the provision of formal open space facilities on the one hand and the general economics of earthmoving and flood control on the other. These three plans are illustrated together with their appropriate road networks as Plans A, B, and C respectively on Figures 7.15, 7.16 and 7.17. The following general points are of interest concerning these outline plans:

1 In each case the physical redevelopment of the valley floor was assumed to take the form of a series of plateaux, rising from the level of the existing 'Gas Board' site on Plot 16 (27 a.o.d.), up to that of the Duffryn Tip on Plot 19 (40 a.o.d.) and Plot 28 (40 a.o.d.). Plans B and C also assume a realignment of the Nant-y-Fendrod and the filling-in of the Swansea Canal.

2 No residential development is envisaged for the valley floor, though its possibility was considered.

3 Amenity and recreational open space is provided in the form of playing fields, extensive areas of landscaping and planting, a network of landscaped footpaths and a number of ponds and stretches of open water. All playing fields and parks are located in areas where there is a demand for them and where they will be readily accessible. The system of paths and riverside walks (see Figures 7.15, 7.16 and 7.17) is designed to draw people down on to the valley floor towards these open space and amenity facilities.

4 Industrial development is concentrated in three main areas: (a) to the north of the A48; (b) in the wedge of land between the river, the main London-Swansea railway line and the A48/B4292 roads; and (c) in the vicinity of the existing Addis Factory and Yorkshire Imperial Metal Company's Works (Plots 50–52). It is envisaged that this development will generally be of a light industrial/distributive/storage nature, with a preponderance of small to medium-sized firms, as is suggested in Chapter 9.

5 In all three cases, it is assumed that the proposed regional and local road improvements outlined in Sections I and II of this chapter have been completed.

6 The estimated cost of earth-moving for each of the three plans (i.e. the cost of removing and levelling existing tips and filling and consolidating marshland areas) was: Plan A, £183,000; Plan B, £932,500; Plan C, £700,000. These costs do *not* include any earth-moving for road construction.

Road network

A consideration of the outline development plans illustrated in Figures 7.15, 7.16 and 7.17, coupled with a knowledge of the probable distribution of traffic movements resulting from any future industrial redevelopment on the valley floor, indicates that a future road network should consist primarily of three elements:

1 A main north–south spine road, linking the northern industrial areas with the A48 trunk road, the docks, the St Thomas railway depot and the east side approach road. This road would also link those areas, in a new cross-river link, with the A4067 (Neath Road) and the town centre.

2 A second north–south route, running parallel to the A4067 along the line of the Swansea Canal and the river Tawe. This route would serve as a distributor road for the proposed industrial and recreational areas situated between the Neath Road (A4067) and the river.

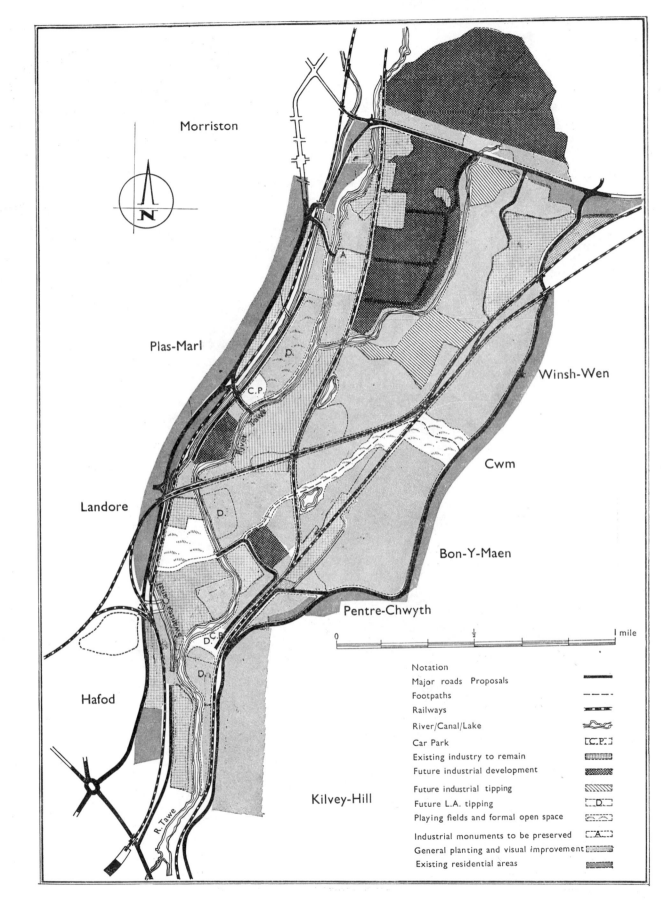

Morriston

Plas-Marl

C.P.

River Tawe

Landore

D.

D.

Winsh-Wen

Cwm

Bon-Y-Maen

Pentre-Chwyth

D.C.P.

D.

Hafod

R.Tawe

Swansea Canal

Kilvey-Hill

Notation

Major roads Proposals	▬▬▬
Footpaths	– – –
Railways	╫╫╫
River/Canal/Lake	∿∿
Car Park	C.P.
Existing industry to remain	▦▦
Future industrial development	▮▮
Future industrial tipping	▨▨
Future L.A. tipping	D.
Playing fields and formal open space	▦▦
Industrial monuments to be preserved	A
General planting and visual improvement	▨▨
Existing residential areas	▓▓

0   ½   1 mile

149   *Figure 7.15* Outline Development Plan 'A' (Minimal formal development)

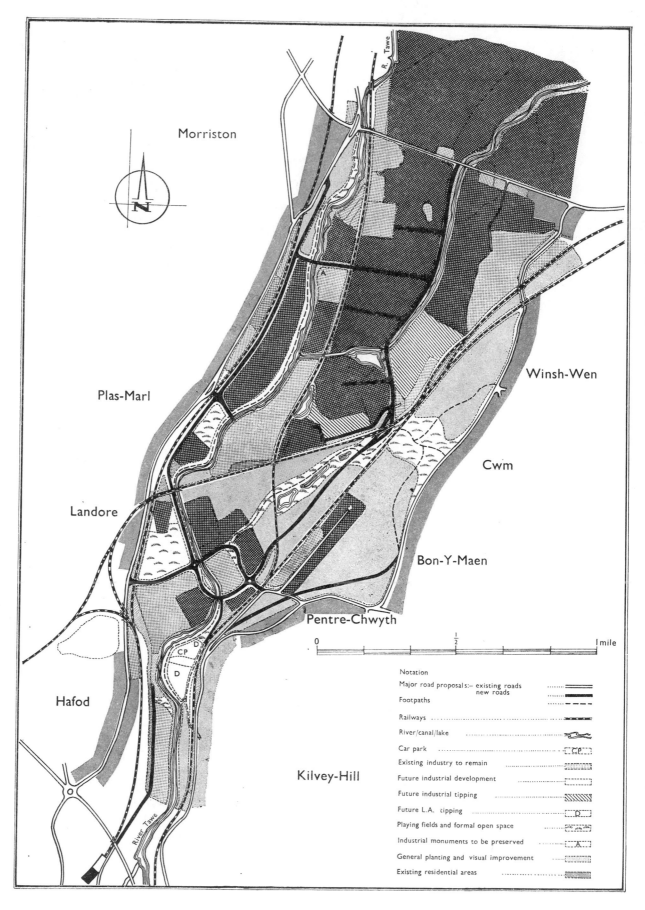

Morriston

Plas-Marl

Landore

Hafod

Winsh-Wen

Cwm

Bon-Y-Maen

Pentre-Chwyth

Kilvey-Hill

R. Tawe

River Tawe

CP
D
D

0   ½   1 mile

Notation

Major road proposals:— existing roads
                              new roads

Footpaths

Railways

River/canal/lake

Car park   CP

Existing industry to remain

Future industrial development

Future industrial tipping

Future L.A. tipping   D

Playing fields and formal open space

Industrial monuments to be preserved   A

General planting and visual improvement

Existing residential areas

Figure 7.16 Outline Development Plan 'B' (Maximal industrial development)

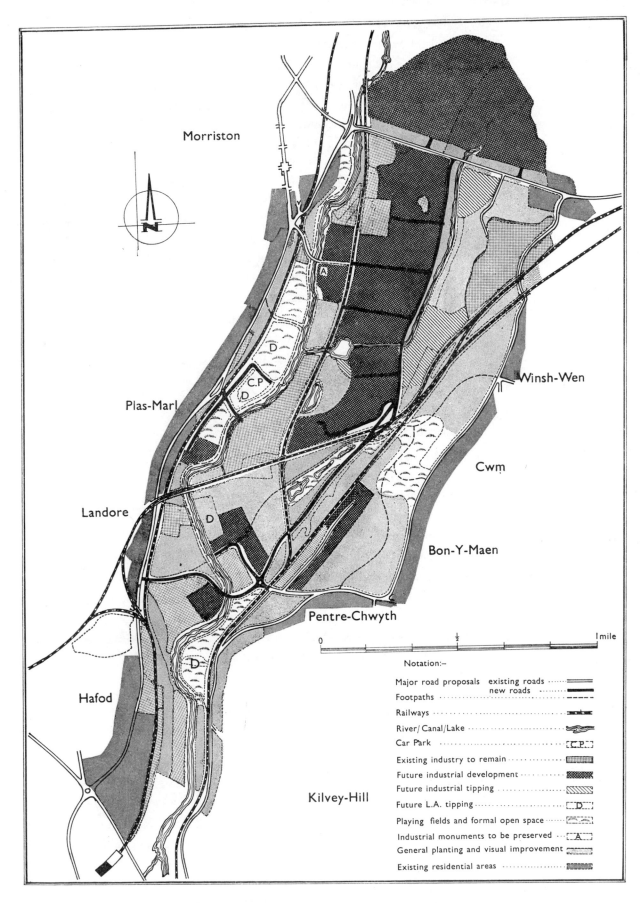

Morriston

Plas-Marl

Landore

Hafod

Winsh-Wen

Cwm

Bon-Y-Maen

Pentre-Chwyth

Kilvey-Hill

A

D

C.P

D

D

D

0   ½   1 mile

Notation:–

Major road proposals   existing roads ········
                                       new roads   ········
Footpaths ···························
Railways ····························
River/Canal/Lake ················
Car Park ···················· C.P
Existing industry to remain ············
Future industrial development ··········
Future industrial tipping ················
Future L.A. tipping ················ D
Playing fields and formal open space ········
Industrial monuments to be preserved ··· A
General planting and visual improvement
Existing residential areas ················

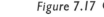
151   *Figure 7.17* Outline Development Plan 'C' (Compromise plan)

3 A new cross-valley route, incorporating a new river bridge in the vicinity of the existing steel and timber truss bridge between Plots 50 and 52, linking the B4292 and A4067 peripheral roads. This route also serves as a common terminal point for the two north–south roads described above, thereby providing a unifying link between the two major sections of the valley floor. Of secondary importance for the redevelopment of the valley floor, such a route would also be instrumental in reducing the current isolation of the east-side residential areas from the rest of the County Borough.

A number of further minor improvements are also essential, including a short section of road running north from the Strand to service Plots 62, 63, 64 and 65.

The actual extent of road construction will obviously depend on the extent of the land use developments that the roads are designed to serve. The basic network outlined above provides a skeletal structure that can be adapted to any future pattern of development on the valley floor. It is both flexible and capable of staged construction. Were only partial redevelopment to be attempted at first, then only a portion of the total network (for example, that serving the proposed light industrial area lying immediately to the south of the A48 (Neath Road) need be constructed. If further redevelopment were undertaken at a later stage, or were the planned distribution of land uses to be modified, then the network itself could be extended or modified as required.

Location of major routes

The location of the three major routes was determined to a large extent by the location of existing railway lines and waterways, and by the need to minimize construction and particularly bridging costs. Despite this desire to keep costs to a minimum no attempt was made to utilize any of the three existing bridges across the river Tawe. These bridges, without exception, are totally inadequate, in terms of both width and bearing capacity, for modern road traffic. Use was made, however, of two existing level crossings (in the vicinity of Upper Bank Station and on the approach to Richard Thomas and Baldwins works) and also of a pair of narrow underbridges passing through the embankment carrying the main London to South Wales railway line. In each case it would be preferable, but considerably more expensive, if these existing facilities could be replaced, respectively, by two overbridges and a new 40 ft wide underbridge.

Description of proposed roads

Main north-south spine road

The major road proposal links the northern and southern halves of the valley into one unit and provides access to the major areas of industrial development. As shown on Figure 7.18 the line of this road runs south from the existing A48 (Neath Road) parallel to the re-aligned Nant-y-Fendrod across Plots 16, 18, 19 and 28, passes under the existing railway embankment via a pair of disused underbridges 14 ft 6 in wide and 40 ft apart and thence along the line of the old Smith's canal to a point level with the existing Upper Bank level crossing where it intersects the proposed east–west route. At the point where the road passes under the railway embankment, it bifurcates into two separate 14 ft wide carriage-

Plate 2 A photographic plan
of the valley as it was in
January 1962

Plate 3   The landscape of industrial dereliction

Plate 4   The view from University College, Swansea, looking towards Mumbles

Plate 5   The Hafod and Middle Bank Works about 1860 (taken from *Le Tour du Monde*, Hachette, 1865)

Plate 6   The ruins of the White Rock Copper, Lead and Silver Works, 1963

Plate 7 A Fabridam (by courtesy of the Firestone Tyre and Rubber Company Ltd)

Plate 8 A mixture of old and new housing on the west side of the valley

Plate 9 New housing development on the distant east side of the valley

Plate 10   The Llansamlet Copper and Arsenic Works in 1961 *before* clearance

Plate 11   The Llansamlet Copper and Arsenic Works in 1966 *after* clearance

Plate 12   A primary school class in the valley

Plate 13   Trees planted on Plot 36 in the winter of 1962/63

Plate 14   The river Tawe at low tide

Plate 15   The river Tawe at high tide

ways. Elsewhere along its length, it is to be constructed to single 30 ft carriageway standards, with provision for right-turn bays where necessary. A series of short, 24 ft wide single carriageway spur roads lead off from this spine road, serving individual development sites. One of these spur roads extends westwards across the Upper Bank–Clydach railway line (crossing it via a new level crossing), to provide access to Plots 15 and 20. This extended spur road replaces the existing inadequate road access from the A4067 via the Beaufort Bridge. This bridge though closed to vehicular traffic has considerable historical and architectural value. It is to be retained as a pedestrian facility. The main north–south spine road is to be constructed in full in Plans B and C. Only its northern segment is included in Plan A.

Second north–south route
A 24 ft wide single carriageway running south along the line of the Swansea Canal and the western bank of the Tawe, from the existing A4067 (Neath Road)/Wychtree Street junction to the proposed east–west route outlined below. This road would act as a distributor route for the various industrial and recreational areas lying between the A4067 Neath Road and the river Tawe. It would also enable a number of existing access points to the A4067 to be closed off and replaced by spur roads leading to the new route, thereby assisting in the creation of the limited access dual carriageway along the line of the A4067 proposed above (p. 145).

Three access points to the dualized A4067 are proposed, one each at the northern and southern terminals of the route and one in the centre, involving realignment of the existing access to Richard Thomas and Baldwins works on Plot 24. The existing river bridge leading to this works is retained as a private works entrance.

Construction of the route in full is proposed in Plan B only. Plans A and C envisage inclusion of only its central section.

East–west cross-river route
The third of the proposals, the east–west cross-river route, involves the realignment of both sections of Station Road east of the Upper Bank level crossing, the construction of a channelled junction with the proposed main north–south spine road, the provision of a new river bridge across the river Tawe immediately south of the existing Addis factory and two further channelled junctions, one with the proposed 'second north–south route' and one with the dualized A4067. This latter intersection was located as shown on Figure 7.18, so as to permit the proposed east–west route to pass under the former Swansea (High Street) to Felin-Fran railway line via an existing viaduct. With the closure of this line, there will be considerably more flexibility in locating this intersection.

This road, which is to be constructed to 30 ft single carriageway standards, is afforded relatively low overall priority, owing to the cost of constructing a new river bridge. Its eastern section is included in all three plans, its whole length only in Plans B and C. The justification for this route, it should be noted, is not the volume of traffic flowing westwards from the Pentrechwyth and Bonymaen housing areas, but rather the need for an east–west link at the southern terminal of the main north–south spine road, to link the eastern and western halves of the valley together and to provide the unity of development discussed earlier. No serious foundation problems are likely to be encountered at the site illustrated in Figure 7.18.

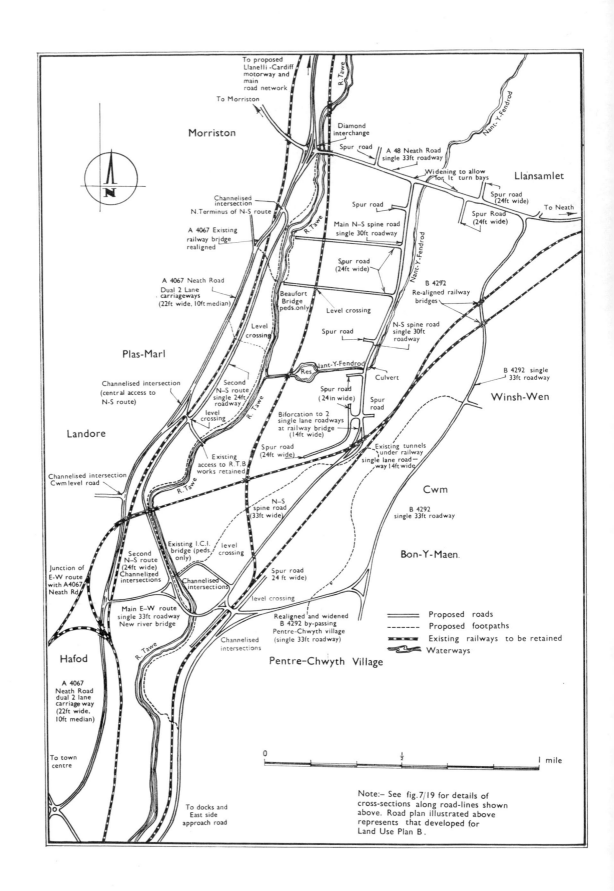

Figure 7.18 Basic road network for Valley floor

Minor improvements

A series of minor improvements are also required. The most important of these is a proposed access road leading north to Plots 62, 63, 64 and 65 from the Strand, replacing the existing unsurfaced track and level crossing at the eastern end of Maliphant Street. This latter access is to be closed off completely.

All the minor improvements and spur roads are to be constructed to single 24 ft carriageway standards. A series of footpaths and pedestrian walks are also proposed and illustrated in Figures 7.15–18 inclusive. These walks are to be surfaced with tarmacadam to a width of 10 ft to be appropriately graded.

Figure 7.19 illustrates the longitudinal profiles of the three major routes, assuming that the earthworks proposed for Plan B have been carried out. The amount of cut and fill shown in these diagrams was used as a basis for the cost estimates discussed later.

Design standards

Road widths for the proposed improvements have already been mentioned in the previous paragraphs. The remaining design standards are in general in accord with those laid down by the Ministry of Transport.[6] In the absence of appropriate British Standards, those of the American Association of State Highway Officials have been adopted. The major standards utilized in the design of the network are as follows:

Design speeds:	1	Dualized portion of A4067/Neath Road	—50 mph
	2	All other routes	—40 mph
Maximum grade:		All routes	—±4 per cent
At grade intersections:		All major intersections to be channelled to accommodate AASHO 'C43' design vehicles. Minimum kerb radii at minor intersections = 35 ft	

In order to keep costs down to a minimum, construction of two new level crossings and retention of two similar facilities is proposed. Although the traffic on the two railway lines involved is likely to remain light, it would be desirable if all four of these junctions could be replaced by grade separations. As such a procedure would obviously increase the construction cost, however, and as none of the crossings appears likely to present severe operational problems, it is proposed that their replacement be awarded relatively low priority. Any surplus funds could more usefully be spent in construction of a new underbridge to carry the main north–south spine road under the embankment of the London to South Wales railway line.

As the results of the soil mechanics and foundation engineering tests indicate (see Chapter 4), the subgrade material on which the roads will be constructed is extremely variable in character. For design purposes it may safely be assumed that a minimum compacted density of 100 lb/ft^3 will be attained in the process of site preparation, and that all roads will be constructed on a base of at least 5 ft of consolidated hardcore. As there is still a distinct possibility of continued settlement, and as suitable construction materials are available in the Swansea area, it is proposed that a flexible form of construction be adopted for all new roads on the valley floor. In this connection the following minimum specifications are proposed as standard:

Figure 7.19 Profiles along proposed road lines

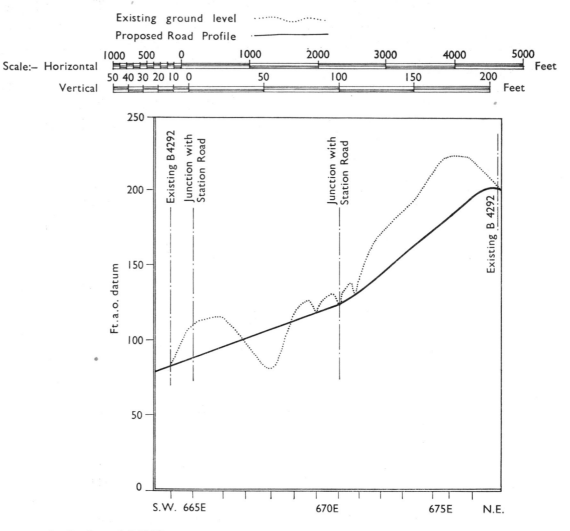

Existing ground level ⋯⋯⋯⋯
Proposed Road Profile ─────

Scale:─ Horizontal
Vertical

1. Realigned B4292

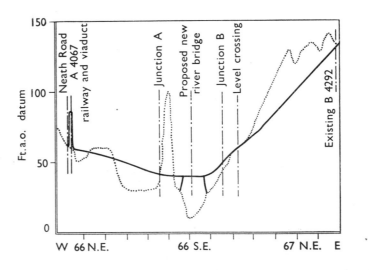

2. Main north–south spine road

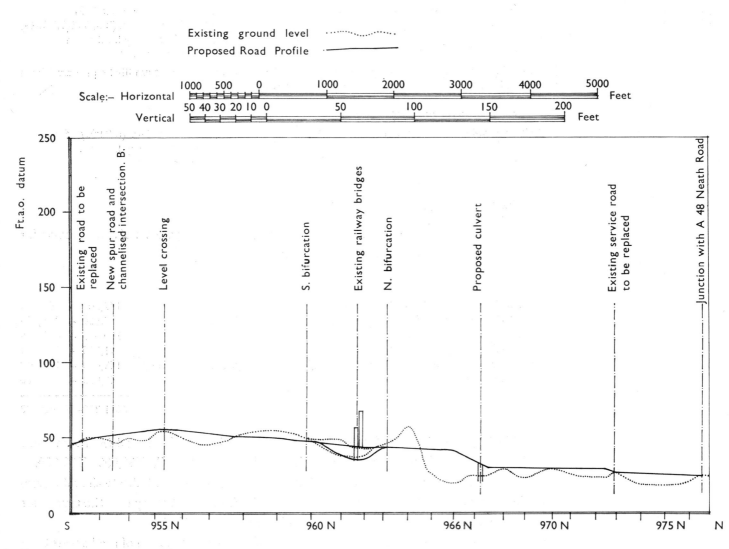

Existing ground level ....
Proposed Road Profile ————

Scale:- Horizontal
1000 500   0   1000   2000   3000   4000   5000   Feet

Vertical
50 40 30 20 10 0   50   100   150   200   Feet

250

200

Ft.a.o. datum

150

100

50

0

Existing road to be replaced
New spur road and channelised intersection. B.
Level crossing
S. bifurcation
Existing railway bridges
N. bifurcation
Proposed culvert
Existing service road to be replaced
Junction with A 48 Neath Road

S   955 N   960 N   966 N   970 N   975 N   N

3. East–west cross river route

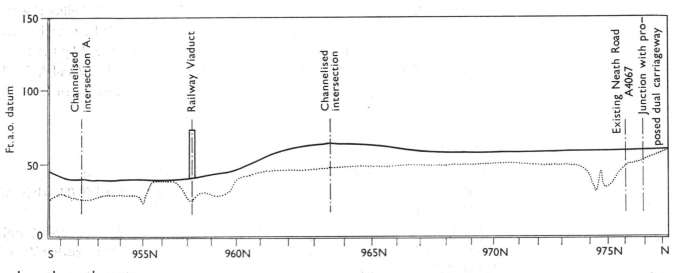

150

Ft.a.o. datum

100

50

0

Channelised intersection A.
Railway Viaduct
Channelised intersection
Existing Neath Road A4067
Junction with proposed dual carriageway

S   955N   960N   965N   970N   975N   N

4. Second north–south route

(a) *All three major routes*

Surface (wearing course)	$\frac{3}{4}$–$1\frac{1}{4}$ in Tarmacadam (B.S.802)
(base course)	$1\frac{3}{4}$–$2\frac{1}{4}$ in Tarmacadam (B.S. 802/B.S.1241)
Base	6 in Wet mix or dry hard stone
Sub-base	6 in Graded stone

('Wet Mix' refers to a graded, pre-mixed, water-bound macadam which might readily be prepared from hardcore of the type available in the Lower Swansea Valley.)

(b) *Spur roads and minor improvements*

Surfacing (combined wearing and base course)	$2\frac{1}{2}$ in Tarmacadam (B.S.802/B.S.1241)
Base	6 in Wet Mix or dry hard stone
Sub-base	6 in Graded stone

Estimated construction costs

On the basis of current figures for the Swansea area, the estimated costs of construction for the road network illustrated in Figure 7.18 are:

	£
North–south spine road (30 ft single carriageway)	142,500 – 190,000
East–west river route (30 ft single carriageway excluding bridge section)	94,500 – 126,000
River bridge (30 ft carriageway)	300,000 – 400,000
Second north–south route (24 ft single carriageway)	91,300 – 107,900
Spur roads and minor improvements (24 ft single carriageway, combined total)	143,000 – 175,000
Footpaths and pedestrian walks	40,000 – 45,000
	£811,300–£1,043,900

Considering Plans A, B and C separately, the estimated costs of the road works involved are: Plan A, £130,000–£180,000; Plan B, £811,300–£1,043,900; Plan C, £550,000–£900,000.

Ranges of probable costs rather than unique estimates are given to indicate the minimum possible and maximum probable expenditures required. In almost every case the true costs are likely to lie closer to the upper than to the lower limit specified.

From these figures it is clear that the provision of an adequate system of road access is by no means inexpensive. The total cost of the proposals illustrated in Figure 7.14 is likely to be in the region of £800,000–£1,100,000. The proposed improvements to the peripheral roads would cost considerably more, between £3,500,000 and £4,000,000, including the cost of new bridges and flyovers. As these peripheral roads are all classified by the Ministry of Transport, any improvement schemes would, once they were approved by the Ministry, become eligible for financial subsidy, 75 per cent in the case of the A4067 and A48, 60 per cent for the B4292. The proposals for the valley floor are not eligible for any such subsidy.

Conclusions

A future road plan for the valley floor is proposed. This plan incorporates:

1. A main north–south spine route, running south from the existing A48 (Neath Road) to the Upper Bank railway station.
2. A second north–south route, running along the present line of the Swansea Canal and the western bank of the Tawe, between Wychtree Street and the existing Yorkshire Imperial Metals factory

Valley floor analyses

3 An east–west cross-river route including a new river bridge joining these two routes with the B4292 and A4067 peripheral routes.

4 A series of minor improvements, including an extension of the Strand northwards to Plot 62 and short spur routes serving individual sites.

5 A network of pedestrian footpaths connecting the surrounding residential areas with the new open space and amenity areas on the Valley floor.

6 The estimated costs of constructing the proposed road network in full is £811,300–£1,043,900 including all bridge works.

7 The proposed network may be constructed in stages according to the timing of development.

Overall plan

This chapter has discussed some of the problems of transportation planning and highway development associated with the redevelopment of the Lower Swansea Valley. It has been shown that a number of improvements, particularly in existing road facilities, are required on both a regional and a local scale if the valley is to be redeveloped successfully. A large number of these improvements are at the same time necessitated by the general increase in traffic with the Swansea area and would consequently be of considerable benefit not merely to the valley area but to the Borough as a whole. It is extremely important, however, that neither the construction of the proposed road schemes nor the improvement of dock and rail services be considered as catalysts for the future development of the valley.

The proposed transportation improvements are merely a part of an overall plan for the redevelopment of the valley, no single element of which is of overriding importance. On their own, they are likely to have relatively little effect on redevelopment. To be successful they must be accompanied by site preparation, flood control and the provision of essential services. Even more important, they must form part of a balanced and realistic set of land use proposals.

Bibliography

1 *Transportation and Physical Planning in the Lower Swansea Valley* (Study Report No. 2).

2 Industrial Association of South Wales and Monmouthshire, Final Report. *Assessment of the Future Highway Requirements of South Wales and Monmouthshire*, Industrial Association of S. Wales and Mon., Cardiff, 1961.

3 British Railways Board. *The Re-shaping of British Railways*, H.M.S.O., London, 1963.

4 Rochdale Committee, Final Report. *Report of the Committee of Inquiry into the Major Ports of Great Britain*, H.M.S.O., London, 1962.

5 R. D. Worrall, *Traffic Studies for the Lower Swansea Valley Project, Traffic Engineering and Control*, London (to be published shortly).

6 Ministry of Transport, Memorandum No. 780, *Memorandum on the Design of Roads in Rural Areas* H.M.S.O., London, 1961.

7 J. R. Scott and J. L. Tanner, 'Traffic Trends and Vehicle Miles in Great Britain, 1938–1960', *Surveyor*, London, 1962, **121** (36 and 9), 654–8.

8 County Borough of Swansea, *Development and Plan—Town Map*, 1960.

9 D. C. Ledger, *The Hydrology of the Lower Swansea Valley* (Study Report No. 3).

Authorship

This chapter was written by Dr R. D. Worrall, Assistant Professor of Civil Engineering and Research Associate, Northwestern University, Evanston, Illinois, U.S.A.

The author would like to express his sincere thanks to Professor O. C. Zienkiewicz, Professor of Civil Engineering at the University College of Swansea, and to K. J. Hilton, Director of the Lower Swansea Valley Project, for their unfailing advice and encouragement during the course of his work.

He would also like to acknowledge the invaluable help that he received from his colleagues on the Project staff, from numerous members of the staff of the University College and from all the firms, public authorities and individuals who answered his questionnaires.

The permission of British Rail to use Maps 1 and 2 of the Beeching Report, Part II, is acknowledged.

Figure 7.7 is based on a series of traffic counts performed by the Swansea Borough Engineer and Planning Officer. Figures 7.8–7.11 inclusive are based on studies performed by the Project staff.

8 The people, their environment and their houses

Three studies were undertaken to assess some of the human factors connected with the dereliction in the Lower Swansea Valley. The first study (*Human Ecology*, 1962) described the valley people in their social and physical environment and considered the social implications of the Project area for the Borough. The second (*Housing*, 1965) assessed the housing need in the whole Borough and in greater detail for the valley area. It was principally concerned with reasons for house location and with future prospects for housing in the valley. The third (*Open Space*, 1965) dealt with the provision and to some extent the use of open space for recreational purposes. In this chapter the main findings of the three studies will be drawn together. It will not be possible in the space limits to present full evidence for many of the statements made. For these, reference must be made to the original reports.

In the three studies the valley was defined rather more widely than the Project area proper. The sociological survey area includes the valley sides, which overlook the valley floor, and which have an economic and historic unity with it (see Figure 1.1). In some cases where administrative data are used the boundary is not precisely coterminous with this. The surrounding wards, for example, extend in some cases beyond the valley as defined here. Where this happens it will be mentioned.

The people and their environment

The pattern of settlement

As industry developed in the valley bottom, so settlements grew up on the hillsides around to house the workers and some of the owners and managers of the undertakings. In some parts the residential development was dense, stretching away from the valley floor and linking with town centre developments in Swansea and Morriston. In other places just a row of cottages was strung along the hillside. Here and there, especially on the east side of the river, were isolated industrial hamlets. Now almost all the industry has left the valley floor: much of it lies derelict and deserted. A new town, in Dr Rosser's phrase, is being built beside the ruins of the old.*

The Project was started and the studies for the Human Ecology Report planned before the results of the 1961 census were available. At that time it was widely believed that there was a movement of people as well as of industry away from the valley. There was visible evidence in support of this view: acres of new houses had been and were being built on the outskirts of the Borough to the north and to the west. The Borough Housing Manager could

---

* C. Rosser and C. C. Harris, *The Family and Social Change*. Routledge & Kegan Paul, 1965, p. 43.

The people, their
environment and their
houses

point to a high proportion of preferences entered for West Cross, an estate on the coast in the south-west of the Borough, among his housing applicants. Rosser and Harris, in a detailed examination of the local authority housing list, confirmed the accuracy of this impression.* As someone put it the 'ecological tide' was running out westwards and it was useless to try and turn it. 'Everybody', it was said, wanted to move westwards. The corollary of this was that 'nobody' wanted to live in the valley area. Yet people were still living there.

The people of the valley

In view of this apparent contradiction, the question was posed whether it was only the old, the poor and the unenterprising who lived adjacent to the derelict areas. Data drawn from the Rosser–Harris sample survey of 1960 were used as the starting point for this analysis.

The demographic structure

Dr Rosser and Mr Harris grouped their material into localities based upon neighbourhood units as in the town plan. The population surrounding the valley fell into three such localities: Morriston/Llansamlet; Hafod/Landore; and Brynhyfryd/Manselton. These include small populations outside the survey area as defined at the beginning of the chapter. This is particularly true of Morriston/Llansamlet, which on its outskirts extends beyond the present definition of the valley. Nevertheless the three localities extracted from the Rosser–Harris data in this way are those which surround the valley in contrast to the ten other localities they defined.

It was estimated that at least a quarter of Swansea lived in these three localities. The demographic evidence refuted the suggestion that it was only the old who lived around the valley. All age groups and both sexes were represented in what can be said to be a normal distribution judged by the standards of the Borough. In the number of generations per household, and in the size of their families, once again the valley localities displayed distributions similar to those of the rest of the Borough.

The socio-economic structure

If the valley people were not particularly the old, were they then the poor? According to Rosser and Harris the Borough as a whole had a concentration of incomes in the £11–15 a week group in 1960. This concentration was even more marked in the valley localities, because there were noticeably fewer higher incomes than average. The valley had in 1960 some, but by no means all, of the poorest people; a few well-to-do, but none of the richest. A population with a similar income distribution could be found in many other parts of the Borough.

The same sort of finding was made about occupation and education. The valley had proportionately more manual workers than the town as a whole, but by no means did all the town's manual workers live there. Nor was it a 'working-class area' in the sense that only manual workers lived there. Over 20 per cent of the population in each of the three valley localities identified are non-manual workers, compared with about 30 per cent in the whole Borough. Each valley locality contains some professional people.

Few of the Rosser–Harris respondents living in the valley in 1960 had been to fee-paying

* Op. cit. p. 60.

schools as children. Those who had been to such schools tended to be found outside the valley in the south-western wards, there amounting to nearly a quarter of the adult population. In fact today all the private schools are in the west and there are none in the valley. Similarly, college graduates tend to live in the western part of the town, although 21 per cent of them are found in the valley. On the other hand the proportion of valley dwellers in 1960 who had stayed at school after fifteen was low, relating to the rather high proportion of unskilled workers.

The Rosser–Harris evidence suggested that the 40,000 or so inhabitants of the three valley localities were not unrepresentative of the population of the Borough in their socio-economic characteristics.

Social need and social deviance

Was the valley an area with a high proportion of the more troublesome? Certain indices were used to test this. They showed families who either exhibited a need for help or who had failed to conform to certain minimum legal standards of behaviour.

The first index was based upon the incidence of children taken into care; the second, the provision of free school meals; the third, the incidence of juvenile delinquency.* These particular indicators were taken simply because they happened to be the ones available. They measure somewhat different things,† but all three have the common factor that a family has been exposed by authority as not doing the job expected of it, either in maintaining and bringing up its children in terms of care and nourishment, or in terms of training the children to keep the law. It could be said that a locality with a high incidence of such exposure was one which was to this extent a liability to the authority.

One part of the valley, let us call it 'A', stood out as having a high incidence of children taken into care; the remainder were well below the Borough average. The school in area A also had a high incidence of free school meals. So did one other school in another part of the valley. Otherwise the incidence of the provision of free meals in valley schools was equal to, or in some cases well below, the Borough average. On the juvenile delinquency index, area A was not particularly high. A school in another part of the valley, area B, had a particularly high incidence of juvenile delinquency at the time the Human Ecology Report was compiled, while a number of schools in the valley were just a little above the town average. On the other hand, two-fifths of the valley secondary schools had a delinquency incidence among their eleven-plus boys which was well below the town average.

At that time only one year's analysis of juvenile delinquency by school was available from the Probation Office. Four years are now available in all; the analysis has therefore been brought up to date, since one year's figures might well give an unrepresentative picture. Indeed the school in area B came out so high because a gang had been caught that year, while gangs in other areas had not. The revised analysis shows the same valley school B at the top of the list with the highest number of convicted delinquents per 100 boy pupils over eleven. There are six schools which have a delinquency rate over the four years, 1961–4,

---

* This information was provided by the Swansea Local Education Authority, Swansea County Borough Children's Committee and the Probation Office respectively.
† Details of the method of construction of the indices and of what they measure are given in Appendix I to this chapter.

The people, their
environment and their
houses

above the Borough average, which is 2·9 delinquents per 100 boy pupils over eleven. Of these six schools two are in the valley (school B plus one other). There are nine schools with a below average rate. Of these schools, three are in the valley. Thus one-third of the schools with a below average rate are in the valley and one-third of the schools with an above average rate are in the valley. As has been said the school which heads the list over the four years is a valley school. The one which comes second is not. The valley school is in one of the oldest areas of town. The second is not. They do have in common two factors: both schools are in localities which according to the Rosser–Harris inquiries have a high incidence of low-income earners as household heads; both also have an above average proportion of large households living in small houses.

These three indices gave no evidence that the people living in the valley were in any sense more of a liability to civic authorities than those in any other part of the town. Three arguments support this conclusion. First, there was very high variation from one part of the valley to another. Second, while there were within the valley small areas where the incidence of particular social problems was above average, in other parts of the town there were areas which had as high or higher scores on the indices used. Third, no one part of the valley had a concentration of all the social problems. An area with a high score on one index had a low score on two others. There was thus not any one part within the valley where people exhibiting a wide range of social problems were gathered together.

The hypothesis that it was only the old, the poor, and the unenterprising who lived on the valley sides had to be rejected. There was no evidence for it. On the contrary, whatever measure was used the people of the valley appeared as a cross-section of the people of the town. They were, in this sense, a 'normal' population.

The environment

Houses

Swansea in common with all other industrial towns which developed in the nineteenth century has a comparatively heavy load of old and obsolescent dwellings.* About 20 per cent of the total 1961 housing stock of about 50,000 houses was built before 1875, that is to say, in 1960 a fifth of Swansea's dwellings were over eighty years old. In addition there were over 13,000 dwellings at that time which were between forty-five and eighty-eight years old.† Age is not necessarily a guide to present condition, but the figure of 10,000 dwellings over eighty years old fits closely with the figure of between 10,000 and 11,000 dwellings with no fixed baths given in the Census of 1961. Some of the older houses have no doubt been modernized and some less old lack amenities. Thus it seems likely that about 10,000 dwellings in 1961 represented the net size of the problem of obsolescence in Swansea.

Between 1959 and 1962 inclusive, less than 1,000 old dwellings were cleared. The clearance rate in this period was 186 dwellings a year. Many have been modernized with the aid of grants, but the rate of improvement, 360 in 1963, is small in relation to what needed to be done in 1961. The rate of improvement without grant cannot be measured until a new

---

* This is a particular feature of the British housing scene. See for example *A Statistical Survey of the Housing Situation in European Countries Around 1960*, U.N.
† A special analysis undertaken by the Town Planning Department of the County Borough is the source for these figures.

Age of Dwellings

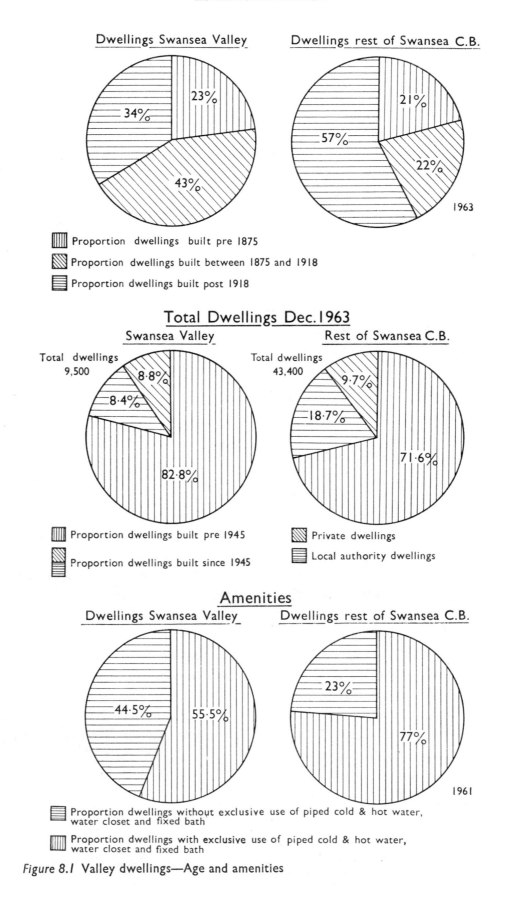

Dwellings Swansea Valley

23%
34%
43%

Dwellings rest of Swansea C.B.

21%
57%
22%
1963

▥ Proportion dwellings built pre 1875

▨ Proportion dwellings built between 1875 and 1918

▤ Proportion dwellings built post 1918

Total Dwellings Dec.1963

Swansea Valley

Total dwellings
9,500

8·8%
8·4%
82·8%

Rest of Swansea C.B.

Total dwellings
43,400

9·7%
18·7%
71·6%

▥ Proportion dwellings built pre 1945

▨ Proportion dwellings built since 1945

▨ Private dwellings

▤ Local authority dwellings

Amenities

Dwellings Swansea Valley

44·5%   55·5%

Dwellings rest of Swansea C.B.

23%
77%
1961

▤ Proportion dwellings without exclusive use of piped cold & hot water,
water closet and fixed bath

▥ Proportion dwellings with **exclusive** use of piped cold & hot water,
water closet and fixed bath

Figure 8.1 Valley dwellings—Age and amenities

The people, their
environment and their
houses

census is taken. It is likely that many major improvements are undertaken without grant. A great many of the dwellings in the valley are old and inadequate by modern standards: 66 per cent of the dwellings (1963) were built before 1919, compared with 43 per cent in the rest of Swansea. In the valley 17 per cent of the dwellings in 1963 had been built since 1945 compared with 28 per cent in the rest of the Borough.* Similarly, at the 1961 Census over 44 per cent of dwellings in the valley were without exclusive use of piped cold and hot water, water closet and fixed bath, compared with 23 per cent in the rest of Swansea. This is shown in Figure 8.1.

It can therefore reasonably be said that while the valley did not have a monopoly of Swansea's obsolescent dwellings it had a high proportion relative to the rest of the Borough. There were other similar areas, south of the town centre and in the vicinity of the docks for example. Indeed small clusters of obsolescent dwellings are scattered throughout the Borough. Nevertheless the valley area remains one of the largest concentrations. Between 20 and 25 per cent of all the old and obsolescent dwellings are found there.

Other buildings

Houses are not the only old buildings in the Valley. The shops, the churches and chapels and the schools all speak of the nineteenth-century origins of much of the area. Indeed in one place an eighteenth-century chapel which was outgrown by its increasing congregation stands next to its nineteenth-century successor. All but one of the schools are over fifty years old, and at least one is over 100 years old. This is again typical of the older areas of most old towns.†

Unmade roads

In Britain, we have come to accept that roads with a tarmacadam or other made up surface are an amenity which one may expect in an urban area. There were in 1962, twenty-one miles of unmade and unadopted roads within the County Borough. To some extent it is understandable that there should be a considerable mileage of unmade roads since the Borough includes a good deal of rural land, but by no means all the unmade roads are on the undeveloped periphery of the Borough. Seven miles, that is one-third, of these unmade roads are found in the valley. They are another legacy of the eighteenth and nineteenth centuries, and one to which no attention has been paid in legislation or financial provision. Making up a road is an expensive proposition, especially when water, electricity, gas, sewerage, and other services run beneath it. Many of the houses alongside the unmade roads are owned by persons of modest means for whom frontaging would be financially difficult. The local authority are unwilling to adopt the roads in their present state. No financial aids are available. Present law insists that builders should make roads properly as they build. This was not formerly the case and consequently many side roads in the valley lack this amenity.

Recreational open space

Because the valley was an industrial area in the nineteenth century the wealthy tended to

---

* Ministry of Housing and Local Government, *Housing Returns*, H.M.S.O., 1964, Appendix.
† National Union of Teachers, *The State of our Schools. A report of the findings of the National Survey of Schools*, 1962.

live farther west. Many of their houses, gardens and parks have now been taken into public use. This is one of the reasons why Swansea East is relatively less well endowed with public open space, and indeed recreational space of any kind, than Swansea West. The other reason is that the cliffs and foreshore accessible for public recreational use are also on the west side, for the docks and associated industry occupy the area of the river mouth and the eastern foreshore. There is a good deal of open space on the east side, but it is much more often derelict open space than it is public open space, or recreational space of any kind.

A summary of all types of public open space, that is open space owned and managed by a public authority and accessible to the public, is given in Figure 8.2. This gives the general impression that a bottle of ink has been knocked over somewhere near the Mumbles Head, most of it spilling in the south-west of the Borough and only a few splashes reaching up the north and east. There are in fact 522·7 acres of public open space in Swansea West constituency and only 234·1 acres in Swansea East. Thus nearly 70 per cent of the total open space in the Borough is in Swansea West. Taking the population at the 1961 census for every 1,000 persons Swansea West had 7·32 acres of public open space and Swansea East had 2·44 acres.

Furthermore, the open space analysis showed that not only is the total provision unequal in this way, but the quality of provision is also unequal. Thus almost all the cliffs, commons, and foreshore are in the south-west area: 700–800 derelict acres match them on the east side. Not only are there more and larger parks in the south-west, but the parks in that area are also of a higher standard.

For purposes of analysis public parks were divided according to the amenities that they provide. These are of course very various and some simple measuring rod had to be used. Parks were defined by Sir Herbert Manzoni* as parkland of over one acre in extent, supplying relaxation in natural surroundings, available free, and with facilities for entertainment and refreshment. Parks in Swansea were assumed to fit this definition and called 'Parks I' if they had grass to play on and a refreshment or ice cream kiosk. Parkland of over one acre with at least seats, and grass to play on, but no refreshment amenities was classified as 'Parks II'. Remaining public open spaces, listed by the local authority as parks, that is those other than playing fields or children's playgrounds, were defined as amenity areas.

There were no parks at all of the standard of Parks I east of the Tawe. Of the fourteen Parks I all but three are ranged along the south-western foreshore. Their catchment areas, taken as half a mile from the park gate, overlap each other. Thus while the provision of Parks I in terms of acres per head of the population for the whole of Swansea is very reasonable, the distribution is uneven between the east and west constituencies and between the valley and the rest of the Borough. The areas which benefit least from this acreage of public open space are the valley and the east side area.

The distribution of Parks II is rather better, as between east and west, but the acreage in Swansea East is less and the amenities are less good. There are certain open spaces listed in the valley area which are quite undeveloped and utterly drab, with neither grass nor a proper hard surface.

The distribution of amenity areas showed that this was a type of development with which the Borough had not much concerned itself. The lower valley sides are punctuated

---

* In an unpublished draft report made to the City of Birmingham in the 1950s.

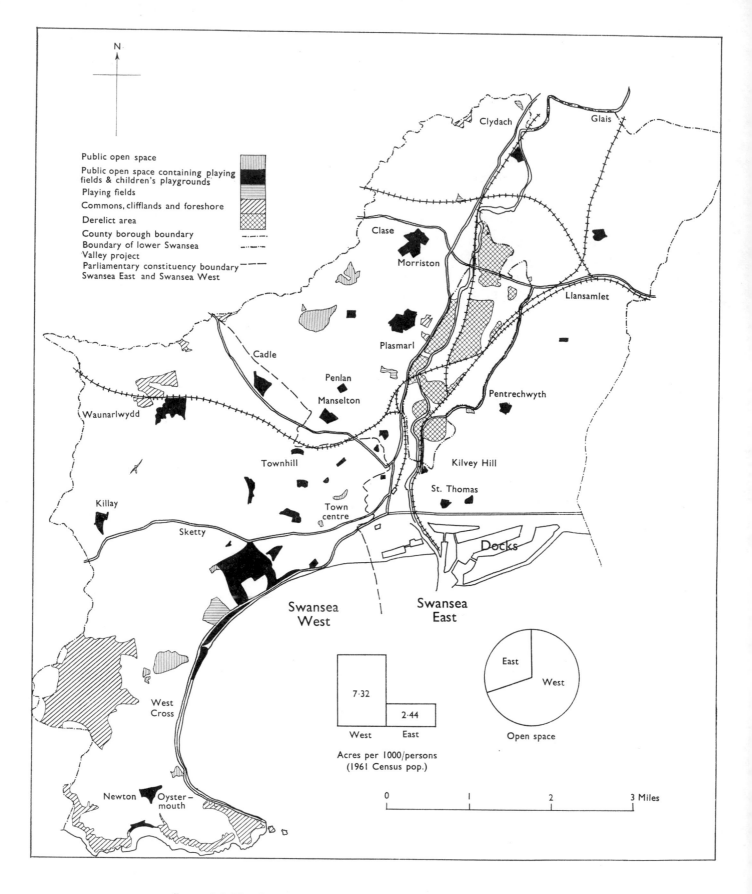

Legend:
- Public open space
- Public open space containing playing fields & children's playgrounds
- Playing fields
- Commons, clifflands and foreshore
- Derelict area
- County borough boundary
- Boundary of lower Swansea Valley project
- Parliamentary constituency boundary Swansea East and Swansea West

Clydach
Glais
Clase
Morriston
Llansamlet
Plasmarl
Cadle
Penlan
Pentrechwyth
Manselton
Waunarlwydd
Kilvey Hill
Townhill
St. Thomas
Killay
Town centre
Sketty
Docks
Swansea West
Swansea East
West Cross
East
West
Open space
Newton
Oyster-mouth

7·32 West   2·44 East
Acres per 1000/persons
(1961 Census pop.)

0   1   2   3 Miles

Figure 8.2 The distribution of public open space, 1963

The people and their environment

with patches of undeveloped and untidy ground among the older houses and odd and untidy corners in new estates left, with builders' rubble still on them, to accumulate further rubbish.

Playing fields, private as well as public, were examined separately. Once again the distribution is weighted to the west, and particularly the southwest, part of the Borough. Not only are there more playing fields on the west side, but the west side playing fields are of a higher standard than those on the east. In addition it seems that sportsmen do not find the playing fields provision in the Borough as a whole adequate. Complaints were made both that there were not enough fields, and that the standards of the courts or pitches were inadequate. These complaints were made by players on the west as well as the east. Since, as we have seen, the east side provision is less good than the west side, it seems certain that the playing field provision on the east side is inadequate.

There is clearly a shortage of recreational open space in Swansea East in general and the valley in particular.

The visual environment

Little is known of the impact of visual environment upon people. To some it seems to matter a good deal; to others apparently very little. At least some people seem aware of their visual environment, others not so.

To the author there is an air of desolation about many parts of the valley sides. Cottages abandoned many years ago give an impression of decay. This is increased in some parts by the remains of dwellings more recently abandoned on account of clearance or closure orders issued by the local authority, but which have not yet been cleared away. There are undeveloped patches between the buildings which add to the sense of dereliction. Empty land tends to be used for dumping rubbish. In one case a scrap merchant's yard has developed and is operating on land at Cwm which is scheduled for educational purposes. The operator has by now achieved established user rights and can only be evicted expensively by compulsory order. In an area of higher standards, less littered by debris, the development of this scrap yard is unlikely to have gone unnoticed for so long. Rubbish, in the shape of old prams, bicycle parts, and wheels, tends also to be dumped in the unculverted streams, a number of which run down from the east side residential development to the Tawe. To the eyes of this observer, such untidy patches constitute an eyesore which downgrades the area. In addition, on the new estates small patches between the houses which neither are part of people's gardens, nor constitute the verges for which the parks department takes responsibility, are left littered with builder's rubble.

The tip scenery of the valley floor is a man made landscape which some observers find simply depressing, and which others, especially in the evening sun, find strangely beautiful. Economic and social historians can be fascinated by the ruins of eighteenth and nineteenth-century industrial plant.

It is clear that in the matter of visual appreciation, subjective and perhaps unmeasurable factors enter. In the course of the studies some points became clear. The impact of the visual scene varies with certain observable characteristics of those who see it. Attention was drawn to the valley by those initiating the research and support was gained for it, at least partly because the dereliction flanks the main railway line for the last three miles of its

The people, their
environment and their
houses

entry into the town. To travellers and to the leaders of government and business the area was seen as a most untidy 'front door'. Those who have lived with it all their lives may not 'see' it at all. One lady assured the author that she liked her house 'because it had such a lovely view'. The author's eyes saw an untidy and little-used railway line bordered by rows of butane gas cylinders. The lady looked above and beyond this to the distant hills. A country-woman by birth, this long view was a comfort to her after living in tight-packed terraced streets where the only view was of the windows of the row in front. She could ignore the untidy foreground. In the same investigation, a study of all those people living around a particular derelict site, it became clear that whether the 'ruins' mattered to a person depended a good deal on where it was in relation to (a) their windows and front and back doors, and (b) the way they ordinarily went to the bus or the shops. A tip or a ruin could be very near (less than 100 yards) but if they could not see it from the house and did not have to pass it on the way they usually went out, then it was of little concern to them. Those who could see it and did have to pass it were more concerned.

Concern, however, tended to take the form less of what it looked like than of what it did or might do. Thus those living near a ruined works were concerned because it was danger-ous: it 'creaked' in the night, they were frightened when the children climbed on it (which they could see them doing from their houses) and they disliked passing it to go to the square to shop. A stagnant pond was disliked and feared because it smelled bad and because a child had nearly drowned in it and others might at any time. Other informants, whose road end was closed by a tip, were less concerned about its appearance than about the nuisance it caused. This tip was being worked for hardcore, and when the wind blew down the street all house cleaning efforts were frustrated by the dust and dirt which blew into the living-room. Similarly those whose houses were on an unmade road bothered more about the dirt this caused than they did about the ruins at the end of the road.

Living on the hillside gives many people views which are wide and long, sometimes to rural hills in the upper valley, sometimes out towards the sea and sometimes to urban hills on the other side of the Tawe. These long views are in part the simple result of sharp con-touring, they are as much the result of a good deal of (derelict) open space. Among those who commented at all upon the visual scene there was a high degree of consensus that these views were valuable, a matter of pride. The views at night were particularly com-mended.

Several informants made it plain that the extent to which they were aware of their visual environment and the extent to which it mattered to them depended a good deal upon their knowledge of other places. One informant, an incomer to the town from the English side of the border, said that he found the dereliction most deplorable. 'It makes the wife and I feel sick every time we come back to it when we've been away. As soon as we reach Pontardawe [a town up the valley a bit from the Project area] we start to feel sick at the sight of it.' Another informant who had been born and brought up in the valley, who was proud of its industrial history and who was a deacon of a chapel there, said 'Well, it's when you've seen other places that it starts to matter to you. I used not to think about it. But since my son and daughter have got married and moved away I go up to England to visit them [one in Warwickshire and the other in Sussex]. When I come back I realize how awful it is and what it could be like. It shows it up when you see those places.'

It may be that the sense of drabness and decay is increased because of the strong contrast between the west side of the town and the east side and the valley area, that is for those who know both. The west side abuts the Gower, an area scheduled as 'of outstanding natural beauty'. The edge of this area comes just within the County Borough boundary on the west side.

People vary in their assessment of the visual appearance of the valley depending among other things on their proximity to dereliction and their knowledge of other places.

The divided borough

Many informants, both private residents and those working in public service on the east side, said they felt neglected. A few reported the contrast in visual terms. More often the references were to services available. In some cases they felt they were not fairly treated, that their colleagues on the west received more attention. In other cases they had no complaint of unfair services, but did complain of a sense of isolation. They felt that they did not belong to the Borough, that they were cut off. There are many physical barriers, rivers, railway lines, tips and boulders which lie between parts of the Valley and the entertainment, business and administrative centres of Swansea.

The transport system of the valley is the subject of Chapter 7. The social consequences of the road pattern and of the unused acres in the valley are relevant here. As shown in Chapter 7, it is not possible to cross the Tawe except on foot for the whole three-mile strip of the Project area. The evidence of the human ecology study was that the effect of this unbridged waste land was to cut the east side off from the remainder of the Borough. There was some evidence, and this was supported by Mr Worrall,* that the east side of the Borough (i.e. east of Morriston and north of Foxhole) looked to Morriston or to Skewen and Neath as its focus as much as, or more than, Swansea town centre. That is to say people living on the east side of the Tawe and north of Foxhole turned their backs on the shopping and commercial centres of Swansea, which for them were across the river. Furthermore, as the later housing study showed, a number of east-siders had been brought up in, and had kin and friendship connections with people in, Morriston, Skewen and Neath.

Nevertheless this east side is part of the County Borough and is administered from the Guildhall, which lies in the south-west coastal strip beyond the business district. Apart from the people who live on the east side, and local government employees assigned to working in it, few people go there or pass through. There is no reason why they should. There are no works and no places of entertainment, and it is not on the main route anywhere. The docks to the south constitute a separate ecological area which is cut off from the valley's east side by the White Rock tips.

On the other hand there are many east-siders in a position to compare east and west Swansea, for while there is little to take those from the west on a trip to the east, there are many reasons connected with work and play to encourage east-siders to travel to the west. Travelling to the west may become a daily journey for east-side children. Nearly a third of all Swansea primary school children go to schools in the valley, but only a quarter of the secondary school children. This is not because there are fewer secondary school children in the area. Altogether more than a third of all Swansea's secondary school children live in the

---

* R. D. Worrall, *Report on Transportation and Physical Planning in the Lower Swansea Valley*, L.S.V.P. report, September 1963, Section 2.7 (*a*).

The people, their
environment and their
houses

valley. The proportion attending secondary schools in the area is a quarter and not a third, principally because over a thousand secondary school children from the valley attend schools outside it. There are no grammar schools, or schools with facilities for a grammar education, in the valley or on the east side. Thus all those children who are receiving a grammar school education must travel to the western part of Swansea for it. So must those receiving a technical education. At the time of survey a school able to give a grammar and a technical education was being planned. Its building has now (1965) begun. It will be a comprehensive coeducational school on an east-side hill-top, and is designed to serve all those on the valley east side as well as those near the docks to the south of it. Those on the west side of the Tawe still have to travel farther west out of the valley to reach a school which will give them a grammar education.

Historically, the works in the valley drew workers from the neighbouring hillsides. Contacts were made between east and west in the place of work. Apart from the accounts given by older informants, there is the evidence provided by what still remains of this older relationship between home and workplace. An analysis of the place of residence of those working in the principal industries which were still functioning in the valley in 1962 showed that there was a distinct tendency for workers to live on the hillside above and around the workplace. The only serious exception to this was one works which had moved from the southern central area of the town to the valley and still drew many of its workers from around that central area. Council house building had also led to a number of workers coming from farther afield. The tendency for place of residence to be near place of work remained noticeable. It seems reasonable to assume therefore that in a sense in the old days the valley united, at least during working hours, the people from the surrounding hillsides. Now that so little industry is left in the valley, it tends to divide the town, to separate east from west, to be a barrier and not a focus.

Conclusions

The environment of the valley is substandard and is isolated from the remainder of the Borough. The environment is substandard in terms of buildings, roads, scenery, services and amenities provided, when judged against the standards of Swansea West, or against the standards of the new towns of the south-east. This is historically the result of the decline of industry and the failure to renew and redevelop other kinds of capital in the valley.

New developments in the valley

The new buildings

It is not true to say that there has been no capital development in the valley. This was in fact an important difference between the valley sides and the valley floor at the time of survey. It is true that some industries were then continuing in operation in the valley, but with the exception of the largest works, the impression given was of contraction and decline, an impression that the valley had not entered the motor age. Since the survey was done one new factory has arrived.

The impression of contraction does not apply to the valley sides and the difference is perhaps best symbolized by the new filling stations opened on the peripheral roads. The new filling stations were a symbol not only in their contemporary architecture, which contrasted so strongly with the old terraced houses and the chapels, but in their assurance that those living and working on the valley sides were increasingly using the internal combustion engine. The twentieth century might have overlooked the valley floor, but its influences were at work upon the valley sides.

In addition the gaps between the old terraces were gradually being filled in. A new bungalow or a pair of 'semis' between two old terraces showed that some people at least were prepared to invest in residential development in the valley. Nor was the development negligible. The eastern hillsides were being developed both by the local authority and by private developers with estates of several hundred houses. While in the rest of the Borough the ratio of post-1945 council to private building is about 2:1, in the Swansea Valley the postwar building is shared almost equally by the private and the public builder, with a slight balance in favour of the private builder. Individuals, whether building for themselves, or speculatively on a larger scale, seem to have had more faith in the valley than have the councillors and officials of the County Borough (Plates 8 and 9).

The population movements

At the time when the Project started it was widely believed, by the Guildhall officials and by other students of social affairs in the University, that people were leaving the valley and moving westwards. It is true that the Borough, both by private and public development, has extended westward in the twentieth century. The movement continues in a south-westerly direction, and seems now to be overshooting the County Borough boundary (Figure 8.3).

In the years between the 1951 and 1961 censuses, the population of Swansea West con-stituency remained virtually stationary. At the same time the neighbouring rural districts on the west, Pennard and Bishopston, showed increases of 31 per cent and 20 per cent re-spectively, a joint net increase of over 900 people. This figure will almost certainly have been augmented in the years since 1961, in which period a further spurt of building in Swansea West itself has also taken place.

Although looked at as a whole Swansea West population did not change between 1951 and 1961, there were movements of populations within the constituency. The older, more central wards, including Townhill, a second-generation housing estate, have declined in size. The peripheral wards, Fforestfach, Mumbles and Sketty, have increased. This is evi-dence of a continuing population movement north and west. This movement seems, from the evidence of new building, to be continuing. The increases in the adjacent rural areas can be seen as an unplanned overspill. It is also probably true that this unplanned overspill has only taken so long to come about because Swansea County Borough is widespread. It has a total acreage of 21,600 (excluding foreshore) and a density of population of only 7·8 per-sons per acre. The acreage is by far the largest of any County Borough of similar popula-tion and penny rate product.*

At the same time as these northward and westward movements were taking place, within and beyond Swansea West, Swansea East increased its net population by $8\frac{1}{2}$ per cent. Again, as in the west, there were differences from one ward to another. The older central wards of Swansea East declined between 1951 and 1961. The major part of the increase in the con-stituency in that period was due to the large Council developments in Penderry Ward. There was also a net increase of 22 per cent in Llansamlet, the ward which embraces the

* Study Report No. I, Table I.

The people, their
environment and their
houses

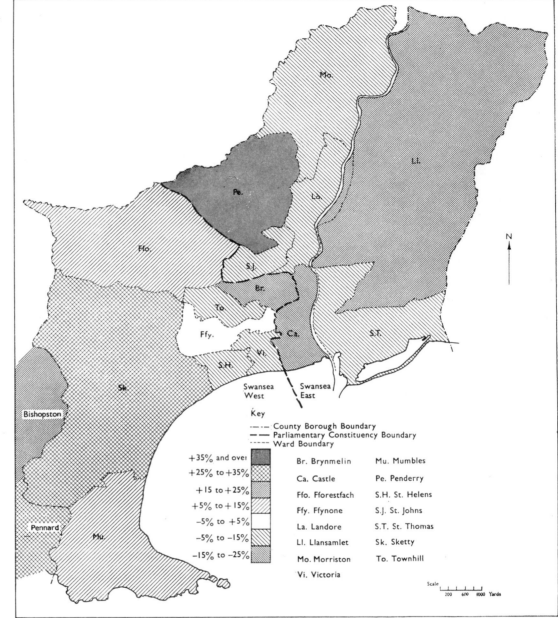

Figure 8.3 Population movements, 1951–1961

northern and eastern parts of the Lower Swansea Valley. Here, while the increase was partly accounted for by east-side council estates, it was also influenced by large-scale private developments in the ward.

The census results therefore suggested that as well as a westward population movement there was also an eastward and a northward movement and this was associated with a certain amount of new building in the valley.

Conclusions: A

1   The population of the Lower Swansea Valley is a normal cross-section of the County Borough of Swansea as measured by its distribution along indices of age, sex, marital status,

Conclusions: A   occupation status grading, educational attainment, income, receipt of free school meals, of children taken into care, of juvenile delinquency, except for some shortage of the most wealthy groups.

2   This 'normal' population is living in a sub-standard environment judged by the standards of the Borough as a whole and of other and newer towns, and in the ways enumerated below:

(a)   The buildings are old and many are in need of replacement and renewal. These include public buildings (e.g. schools) and residential buildings.

(b)   There is a shortage of acres of open space per head of population. Provision at 2·44 acres per 1,000 persons in Swansea East is below the Swansea West level (7·32 acres per 1,000 persons) and below the recommended national figure (6 acres per 1,000 population for playing fields alone). Such open space as is provided is of a lower standard than that in Swansea West.

3   Because of its excellent position in relation to road and rail transport the valley offers possibilities for the provision of recreational amenities for the sub-region as well as for the valley and the east side.

4   Despite 1 and 2 above, there is no net loss of population in the valley. Population is declining only in the older wards to the south of the area. East and north of the valley the population is increasing.

5   Building and the improvement of buildings is being undertaken extensively in the valley and on balance (up to 1963) by private individuals and companies slightly more than by the local authority.

Recommendations

1   The valley should be upgraded and developed to continue to house a quarter of the town's population, including the increases to 1981, i.e. there should be a net increase in the population of the area in order to retain the present proportion. (This recommendation is made in the light of the conclusions of the Appendix on Climatology and Air Pollution of the Lower Swansea Valley (see p. 292), which shows that air pollution levels are not high by comparison with other urban areas, and that 'climatic factors are not likely to play a major part in assessing the future development potential for the Lower Swansea Valley'. It is recognized, however, as that Appendix states, that more study is necessary before the microclimatology of the valley is fully established, particularly as the presence of inversions is proved. It is recommended therefore that before residential developments take place on any sites other than the hill slopes, a more detailed climatic study of the proposed site be undertaken.)

2   Part of the derelict areas of the valley should be developed as open space. In particular, two parks are suggested, one on the east and one on the west of the Tawe.

In both cases these should run down from the hillside to the river. The park on the east of the Tawe should start in the old colliery tip behind Cwm school and run down to the river linking with the College plot, while that on the west of the river should start on the common land of Graig Trewyddfa and run down to the Tawe's west bank.

The people, their
environment and their
houses

3   There should be a riverside walk with which the park on the west of the Tawe could link up.

4   Certain tip areas should be used for such developments as adventure playgrounds and bicycle tracks.

5   Part of the area should be developed as free ranging open space.

6   Playing fields similar to the King George V playing fields on the Mumbles Road in Swansea West should be developed to the north of the area.

7   The recreational space should include provision for an indoor recreation centre for winter recreation in particular and including such amenities as an ice rink.

Houses

Housing demand and housing need

Whether more houses are wanted in the valley can only be decided in the light of the overall housing situation in the Borough. Within this frame the particular conditions in the valley may be examined. Taking the Borough as a whole the housing situation has greatly improved since the war and the record of house building is a creditable one. Nevertheless evidence displayed in the Housing Report suggests that the housing problem in Swansea is by no means nearly solved. Its nature is changing, but much remains to be done.

Estimates were made which suggested that the population of the Borough would be at least 170,000 by 1971 and 175,000 by 1981. These were conservative estimates and slightly lower than those of the Registrar-General because they assumed a lower birth and higher death rate than it would appear he assumed. They also assumed that the rate of immigration between 1961 and 1971 and again from 1971 and 1981 would be the same as that between 1951 and 1961. Any increase in the birth or immigration rates, or noticeable fall in the death rate (all three of which are more likely than movements in the opposite direction), would of course lead to upward revision. The estimates are to be looked upon therefore as minimum figures.

The number of houses required depends upon the way the total population is divided up into households. One of the reasons for the continuing housing shortage despite the tremendous amount of house building that has gone on is that the population is nowadays divided up into a great many smaller households than it used to be. The number of people in a household on average in the Borough has fallen from 4·42 in 1921 to 3·17 in 1961. There is evidence to suggest that in Swansea this fall will continue for a while yet. A household size of three persons per household has therefore been assumed for 1971 and 2·9 for 1981.

These estimates suggest that from 1961 to 1971, 5,600 dwellings will be needed to keep pace with population growth and a further 3,600 between 1971 and 1981. In addition to this there was still a gap between the number of households and the number of dwellings of 1,700 at the 1961 Census. It also seems probable that 1,000 additional houses are needed to reduce overcrowding and provide dwellings for 'concealed' households (that is, where two families are living as one household but would prefer to divide into two separate houses, and thus two households, if they could get suitable accommodation). These calculations suggest that, in the Borough, to keep pace with household formation and population growth and to reduce the sharing of dwellings and overcrowding, 8,300 houses would be needed between 1961 and 1971, an annual building rate of 830 dwellings. Assuming this rate was achieved, 3,600 dwellings would, on these estimates, cope with the new households formed between 1971 and 1981. These building rates do not allow for any slum clearance, nor for the destruction of dwellings for development of any other kind (e.g. roads, offices, shops).

It was estimated that there are at present 10,000 dwellings needing replacement or modernization. From June 1961 to June 1964, 941 dwellings were vacated unfit, or for other similar reasons. In that period the gross building rate was nearly 1,400 a year taking public and private building together. The net rate was just over 1,000 dwellings a year, the local authority being responsible for 46 per cent of this total in this period. At this rate of building it should be possible to cope with population increases of the order estimated here and at the same time to clear unfit dwellings at a rate higher than that which has been achieved in the first three years of the decade. At the rate indicated above it would take twenty years to deal with the dwellings that probably already need replacing; but by that time there will be a further 13,000 houses in the town all of which will be over sixty years old and many already over eighty years old.

In the valley

If the valley is to retain its present position in the Borough as a residential area in terms of the numbers of inhabitants that it houses, then something like a quarter of the future new housing should take place in this area. Furthermore since something like one quarter to one-fifth of the old and obsolete houses appear also to be in the valley area, then it should receive at least one-fifth and probably a quarter of the clearance effort, if parity between one area of the town and another is to be the criterion. It is possible, on the other hand, that concern may be felt to draw population back towards the town centre, both to avoid using up more agricultural land or other open space for residential purposes, and at the same time to renew the older housing areas and the derelict industrial areas in the valley.

Already events have moved to start the process of change from what was once an essentially industrial quarter of the town into a residential quarter. The departure of industry from the valley bottom has been associated with the arrival of sizeable housing estates both public and private on the east side and also the development of new houses in gaps among the old. In terms of the future housing in the valley it is important to notice this difference that while industry appears to be leaving the valley the people have not gone. On the contrary the residential areas are expanding, not contracting. The older houses are not voluntarily abandoned. If one family moves out, another moves in. It is only when the Medical Officer of Health declares a house unfit, or when an area is wanted for clearance and redevelopment, or a road has to be widened, that the houses are abandoned. They are abandoned at the will of the authority, not of the people.

Many of these houses are already ripe for renewal. Some of them the Medical Officer has already listed. Others will certainly be ripe for renewal in the next ten years. The valley sides in fact will constitute a major problem in urban renewal of a kind that is bound to exercise many authorities in the 1970s. Nor are all these older houses rented. Many are owned and many, but not all, by owners who have maintained them well. Many have improved their houses extensively, both with and without the aid of improvement grants. Such houses are scattered among less well maintained and unimproved dwellings, thus adding to the problems of urban regeneration.

The people, their
environment and their
houses

Both because of factors of this kind and because of the impossibility of clearing at one
fell swoop all the old houses, it is clear that in the renewal of the valley sides a rather
sophisticated form of urban redevelopment will have to be employed which blends old with
new. In addition, while it is clear that people are willing to live in the valley, they do so
within certain economic limits. That is to say that there are few who would willingly live
in the valley if they could afford a better house in a select residential area on the west.
However, most people are realistic and accept the best that they can get within the limits
of what they can afford.

To sum up:

1   The Borough still needs to build new houses (both public and private) (a) to accommodate
an expected population increase to 1981, over 9,000 dwellings; (b) to reduce overcrowding
and sharing, 2,700; (c) to replace outworn houses; also, (d) it needs to improve those that
can be brought up to standard. Together (c) and (d) involve a total of 10,000 dwellings.
2   The concept of the valley floor as a problem of industrial dereliction considered
separately from the valley sides is artificial in terms of the present problem.
3   A quarter of the new housing and a quarter of the housing designed for replacement
of obsolete property should be built in the valley to maintain its present position in the
Borough. More could be built there to pull the population back from the periphery.

House location

For whom would houses in the valley be the best answer to their circumstances? To answer
this question studies were made of the occupants of new houses in the valley as a guide
to the extent and type of new housing that could reasonably be recommended for the area.
(Details are given in Appendix 2 to this chapter, p. 183). Particular attention was paid to
persons' reasons for locating in their present house. Ideally all newcomers to the valley
and all occupants of newlybuilt houses in the valley should have formed the subject of the
inquiry. This, however, was not possible. Attention was therefore paid particularly to
those people who had come to live in postwar housing estates on the east side of the valley.
This location was chosen as being one of those thought to be the least favourable. It was the
east side of the river which in terms of local myth and local language, at least for west-
siders, is 'beyond'.* The Housing Manager reported initial and continuing difficulty in
letting houses in this area, which he attributed to the general belief that 'nobody' wants to
live on the east side. Persons located in new houses here were thought likely to be a
guide to the possible occupants of other new valley houses.

There were two kinds of postwar housing estates on the east side, council and private.
The private houses were all for sale when first built. Therefore owner-occupation and
council tenancies were the only types of tenure of new houses. The two forms of tenure
represent two quite different methods of acquisition. Examples of both were therefore
examined. To discover whether east side occupants had any distinctive characteristics,
they were compared with occupants of similar houses on the west side. Details of the
method and of the findings summarized below are given in Appendix 2.

---

* 'Beyond' is used locally to describe a suggestion or action which is too extreme to be tolerated, which is outside
any acceptable limits.

Fifty households in each of the four postwar estates were compared, two in the valley and two in Swansea West. One estate in each area was privately owned and one in each council owned. The council houses in both estates were of similar age, rent and rateable value. The private estates were among the cheaper on the market in 1960–3, of similar age and size, but the west side houses were, for locational reasons, more expensive and of higher rateable value. The Private West householders on average were of higher socio-economic status than Private Valley, which occupied a medium position between Private West and the Council estates. The total household earnings in Council Valley were greater than in Council West. Both private estates have a concentration of men and women between twenty-five and thirty-five and of children under five; the adults on the council estates cluster between thirty and fifty-five and the children between five and fifteen. This seems to be the result of the wait for a council house. Private West has more families at the first stage of the family cycle, Private Valley at the second, while the council estates are approaching the phase of dispersal. Only in Private West had a substantial number not entered the phase of procreation before acquiring a house. More householders in Private Valley appeared to be frustrated council house tenants than in Private West.

Contrary to expectation, householders brought up in the east had moved to Private West *less* often than householders brought up in the west had moved to Private Valley. A similar but less marked movement among the total household membership was discernible in the council estates. Alongside the movement westward appears to be another movement eastward.

Household heads living in the private estates appear to have fitted their house to their workplace more aptly than those in either of the council estates. Other members of the household are better placed in this respect in both western than in either of the valley estates. Those working in industry, especially heavy industry, appear to be better placed for their journey to work when living in the valley or on the east side. Those working in commerce or services are better placed in a location like Private West.

In Private Valley most people paid between £2 15s and £3 15s weekly in mortgage and rates; in Private West some paid less than £2 5s, the largest single group paying over £3 15s. In both council estates almost everybody paid less than £2 5s (average £2). Rents and allied outgoings were related to income. Attention was drawn to the considerable proportion in all cases, but particularly on the council estates, who had less than £6 a week left out of the household head's take-home pay after these regular outgoings were met, i.e. less than £6 for food, clothes, entertainment and all out-of-pocket expenses.

Greater affluence had made the exercise of some choice in house location possible for occupants in Private West, but many here, as most in Private Valley, had bought the only house they could afford. Most council tenants had accepted the first house offered them. The least contentment with the house and its location was in Council West. Council Valley, while more difficult to let initially, produced more contented tenants. Location near the Borough boundary on the west strained the economic resources of council tenants because of the cost of the journey to work and to town. Private Valley residents were disappointed with the absence of services and amenities on the estate. The private estates, and especially Private Valley, lacked amenities more seriously than the council estates. Location choice for council tenants was made largely by the local authority letting committee. Few applicants at the time these estates were let felt they could afford to reject an offer. Location

The people, their
environment and their
houses

choice for private owners appears to relate to the householder's available income and/or wealth, and to the place of work of the household head, within a status ranking of areas which puts the south-west at the top.

Summary

1   There is a movement from Swansea West to Swansea East of persons in an income group up to and just above the national average wage and particularly of those working in the north, east and south-east of and around the Borough.

2   The reasons which have taken people to the valley have been mainly economic, principally cheap houses and reduced costs of travel.

3   Council house applicants do not always know well the geography of the whole Borough nor the respective merits in terms of their life situation of various house locations. This partly accounts for resistances to east side council estates.

Rents, mortgages and the ability to pay

The rents of older properties on both sides of the valley are sometimes less than 10s a week and rarely more than 30s a week. A sample survey of the Hafod/Plasmarl area in 1962 showed that 80 per cent were paying less than 27s 6d a week and 43 per cent were paying less than 22s 6d. In another study in 1964 in four separate areas around the valley sides at least two-thirds of the householders were found to be paying less than 25s a week. In one area 38 per cent paid less than 10s a week. In one area only were as many as a quarter of the respondents paying more than £1 15s a week. In none of the other areas, generally speaking, were more than 20 per cent paying rents as much as this. Nevertheless in a few cases rents of over £3 a week for parts of these old houses were recorded. One characteristic of the rent structure worth noting was that there appeared to be no steady relationship observable between the rent paid and the dwellings and amenities received for that price.

In contrast, the rents of the new properties, some of them built among or adjacent to the old, are much higher. Rents on the council estates studied averaged £2 a week inclusive, and ranged from £2 15s to £3 15s for most on the private estates. In 1965 new council rents on the east side were £4 or £5 depending on the size of the house and private properties were still available for total outgoings of less than £4 a week.

In considering the future of housing in the valley, occupants' ability to pay must be borne in mind. Within this frame the economic cost of new houses must be examined. It has been shown in a number of national studies that a considerable section of the population cannot afford the economic rent of a new house.* If it is assumed that the maximum a man can afford to spend in housing outgoings is 25 per cent of his income, this would certainly appear to be so. At this level it would seem, on the evidence of the Ministry of Labour (1962), that over a third of the population could afford to spend a maximum of £2 10s on total house outgoings (i.e. rent and rates or mortgage and rates). Many household heads at present spend only 10 per cent of their income on such outgoings. At this level, over a third of the population could afford to spend only £1 a week. The evidence of the present surveys, and of others, is that for a new house people are prepared to spend more than this, indeed

* e.g., L. Needleman, 'A long term view of housing', *Economic Review*, 18 November 1961.

in some cases to exceed 25 per cent. If therefore one assumes that 20 per cent of the household head's income will be spent on housing, then housing must be available for a third of the population at £2 a week or less.

In the estates most of the respondents came within this 25 per cent limit in terms of their basic wage, and in many cases the household head's take-home pay was more than the basic wage.* The household heads' incomes on these estates were higher for the most part than the third of the population mentioned above.

These findings indicate that:

1 Occupants could be found for houses in the valley which had a rent suitable for those with a weekly income (at 1963 rates) of £10 to £20. That is to say the total outgoings including rates should fall in the group £2 10s–£5 a week. The clustering of incomes is likely to be about £15 and therefore a maximum rent of £4 may be thought to be desirable (1963 prices).

2 A number of low-income receivers at present occupying low-rent accommodation in or near the valley are likely to be displaced by urban renewal. There is a case for rehousing them in the valley in special low-rent dwellings. The proximity to the town centre will keep their living costs down compared with a move to the periphery; they are also more likely to find occupations in the town centre area suitable to their skills.

Conclusions: B

1 The weight of land development in the valley has shifted from industrial to residential development.

2 The conception of the valley floor as a problem of industrial dereliction considered separately from the valley sides thought of principally as residential areas is artificial in terms of the present problem.

3 The Borough still needs to build new houses to accommodate an expected population increase, to reduce overcrowding and sharing, and to replace outworn dwellings.

4 There is a movement from Swansea West to Swansea East for persons in an income group up to and just above the national average and particularly of those working in the north, east and south-east of and around the Borough. Persons' reasons for locating on the east side are largely economic, principally cheap houses and reduced travel costs.

5 Council house occupants appear less well placed in relation to place of work and council house applicants seem sometimes insufficiently informed of the geography of the town when choosing or accepting a council house.

Recommendations

1 Where parts of the valley sides need redeveloping contiguous areas of the valley floor should be taken over for residential development, thus making houses available near to

---

* Take-home pay is here defined as basic wage *plus* any overtime or bonuses *less* National Insurance, tax and any other payments which are stopped at source.

The people, their
environment and their
houses

those being replaced. (This recommendation is subject to the rider that any sites taken for residential development should be in areas where the level of the valley floor has been raised by tipping, and, in view of the present partial nature of the climatological information, a more detailed climatological study of the proposed sites should be undertaken in advance of development. This further study is recommended although the indications of the present studies of air pollution and climatology (see the Appendix on Climatology and Air Pollution, p. 292) are that air pollution is low and climate not likely to be a major barrier to development in the valley.)

2   Houses should be built, suitably interspersed with open space and other relevant amenities such as primary schools, shops, meeting places, on undeveloped land: (a) on the east side of the valley up to the railway; (b) on the west side of the valley up to the Tawe.

3   Care should be taken to graft new settlements on to existing ones.

4   If the centre of the valley is not taken up by industry it would be appropriate to extend the housing development right across the central area from east to west.

5   Any housing in the valley should be at a cost suitable for those with a weekly income (at 1963 prices) of £10–£20, i.e. the total outgoings on the house including rates should be in a range of £2 10s–£5 per week. Since the clustering of incomes may well be around £15, a maximum rent of £4 may be desirable (1963 prices).

6   In addition, since the number of low income receivers requiring rehousing is likely to increase as they are displaced by urban renewal, including those displaced from the valley sides, there is a case for siting here specially low-rent dwellings for the lower income groups because (a) its proximity to the town centre will also reduce their living costs and (b) it will make labour available in that area.

7   Occupants are most likely to be found for houses in the valley from among those who work to the north, east, and south-east of the Borough and in the town centre.

8   Houses or bungalows are likely to be more acceptable than flats or maisonettes.

9   Attention should be paid in housing administration and housing management to (a) fitting houses in the valley to the client's life situation especially his income and place of work; and (b) explaining the implication of locations to each in relation to his life situation.

General Recommendations

In addition to the recommendations of the two parts A and B the following general recommendations are made:

1   The valley sides and valley floor should be looked upon as one urban renewal exercise with a master plan carried out through detailed development of small areas by stages.

2   In view of the *already existing* large increase in residential use care should be taken in the development of new industry to avoid any air pollution.

3   Further research should be undertaken into (a) the physical structure of dwellings; (b) the social fabric, to avoid unnecessary destruction of dwellings or of social life.

Appendix I   Social need and social deviance indicators

Children in care
A child may be taken into care for a longer or shorter period, perhaps because there are no kin to mind it in a crisis, such as when the mother has another baby, and so the local authority has to act instead. It may be that the court has deemed that the parents are not fulfilling their role as child rearers adequately and therefore have taken the child into 'care and protection'. Similar cases elsewhere may go undetected and the better off may pay for services (such as child minding during childbirth) which for the less well off are provided by the authority. Relative poverty and a failure to conform to accepted standards of child rearing and maintenance are both involved in this index.

Free school meals
Free school meals are made available to certain children in need . They provide an indication of the location of low-income homes. A child may be in receipt of free school meals because his father is sick or dead, or has deserted the mother, or because the father earns inadequately (this may or may not be the man's fault) or because the father is out of work due to, say, technological change which has closed a local factory and made his skill redundant.

Juvenile delinquency
The juvenile delinquency index measures the number of youngsters who have broken the law and been caught doing so. Variations in incidence from place to place may be due to a greater amount of law-breaking, to greater police vigilance, or to parental inability to extricate their children from scrapes.

Index construction
In all cases the index related the incidence of the problem to the relevant child population at risk. The areas investigated were school catchment areas, smaller than the three Rosser–Harris localities discussed above. Free school meals were analysed by school and the index constructed as the number of free meals provided per pupil per school. The juvenile delinquency index was confined to boys over eleven, the group with the largest number of delinquents in it. The index was constructed by relating the number of male delinquents over eleven per school to the number of boys over eleven in that school. The child care figures were available for home areas and not for schools. They were therefore analysed in a way which was as far as possible coterminous with the school catchment areas. The index was constructed by relating the number of children taken into care to the estimated child population of that area.

Appendix 2   House location studies

The studies were of postwar housing estates in the valley. These were of two kinds, council and private. The private houses were all for sale when first built. Therefore owner-occupation and council tenancies were the only types of tenure of new houses. The two forms of tenure of course represent two quite different methods of acquisition. Becoming a council house tenant involves applying for a house and then waiting to reach the top of the list in

The people, their
environment and their
houses

order to have one's application considered. This wait had been ten to thirteen years for many who moved into council houses on the east side in the late 1950s. If the application is granted, once the wait is over the applicant is offered a house which may or may not be of the kind he wanted or in the place he originally requested. There is rarely much choice, except to refuse the house offered. Those in desperate housing circumstances are fearful of such refusal. It inevitably prolongs the wait and risks the disapproval of housing officials. The process of buying is different. It is a matter of deciding how much one can afford in initial deposit and in weekly mortgage outgoings. In fact the freedom may be no greater than that of the council tenant because there may be only one house, or type of house, or location, which fits the terms the buyer has set himself. But he has set the terms himself and accepting his own terms is to him different from being allocated a dwelling according to terms laid down by some superior authority as a council tenant has to do.

The conditions of the two types of tenure once the occupant is installed are also very different. In the case of the council tenant he pays a rent which includes his rates and he is not responsible for any major maintenance of the dwelling. The owner-occupier has his debts to repay, his rates to pay and his house to maintain.

For all these reasons it seemed wise to look at both council and private houses to establish the socio-economic characteristics of occupants of east side postwar housing. There were several private and council housing estates on the east side. In one area a council and a private estate were side by side. The private one of the two had apparently belied the beliefs of Guildhall officials by selling very quickly when advertised. Many explanations were offered of why this should be so when 'nobody would ever dream' of buying a house there. None of the explanations included the fact that some people did want to live there, or at least chose this location as being more suitable or less disadvantageous than any other. For this reason, and because of the proximity of the council and the private estates, this pair was chosen for examination. It is not claimed that the results apply to all east-siders, but only to the two estates examined. It is felt, however, that since they are so close together factors of geography will in these two cases have the same effect. Thus any differences between the occupants of the two estates are more likely to be due to the different tenure arrangements than to location.

Our concern in looking at east side occupants was to discover whether there were any peculiar or distinctive characteristics about them which differentiated them from people living in other locations. In particular, we were concerned to know how east-siders differed, if indeed they did, from west-siders. It might theoretically have been possible to compare east-siders with the rest of the Borough. A number of things were against this, the overriding practical consideration being that there were no data available for the Borough as a whole about persons' reasons for location in their present house. Even had there been, such comparison would not have been satisfactory, and would have been most unlikely to yield the results looked for. There are many reasons which affect house location, the size, type and cost of the house being obvious ones. In order to point up the factors leading to east side location in postwar housing it was felt wise to control as many of these variables as possible. It was therefore decided to compare the two east side estates with two west side estates. Two west side estates were chosen as being as similar as possible to the east side estates in cost (i.e. either price or rent), in rates and in age of building.

The private estate on the east side, which will be called 'Private Valley' here, was matched with the most similar private estate of comparable age that could be found on the west side. The council estate, 'Council Valley', was similarly matched by part of a large west side council estate, which went into occupation about the same time as Council Valley and had about the same rateable value and rent ranges. The two council estates were in fact both older than the two private estates, amounting to five years on average, and the west side private estate was slightly younger than the east side private estate. The newest houses were still being built on Private West and the oldest houses were on the council estates and were about eight years old.

It was hard to get as good a comparison as one would have liked in the case of the private estates, because it seems that location on the west is so highly valued that it adds a good deal to the purchase price of west side houses. The variables with which we were concerned were in fact interdependent. So the cheapest estate on the west side was chosen as being the one which was as comparable as one would be likely to find with Private Valley. The houses in Private West and Private Valley were of essentially the same size and construction, the gardens on the east being, if anything, a little larger than those on the west. Yet the houses on the west cost about £1,000 more. For the house that one paid £2,000 for in the east, one paid £3,000 in the west.

Having selected the housing developments to be considered, an area within each was demarcated. The area chosen in each case was a census enumeration district. About fifty individuals were interviewed in each of the four estates. (Sampling fractions varied in each estate: $\frac{1}{9}$; $\frac{1}{9}$; $\frac{1}{7}$; $\frac{1}{8}$.) Their names were drawn at random from the electoral register, that part of the register being used which covered the relevant enumeration districts. (Enumeration districts and polling districts are unfortunately not coextensive.) The advantage of using a census enumeration district was that the sample results could be checked against the census data.

Interviews were conducted with the aid of a schedule. This had been drawn up after a number of relatively unstructured, detailed and lengthy interviews had been undertaken with a few residents on the estates about their social and economic background and about their housing history and hopes. The 200 schedule interviews were undertaken in the autumn of 1963, after a pilot run, by a team of specially trained temporary interviewers and by the author and her assistant, Mrs D. Yeoman. Respondents were assured that their replies would be treated as confidential: all names and addresses were removed from schedules and replaced by code numbers immediately upon receipt at the office.

Replies were subsequently punched and sorted on IBM machines. The analysis proceeded principally by comparing the characteristics of each of the four estates.

The socio-economic characteristics of the occupants

The occupants of Private West were a good deal different in a number of important respects from those of Private Valley (see Table 8.1).

They were generally a good deal better off, had had longer education and were of a rather higher occupational status. As the table shows, 77 per cent of Private West household heads were non-manual workers compared with 18 per cent in Private Valley. In this and some other respects Private Valley householders were more like those in the two council estates studied than they were like the householders in Private West. In the east-side

The people, their
environment and their
houses

council estate (Council Valley) only 6 per cent of household heads were non-manual
workers, and in Council West 16 per cent were. In terms of education also, while some
householders in Private Valley were educated for as long as some in Private West, in general
their education resembled that of the household heads on the council estates rather more.
In terms of their income, the household heads of Private Valley also occupied a middle
position as the table shows. In Private West over three-quarters had a weekly take-home
pay of £15 a week or more. In Private Valley rather less than two-thirds had achieved this
amount, in Council Valley less than half, and in Council West only 20 per cent.

Table 8.1   Socio-economic characteristics of the four estates

(Figures in percentages)

	Private Valley	Council Valley	Private West	Council West
Household head only				
Occupation				
Non-manual	18	6*	77*	16
Manual	82	94	21	84
Education				
Left school at fifteen or under	87	100	40	98
Take-home pay				
Less than £10	2	16	3	20
£10 and less than £15	36	42	21	60
£15 and less than £20	42	33	38	16
£20 and over	20	9	38	4
Total household income				
Less than £10	0	12	4	9
£10 and less than £15	29	22	12	55
£15 and less than £20	43	38	21	27
£20 and over	28	28	63	9
Number in sample	55	51	47	52

* One unclassified

Demographic characteristics, housing routes and family phase

Figure 8.4 shows the age–sex structure of the four estates and, for comparison, that of the
County Borough. It will be seen that the shape of none of these structures resembles that of
the town. All four estates have bulges in some age groups and almost complete absences of
anybody of that age in other groups. It will also be seen that this tendency is most marked in
the two private estates although it is by no means absent in the two council estates.
Furthermore, the two private estates resemble each other, and so do the two council
estates, but between the two types of tenure there are considerable differences. Both
private estates have a concentration of men and women between twenty-five and thirty-five
and of children under ten, but particularly under five. In the council estates the adults tend
to bunch between thirty and forty-five in Council West, and thirty and fifty-five in Council
Valley, and in both cases the children tend to be between five and fifteen with far fewer
under five than in private estates.

Examination of the family phase of the families on the estates confirms the impression
given by the age–sex structure figures. It shows that in Private West there are a number of
young married couples who have not yet started their families and a number who have.

There are fewer older couples with older children, most of them being immigrants to the town. In Private Valley most of the young couples have already started their families. In the council estates the couples tend to be middle-aged with school-aged children. In Private Valley almost all household heads were fathers of families, or married men. This was true of most in Private West but here a certain number of unmarried people had bought houses and also some had come here upon retirement. In the council estates, while most household heads were married, the provision of old persons' dwellings led to a certain number of single or widowed old people on these estates.

Age – Sex Structure of the sample populations and compared with the County Borough

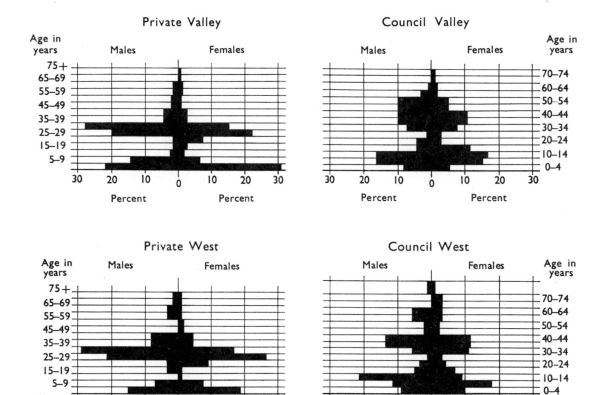

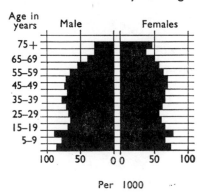

Figure 8.4 The age–sex structure of the four estates

The people, their
environment and their
houses

Analysis by the housing routes which householders had taken since their marriage is summarized in Figures 8.5 a–d. The analysis shows certain interesting differences between the estates. These differences relate to the present demography and family phase of the residents and also to their socio-economic characteristics. The diagrams show that a third of those living in Private Valley in 1963 had started life living in one or other of their parents' houses, compared with 12 per cent in Private West. A number in Private Valley had started in rooms whereas a third of the Private West owners had started in a private flat. This seems likely to reflect the greater affluence of the present owners in Private West compared with those in Private Valley. The major differences between the council estates and Private Valley are that while as many or more started out by living with their parents straight after their wedding, and some were still under the parental roof when they received a council house key, many had left their parents for other kinds of accommodation—rooms, or a rented house—before entering a council house.

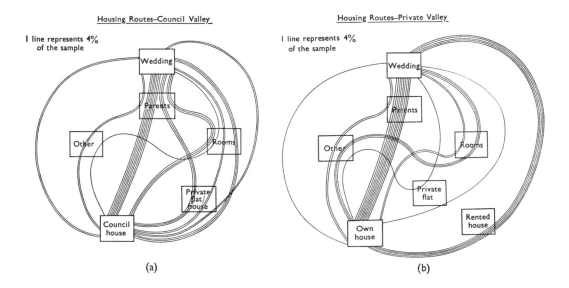

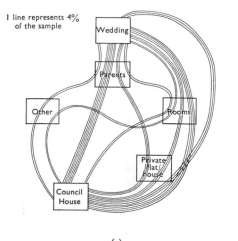

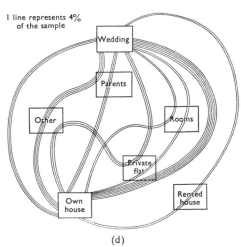

Figures 8.5(a) (b) (c) and (d) Housing routes

This and the age differences seem to be connected with the wait for a council house which was ten to thirteen years when Council West and Council Valley went into occupation. Council tenants had therefore reached middle age and had school children before they had a council house (any council house, not necessarily the present one). They had also in more cases had to leave the parental roof in search of other accommodation before they had a council house. By buying a house in Private Valley householders had short-circuited, as it were, the rather long routes many on the council estates had gone through before reaching their present type of tenure. The family phase analysis showed that many of them had already one child before they bought the house in Private Valley. In this they differed from those in Private West. It will be seen that here a higher proportion were able to go straight into their own owner-occupied residence after the wedding. This also fits the family phase analysis which showed that a far greater number here had not started a family before they acquired a house. This explains why the proportion of children in general and children under five in particular is lower in Private West than it was in Private Valley.

Housing aspiration

To some extent it may be true that residents in the private estates were frustrated council house applicants. In Private West 21 per cent had applied to the council before moving to their present house; in Private Valley as many as 52 per cent had done so. When those who had not put their name down were asked why they had not done so, a number in both cases said it was because they had always wanted to own a house of their own. However, nearly half in Private West compared with only two out of twenty-five in Private Valley said it was because they were against living in a council house. Had they been offered a council house, 42 per cent in Private Valley but only 24 per cent in Private West would have taken it. To a greater extent therefore in Private Valley than in Private West can it be said that the residents were frustrated council house applicants.

Place of origin

The way in which the waiting list for local authority houses worked in the period under review favoured those who had lived in the town for a number of years. Without waiting to reach the top of the list there were only two ways in which an incomer to the town could get a council house. One would be that he had a council house in another local authority area which he had been able to exchange with somebody who had a council house in Swansea and who wished to move to the incomer's place of origin. Such there are, but they are few in number. The other route is for those who come as 'key workers' and for whom local authority houses are provided by arrangement between their employer and the local authority. Again these are few in number. Thus for the most part incomers have to take a private house, that is buy one or rent one privately. For these reasons many more in the private estates than the council estates were brought up outside the Borough as Table 8.2 shows.

This is true both for household heads and for other adult members of the household. The table also shows that of those household heads who were brought up in the Borough, 21 per cent in Private Valley came from the west, and 36 per cent from the east, while of those

The people, their
environment and their
houses

now living in Private West 30 per cent came from the west and only 4 per cent came from
the east. It therefore seems that householders brought up in the west have more often
moved to the east, than those brought up in the east have moved to the west. This is a
surprising finding and quite contrary to the expectations which followed from the emphasis
key informants, including local authority officials and students of the social life in Swansea,
had laid upon a drift to the west. The present finding remains the same, however, when
those brought up within a fifteen mile radius of the Borough on east or west are added in.
Twenty-six per cent of those living in Private Valley were brought up on the west side,
whereas 8 per cent only of those now living in Private West were brought up on the east
side. Fifty-one per cent of those now living in Private Valley were brought up on the east
side and 40 per cent of those now living in Private West were brought up on the west side.
The surprising thing is the small proportion (8 per cent) of west side dwellers who have
come from the east.

Table 8.2   Place of upbringing

Of household heads Geographic areas	Estates							
	Private Valley		Council Valley		Private West		Council West	
	No.	%	No.	%	No.	%	No.	%
West { Swansea: not valley	8	14	9	17	13	26	25	43
Swansea Valley	4	7	2	4	2	4	11	19
Outside Borough*	3	5	0	0	5	10	0	0
West total	15	26	11	21	20	40	36	62
East { Swansea Valley: North and East	14	25	15	28	1	2	2	4
St Thomas	6	11	15	28	1	2	8	14
Skewen, Neath, Port Talbot, etc.	8	15	3	6	2	4	2	3
East total	28	51	33	62	4	8	12	21
Other { In Borough	0	0	0	0	6	12	3	5
Outside Borough	13	23	9	17	20	40	7	12
Total	56	100	53	100	50	100	58	100

Of other members of the household (adults only) Geographic areas	Estates							
	Private Valley		Council Valley		Private West		Council West	
	No.	%	No.	%	No.	%	No.	%
West { Swansea: not valley	17	29	12	20	10	19	35	55
Swansea Valley	5	9	5	8	1	2	5	8
Outside Borough*	12	21	0	0	7	13	1	2
West total	34	59	17	28	18	34	41	65
East { Swansea Valley: North and East	8	14	18	29	1	2	1	2
St Thomas	4	7	16	26	3	5	3	5
Skewen, Neath, Port Talbot, etc.	2	3	1	2	1	2	1	1
East total	14	24	35	57	5	9	5	8
Other { In Borough	0	0	3	5	12	23	3	5
Outside Borough	10	17	6	10	18	34	14	22
Total	58	100	61	100	53	100	63	100

* Within fifteen-mile radius

It is true that there were a number now living in Private West from whom interviewers failed to get an accurate account of the district in Swansea from which they hailed, but even if all came in fact from the east side, there would still be more west-siders moving east than east-siders moving west. It is possible that at the time the houses were offered for sale there were more west-siders than east-siders looking for houses. In that case one would expect there to be more west-siders on any new estate at that date. Nevertheless, despite the contrary myth that 'everybody' wants to move west, on the estates studied west-siders had certainly moved east in greater numbers than east-siders had moved west. It looks as if there is perhaps one current flowing westwards and alongside it another current flowing eastwards. In both cases there is a net movement away from the older central areas. Moving west are non-manual workers in commerce, trades and professions. Moving east are industrial manual workers and a few in trades, commerce and the professions.

This pattern of movement does not apply to the household heads interviewed in the two council estates. Here the proportions balance neatly as Table 8.2 shows. Sixty-two per cent of those living in Council West were brought up either in the western part of the Borough or within fifteen miles on the west side. Equally 62 per cent in Council Valley were brought up either in the east of the Borough or within fifteen miles on the east side. Twenty-one per cent have crossed from west to east and 21 per cent have crossed from east to west. (Five per cent in Council West were brought up in the Borough, area unspecified.) The local authority do try and take home area into consideration in the allocation of houses as well as the wishes of tenants about where they would like to live. It would seem that they have been equally successful in doing this for household heads in both cases. Nevertheless on examination there is an interesting trend in the place of upbringing of other adult members of the household. While 28 per cent now living in the east were brought up in the west, only 8 per cent now living in the west were brought up in the east. Again easterners are turning up less often on the west side than westerners are turning up on the east side. Thus there is still, even in the council houses, some evidence of a net eastward flow and no evidence of a net westward flow.

Place of work

The distance, time, and expense involved in the journey to work was analysed in some detail for household heads and for secondary earners in the household. The general conclusions were fairly clear, and are illustrated in Figure 8.6.

The relationship between the location of their house and their place of work was quite important for household heads on the private estates. Sixty-six per cent of those living in Private Valley work either in the town centre or outside the Borough on the east side; 55 per cent of those living in Private West work either in Swansea West or the town centre and a further 12 per cent elsewhere on the west side. In both cases about 20 per cent work outside the town and its immediate vicinity altogether; 4 per cent from Private Valley work in the west of the Borough; 12 per cent in Private West work in the east. Thus it seems likely that, in choosing their house, household heads have had regard to the journey to work. It should be said that the cost of this is likely to bear rather more heavily on those with lower incomes, both relatively and absolutely. Relatively it bears more heavily in the sense that the same travel cost forms a larger proportion of a lower income, and

The people, their
environment and their
houses

absolutely in the sense that less is left for other expenditure. This differential is increased by the fact that a third of respondents in Private West had their travel expenses paid one way or another by their firms, often generously enough to cover all or part of non-business travel as well. Twice as many living in Private West benefited in this way as in any of the other three estates studied. To the extent of their subsidy these Private West respondents could afford to disregard the location of their house in relation to the location of their work. In so far as they also had a higher income this factor would be less important for them anyway. They can in effect afford to pay more for location because they have subsidised travel.

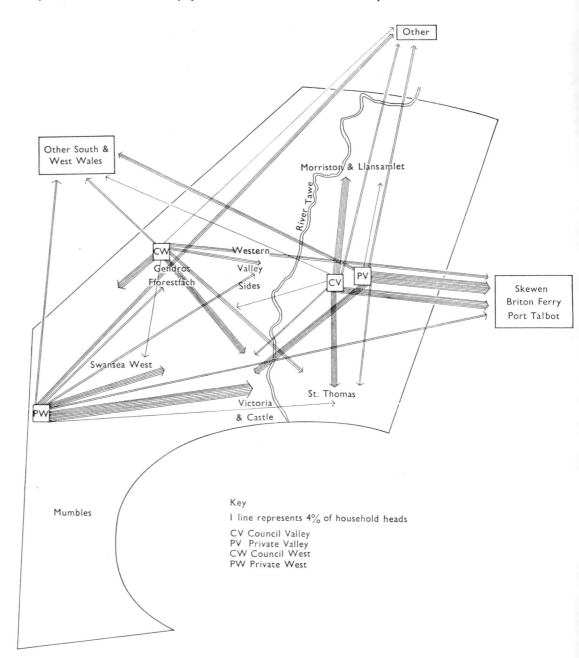

Figure 8.6(a) Journey to work for heads of households

    Place of work and place of residence appears to fit rather less well for household heads on the council housing estates studied and to fit better in Council Valley than in Council West, as Figure 8.6 shows. Thus from Council Valley a quarter of the household heads travel a little way north to Morriston or Llansamlet; another quarter of them travel a little way south to the dock area and rather over a quarter travel out of the Borough to the eastern industrial area where so many of their neighbours in Private Valley work. Three-quarters of household heads thus work within reasonable distance of their houses (for many not more than two miles) in an arc around the estate. This is not true of Council West. There about a quarter of the household heads travel into the town centre (about three miles) and nearly another quarter to the industrial area in the north-west of the Borough. The remainder, in total just over half, travel widely around the Borough, a fifth crossing the Borough to work, 10 per cent going down to the dock area and 10 per cent eastwards beyond the Borough boundaries, a journey of at least an hour in all. An earlier section described how the close tie between home and workplace, between hillside and valley had ceased to be. Some relationship of house place to workplace seems to remain, however, where people are given sufficient choice. Industry is now more scattered than it was and longer travel distances are tolerated. Nevertheless those working on one side of town seem to prefer to live on that side of town. Thus we have a tendency for industrial workers concerned with the industry that now lies around the Borough in an arc from north to east to live on the northern and eastern sides of town.

The place of work of secondary earners is a factor which also has to be considered. It is one which will become more important within the next five years when more of the wives get all their children in school and therefore start to think of going out to work again. Such a move can be expected from an analysis of the present family stage of the women workers: as is common in other parts of the country few mothers of very young children go to work. More go out when the children are in school and more again when the children are working themselves. There will be more secondary earners appearing again in another ten years or so when the children of today on the estates become teenagers and come on the market for jobs.

The evidence is that at present the secondary earners are less well placed for jobs than are the heads of households, particularly on the east side (see Figure 8.6b). The striking fit between house and work location that was observed in both the east side estates does not apply to the wives and children who work. Most of the household heads find work in the eastern area, but only a fifth of secondary earners can. From Private Valley over a fifth of members of the household other than the head have to cross right over to the west or north-west of Swansea to work, and just over a half of them work in the town centre.

In Private West on the other hand the secondary earners are better placed. Eighty-two per cent of them work either in the town centre, which is of very easy access from Private West, or they work in the area itself. Their journeys are less long than those of the household heads. The relatively high household incomes in Council Valley compared with Council West are largely to be explained by the greater number of secondary earners in Council Valley. Over a fifth of them cross to the west to work, a difficult trip. Thirty per cent work in the town centre. Nearly a half have been able to find work in that arc around the estate where many of the householders work, to the north, to the south in the docks, or outside the Borough eastwards. In Council West the secondary earners work on the west side, in the north-west industrial estate, the town centre or on the western valley sides. They would in fact be better placed for finding work for secondary earners in many occupations than those in Council Valley. The fact that there are fewer of them is probably to be explained by factors connected with the size of the family and the stage of the family cycle reached.

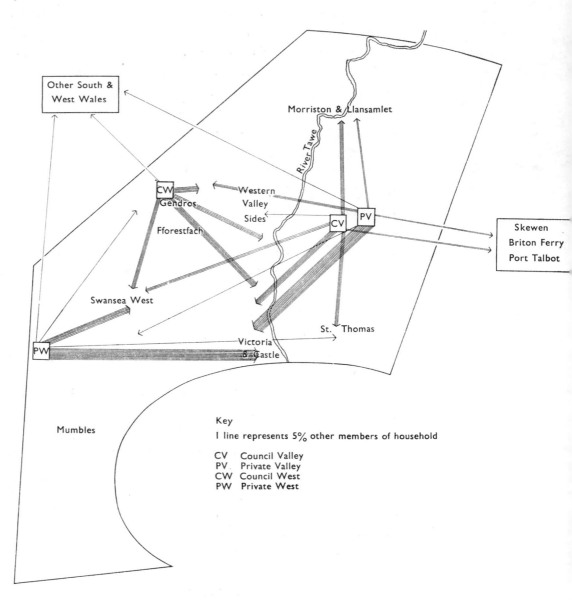

Figure 8.6(b) Journey to work for other members of the household

The cost of living in a new house

In Private Valley most people were paying between £2 15s and £3 15s a week in mortgage and rates, the average being just over £3. In Council Valley and in Council West almost everybody paid less than £2 5s, the average being about £2 a week for rent and rates combined. In Private West the pattern was different. There were a number of people who paid less than £2 5s while the largest single group paid over £3 15s a week.

Table 8.3 relates these housing costs to people's incomes. It is considered in the housing report that it is against the income of the head of the household that the ability to pay should be measured. The wages of the secondary earners cannot be looked upon as suffici-

Table 8.3 Rent, mortgages and rates by Basic wage

| Income basic wage | Rent/Mortgages and Rates | | | | | Total known | Don't know | Total | Average rent/mortgages and Rates |
	Less than £2 5s	£2 5s–£2 14s	£2 15s–£3 4s	£3 5s–£3 14s	£3 15s and over				
Private Valley	No.	No.	No.	No.	No.	No.	No.	No.	£
Less than £10									
£10–£14	1	6	13	8	1	29	0	29	3.03
£15–£19	0	3	8	1	2	14	1	15	3.07
£20 and over	0	0	2	3	2	7	0	7	3.50
Total known	1	9	23	12	5	50	1	51	
Don't know	0	0	2	2	0	4	1	5	
Total	1	9	25	14	5	54	2	56	
Average basic wage*	£8.0	£13.83	£14.89	£16.67	£18.75				
Council Valley									
Less than £10	4	1				5		5	2.10
£10–£14	29	0				29		29	2.00
£15–£19	5	0				5		5	2.00
£20 and over	2	0				2		2	2.00
Total known	40	1				41		41	
Don't know	12	1				13		13	
Total	52	2				54		54	
Average basic wage*	£12.89	£8.0							
Private West	No.	No.	No.	No.	No.	No.	No.	No.	
Less than £10									
£10–£14	1	0	3	3	0	7	0	7	3.07
£15–£19	2	1	2	1	9	15	0	15	3.46
£20 and over	0	0	0	3	10	13	1	14	3.89
Total known	3	1	5	7	19	35	1	36	
Don't know	6	0	0	4	4	14	0	14	
Total	9	1	5	11	23	49	1	50	
Average basic wage*	£19.25	£18.75	£14.25	£16.95	£22.5				
Council West									
Less than £10	4	1	0			5		5	2.10
£10–£14	26	6	1			33		33	2.00
£15–£19	5	2	0			7		7	2.14
£20 and over	1	0	0			1		1	2.00
Total known	36	9	1			46		46	
Don't know	10	2	0			12		12	
Total	46	11	1			58		58	
Average basic wage*	£12.54	£13.11	£11.25						

* Average basic wages were calculated upon a finer grouping than that shown here.

ently continuous or regular to count against such permanent outgoings as those for a house. In Private Valley, where the average outgoings were just over £3 a week, the average basic wage of the household head was about £15, and almost everybody fell into the £10–£20-a-week income group. In Council Valley, and Council West, where the average outgoings were about £2, the average basic wage on both estates was about £12 a week. In Private West the pattern was different. A number of those who were paying less than £2 5s a week had a basic wage of nearly £20 a week while the group who were paying over £3 15s a week

The people, their
environment and their
houses

earned over £22 a week on average. A considerable section of householders in Private West paid between £3 5s and £3 15s a week and earned around £17 a week. The explanation of the distributions in Private West seems to be that there is a small section of the people on the estate who were able to put down a larger deposit than the minimum necessary and therefore have low outgoings. There seem to be a number of reasons why this is so. Some are simply better off, others are older and had owned a house previously to coming to this estate, yet others were helped in buying their house by their parents. For some people in Private West there is what might be called an inversion effect: those who are better off for this very reason have lower outgoings. For the rest on Private West they have higher outgoings as well as higher earnings than those in Private Valley.

Table 8.4 shows how much is left (a) out of the household head's basic wage, (b) out of his take-home pay, and (c) out of the total family income when the regular household commitments have been met. Regular household commitments were defined to include expenditure on rent and mortgage and rates, on travel, on fuel, on insurance, on hire or hire purchase of equipment and furniture. The remainder is what is left for food, clothing, entertainment and all other out-of-pocket expenses. Attention is drawn to the considerable proportion in all cases, but particularly in the council estates, who have less than £6 a week left out of the head's take-home pay.

Table 8.4 Regular household commitments by basic wage of the household head, his take-home pay and the total household income

(a) HhH. Basic wage less regular household commitments

	Less than £6	£6– £9	£10– £14	£15– £19	£20– £24	£25 and over	Total known	Don't know	Total
Private Valley									
No.	21	18	6	4	2	0	51	5	56
%	41	35	12	8	4	0	100		
Council Valley									
No.	20	16	4	0	1	0	41	13	54
%	49	38	10	0	3	0	100		
Private West									
No.	5	11	9	6	2	3	36	14	50
%	14	31	25	17	5	8	100		
Council West									
No.	24	17	4	1	0	0	46	12	58
%	52	37	9	2	0	0	100		

(b) HhH. Take-home pay less regular household commitments

	Less than £6	£6– £9	£10– £14	£15– £19	£20– £24	£25 and over	Total known	Don't know	Total
Private Valley									
No.	11	21	14	4	1	0	51	5	56
%	22	44	24	8	2	0	100		
Council Valley									
No.	16	15	9	1	0	0	41	13	54
%	38	38	22	2	0	0	100		
Private West									
No.	5	15	10	5	1	1	37	13	50
%	13	41	27	13	3	3	100		
Council West									
No.	20	22	7	2	0	0	51	7	58
%	39	43	14	4	0	0	100		

Table 8.4—*cont.*

(c) *Total HhH. Income gp less regular household commitments*

	Less than £10*	£10– £19	£20– £29	£30 and over	Total† known	Don't know	Total
Private Valley							
No.	27	22	5	0	54	2	56
%	51	40	9	0	100		
Council Valley							
No.	19	28	2	0	49	5	54
%	40	56	4	0	100		
Private West							
No.	11	29	5	3	48	2	50
%	23	61	10	6	100		
Council West							
No.	34	19	2	0	55	3	58
%	62	34	4	0	100		

* This group appears likely to split up in the following way, but less confidence can be placed in this breakdown than in those given above.

	Less than £4	£4–£5	£6–£9	£10 and over
Private Valley				
No.	2	6	19	27
%	4	11	36	51
Council Valley				
No.	5	2	12	19
%	11	4	25	40
Private West				
No.	1	2	8	11
%	2	4	17	23
Council West				
No.	7	5	22	34
%	13	9	40	62

† Known totals are larger in this table than others because some persons were willing to indicate a general household income group, but no fuller or more individual details.

Reasons for house location, and satisfaction with it

In the case of the council house tenants the principal reason for location in this particular house was that it was the house they were offered by the council and, in most cases, they accepted it because although it might not have been quite what they had wanted it was so much better than the house they were living in previously. There is, furthermore, the possibility after some years as a council tenant of getting a transfer to a more suitable house. Quite a number of tenants reported their dissatisfaction with their present house and their desire for a transfer as soon as possible. The degree of satisfaction with houses in Council West seems to have been lower than that in Council Valley judged by the amount of movement there had already been, and the number of intentions to move that were reported, as well as by the actual complaints made. The intentions to remove for all four estates are shown in Table 8.5. The greater degree of contentment among occupants of Council Valley compared with those of Council West might superficially appear to contradict the Local Housing Authority's view about the unpopularity of the Council Valley location. However, the Housing Department agree with what we felt to be true that, once they are installed, the Council Valley residents are more content than the Council West residents. It may well be that, having to overcome a real or imagined hostility to the estate, the housing management made a greater effort to fit the tenant to the house and to the estate and, having produced a better 'fit', also now has more contented tenants. It certainly is true that more respondents in Council Valley reported that they had a house where they wanted it and that they were able to choose among one or two when their name came up. To this extent they felt they had had a greater freedom of choice than those, the majority, who were offered one on a 'take it or leave it' basis. (This is how the applicant sees it, whatever may have been the official procedure at the time.) It may be that, initially at least, it was not felt that Council West presented particular difficulties and tenants themselves may not have anticipated difficulties in accepting a house here. There may not therefore have been such an opposition to overcome in placing people on the west side.

Table 8.5   Thinking of moving

	Private Valley		Council Valley		Private West		Council West	
	No.	%	No.	%	No.	%	No.	%
Yes and taken steps	10	18	4	8	6	12	15	26
Yes, but no steps taken	6	11	1	2	6	12	6	11
Not	40	71	48	90	38	76	36	63
Total known	56	100	53	100	50	100	57	100

Although particular difficulties were not anticipated either by the authority or by the tenants, Council West appears to have produced difficulties and these help to explain the discontents found there. It has already been seen that residents in Council West have a longer and more expensive journey to work than residents in Council Valley. This eats into their resources both of time and money. Although they do not have to go around the derelict area before they reach town, the journey is no shorter or cheaper for them than it is from Council Valley. In addition the households in Council West, as has already been indicated, certainly seem to be poorer on average than those in Council Valley. Thus in Council Valley 34 per cent have a total household income of less than £15 a week; in Council West nearly two-thirds (64 per cent) fall into this category (Private Valley, 29 per cent, Private West, 16 per cent). If the west-siders are poorer and find it more expensive both to get to work and to get to town for shops and entertainment, this might perhaps explain at least in part their relative lack of contentment.

The principal reason for location in Private Valley was simply, as so many respondents told us, that 'it was the only house we could afford' (see Table 8.6). As we have seen earlier, if these very cheap houses had not come on the market (some were as cheap as £1,200 at the start of the development), many of their occupants would, at the time of survey, have still been waiting in their parents' houses for a council house key to be offered to them. Not all of them are tremendously happy with the house or with its location as Table 8.5 showed. In particular they complained of the lack of amenities on the estates, no shops, no chemist, no playground, no nursery school. Nevertheless it was a new house and it was a house of their own. For most, but not all, it was within their means.

Table 8.6   Reason for buying this house

	Private Valley		Private West	
	No.	%	No.	%
Reason				
Cost in relation to house type	34	61	14	28
House type	1	2	9	18
Cost	11	19	8	16
Location	8	14	11	22
Type of area	0	0	5	10
Other	2	4	3	6
Total	56	100	50	100

In Private West many similar responses were received, but it was clear that residents here had been able to consider other factors than cost a bit (see Table 8.6). That is to say within the price they had set themselves there was some choice. They wanted a western edge location and could afford to pay the extra £1,000 this involved. Many of them wanted a new house and found that these were the most suitable new houses they could afford.

The market is of course not perfect. For those on the east in a sense the west side houses do not exist, nor the east side ones for those house-hunting on the west. Table 8.7 shows the extent to which people knew of and had considered living on the other side of town and when they did know about developments on the other side why they had not taken a house there. To some extent it seems likely that the west-siders who went east did so because there were no west side houses they could afford. Since there were no such cheap houses in the west, there was nothing comparable to the cheap Private Valley to pull easterners to the west. Economics, in the shape of how much can be afforded in weekly housing outgoings, location of workplace, and the part of town which is familiar, or which is adjacent to what is familiar, seem to be the principal reasons residents have for locating in the house they are at present in. In the case of council tenants the decision is often made at a remove further back. The outgoings which are possible for them lead them to be council tenants and not to buy, and then, at least until they can get a transfer later on, their location is decided for them by the letting committee. Sometimes the committee may be able to meet their wishes and sometimes it may not. For private occupants the reasons given would seem to operate in the order they were listed in, thus occupations, both in the amount of money earned and the location of the workplace, are important determinants. The higher the earnings or other sources of income or wealth, the greater the freedom of choice, and because car ownership and travel subsidies also increase with income the greater the freedom of location in relation to workplace.

Table 8.7   East–West choices

	Respondents in Private Valley		Respondents in Private West	
Looked at a house	*in Private West*		*in Private Valley*	
	No.	%	No.	%
No, because:				
Did not know houses for sale there	4	8	4	8
Don't know the area, too far away	9	18	5	11
Too expensive for us there	19	38	0	0
Not our sort of place, didn't like the area	0	0	24	51
Total number	32	64	33	70

The people their
environment and their
houses

Table 8.7—*cont.*

	Respondents in Private Valley		Respondents in Private West	
Looked at a house	*in Private West*		*in Private Valley*	
	No.	%	No.	%
Yes, but did not buy because:				
Disliked the house/area	4	8	7	15
House too dear	9	18	1	2
Other	5	10	6	13
Total Yes	18	36	14	30
Responses	50	100	47	100

	Respondents in Council Valley		Respondents in Council West	
Council tenants who would have taken a house	*in Council West*		*in Council Valley*	
	No.	%	No.	%
Yes	16	31*	21	36*
No	36	69	31	54
Don't know district	0	0	6	10
Total	52	100	58	100

* Differences between these proportions are significant at the 1 per cent level.

Bibliography

1. T. Brennan, E. W. Cooney and H. Pollins, *Social Change in South West Wales*, Watts, 1954.
2. D. Cole and J. Utting, 'The Economic Circumstances of Old People', *Occasional Papers on Social Administration*, **4**, 1962.
3. County Borough of Swansea. *Financial and Statistical Digests*, 1960–63.
4. County Borough of Swansea. *Annual Reports of the Medical Officer of Health*, 1960–62.
5. J. B. Cullingworth, *New Towns for Old: The Problem of Urban Renewal*, Fabian Society, 1962.
6. J. B. Cullingworth, 'English Housing Trends', *Occasional Papers on Social Administration*, **13**, 1965.
7. D. V. Donnison, C. Cockburn and T. Corlett, 'Housing since the Rent Act', *Occasional Papers on Social Administration*, **3**.
8. D. V. Donnison et al., 'Essays on housing', *Occasional Papers on Social Administration*, **9**.
9. General Register Office, *Census 1951*, H.M.S.O.
10. General Register Office, *Census 1961*, H.M.S.O.
11. General Register Office, *Occupational Classification*, 1960, H.M.S.O.
12. P. G. Gray and R. Russell, 'The Housing Situation in 1960', *The Social Survey*, C.O.I., 1962.
13. Hilda Jennings, *Societies in the Making. A Study of Development and Redevelopment within a County Borough*, Routledge & Kegan Paul, 1962.
14. Nathaniel Lichfield, 'Rehabilitation of Twilight Areas', *Housing Review*, Vol. II, No. 5, September/October 1962.
15. Nathaniel Lichfield, 'Economic Aids in Urban Planning and Renewal', *Town Planning Review*, July 1963.
16. T. Lynes, 'National Assistance and National Prosperity', *Occasional Papers on Social Administration*, **5**, 1962.
17. Ministry of Housing and Local Government, 'Living in a slum'. A study of people in a central slum clearance area in Oldham (mimeo.), 1963.
18. Ministry of Housing and Local Government, *Housing Return for England and Wales*. Appendices since 1945.
19. Ministry of Labour, *Family Expenditure Survey Report for 1962*, H.M.S.O., 1963.
20. C. A. Moser and Wolf Scott, *British Towns*, Oliver & Boyd, 1961.
21. L. Needleman, 'A Long Term View of Housing', *Economic Review*, **18**, November 1961.
22. Colin Rosser and Christopher Harris, *The Family and Social Change, A Study of Family Kinship in a South Wales Town*, Routledge & Kegan Paul, 1965.
23. Susanne H. Spence, 'The Prospects for Industrial Use of the Lower Swansea Valley: A Study of Land Use in a Regional Context' (Study Report 6).

Bibliography
24. Town and Country Planning Association, *Housing in Britain*. A Survey commissioned by the Town and Country Planning Association and carried out by O. W. Roskill, Industrial Consultant, 1964.
25. C. Vereker and J. B. Mays, *Urban Redevelopment and Social Change*, Liverpool University Press, 1961.
26. R. Wilkinson and E. M. Sigsworth, 'A Survey of Slum Clearance Areas in Leeds', *Yorks Bulletin of Economic and Social Research* 15, May 1963.
27. R. D. Worrall, 'Report on Transportation and Physical Planning in the Lower Swansea Valley, 1963. (Study Report 2).

Authorship

This chapter was written by Mrs Margaret Stacey, Lecturer in Sociology, University College of Swansea.

She wishes to express her indebtedness to Dr C. Rosser and C. C. Harris, who kindly allowed her to have access to unpublished analyses and original questionnaires. She had herself done some of the interviewing for the survey (ref. 22) in the Borough.

She is also indebted to Professor W. M. Williams, A. V. S. Lochhead, K. J. Hilton and Dr J. B. Loudon for their help in its preparation.

Acknowledgements to the many people who helped in the preparation of the original reports on which this chapter is based are to be found in those reports.

The local authority and the Ministry of Housing and Local Government have provided access to unpublished data.

9 The prospects for industrial use: a study of land use in a regional context

The nature of the problem

The economic study of the Lower Swansea Valley was directed primarily towards attempting to determine whether the land was of potential use as an industrial site. In this assessment, the two main considerations have been the prospects for economic growth in Swansea and West South Wales, and the suitability of the area to meet any future demand for industrial land. This chapter is concerned to show the economic background of the West South Wales region—a background against which future development of the derelict area must be seen—and to analyse the feasibility of preliminary investment in industrial development on the site.

Chapter 2 traced the decline of the various industries which once thrived in the Lower Swansea Valley. In order to make any useful forecast about the industrial future of the area, it is necessary to stress again the changes which brought about the decline. Not only have there been changes in people's demands for products but industry's own requirements have also changed. Again, industrialists no longer need necessarily locate their works near coal or canals, or even near railways. An essential need for all industry, however, is good road access: this is a facility the Lower Valley lacks, and one which, as Mr Worrall points out in Chapter 7, can only be provided at considerable cost. The concentration of industry, and particularly the integration of steel and tinplate works, in a few vast works has tended to replace the many smaller works. This has not only contributed to the decline of the Lower Valley, but has also in part accounted for its failure to attract new industry. The Lower Swansea Valley is so cut about by disused railway lines, by the canal, the river and the tips, that it was unable to supply, other than at very great cost, the considerable acreages of adjacent land which were in demand by the major heavy industrial undertakings that have come into the area since the Second World War. At the same time, when the Swansea Corporation and the Board of Trade were faced in 1945 with a new industrial location policy, and with the needs of industrialists, they tried to locate new industry coming into the town further from the highly residential areas than their forefathers had done. The decision to place the trading estate at Fforestfach, on the west side of Swansea and well away from the town centre, took account not only of businessmen's desires for pleasant surroundings for their factories, but also of Swansea's need to compete with other Development Areas which possibly did not have the same industrial dereliction problem. Also, although its immediate postwar appearance was not attractive, the Lower Valley was far more active and alive than it has since become. While the outlook for most of the industries represented in the Lower

Valley was poor, many of the smaller works were still functioning, so that the disamenity aspects of the area were offset by the fact that it still employed a high proportion of the town's labour and contributed considerable rate revenue. In 1945 the Borough would have been involved in the acquisition of much active industrial land if it had been decided to locate an estate of the size of Fforestfach in the Lower Valley. In fact, north of the main railway line only 40 acres of land were then vacant.

While industrial land use is one possibility for the Lower Valley, and is therefore worthy of attention as part of the overall study of the area, it should not be assumed that present demand for industrial land in Swansea exceeds supply. The comparative advantages of the derelict land and other industrial sites in Swansea are referred to later, but it may be mentioned at this stage that there are already areas of land scheduled for industry in Swansea which remain unfilled: 23 acres at the Swansea Industrial Estate at Fforestfach are already laid out with service roads, lighting, drainage, etc., while a further 45 acres suitable for development are unprepared. Apart from smaller individual sites within the County Borough, there are also extensive areas of very low agricultural value just beyond the County Borough boundary within the Neath Rural District. Hence the failure of the pressure of demand for land to solve the problems of the Lower Swansea Valley. It is significant that the districts of industrial dereliction in Great Britain tend to be concentrated in areas of higher than average unemployment. It appears that in the more prosperous regions the demand for land for industrial development in recent years has caused potentially derelict land to be reclaimed before it had become an established feature of the landscape. Basically, assuming a certain demand for land for industrial purposes, the economic feasibility of reclamation largely depends on the other demands for land in the vicinity of the derelict district. A rise in the price of alternative sites—due for example to an increase in the demand for amenity or agricultural purposes—will reduce the cost of reclaiming derelict land in relation to the price of alternative land. However, it cannot be assumed that in every instance where greenfield sites are used for development the site has necessarily a significant agricultural or amenity value. In the case of the Swansea area, there are considerable acreages of land which are either sand dunes or at best rough grazing, for which there may be as little demand as there is for the derelict land. In comparison with such land the real cost of the reclamation of derelict land is, or approaches, the cost of its acquisition and reclamation.

The point at which it becomes economic to reclaim the land appears to be the point at which the cost of acquisition and reclamation is equal to the cost of acquiring alternative sites. When the alternative sites are themselves of low agricultural or amenity value, this economic point of reclamation becomes further removed. And since the difference between costs of development on non-derelict and derelict land is reduced as the value of the non-derelict land rises, it seems that initial development of the less costly areas of dereliction will, in the long run, reduce the total cost of an overall development plan.

Broadly speaking, and as would be expected, the derelict land is cheaper than land elsewhere in Swansea; the difference in value per acre can vary between £350 and £2,750. This means that for certain industrial undertakings, where land represents a high proportion of total costs ('land intensive' industries), the Lower Valley may prove to be attractive. It is apparent, however, that the derelict land would involve high site preparation costs and that these have to be set against low land acquisition costs. This would apply to all potential

The prospects for
industrial use:
a study of land use in a
regional context

land uses, not just industry, and indeed the land may well hold even more attraction for land intensive amenity and housing provision than for industry. A private housing enterprise has succeeded in selling low cost houses on the east side of the Project area despite the obvious lack of amenity there. It is apparent that given a high existing demand for low cost accommodation, and with land representing an important feature of house building costs, the unattractiveness of the Lower Valley is a positive inducement to building. This of course may be a short-term factor since the effect of such building will be to improve the appearance of the area which will, in turn, help to raise land prices. Similarly, where there is a demand for parkland or playing fields in the east of Swansea, these might be provided more cheaply on the derelict land than on greenfield sites which might be available, and the problems of foundations and levels would be less serious than for industrial buildings.

The regional background

It must be emphasized that the problem of regenerating the Lower Valley for industrial use has to be seen within the context of the economic prospects for the West South Wales region as later defined. Since the main economic force determining the future of the derelict area is likely to be the demand for industrial land in this region, it has been necessary to study in some detail the prospects for regional growth. An attempt has therefore been made to analyse—mainly for the period 1951–81—the population and employment structure of the West South Wales region. An investigation has also been made into the location motives of firms that have come into the region since the Second World War, and of their experiences.

Regional statistics are notoriously inadequate in Great Britain. However, with the help of various government departments concerned, it is hoped that the best use has been made of such details as are available. There are three basic sources of information: Ministry of Labour Insured Employee statistics, the Registrar-General's mid-year estimates of civilian population for the relevant area, and a survey of postwar manufacturing firms in West South Wales which was undertaken by means of interviews and postal questionnaires. Other sources, particularly the Census of Population for 1951 and 1961, were used. One particular point needs to be made about the three main sources referred to above. Since the region taken for study, West South Wales, is not an officially recognized Standard Region, the geographical boundaries taken by the statisticians do not exactly coincide, so that where direct comparisons are made (for example in Activity Rate calculations, in which the insured employee population is related directly to total population of working age) allowance has to be made for this fact. The West South Wales region as studied is one which observes empirical and pragmatic boundary lines rather than precisely geographic ones. For statistical purposes it has been necessary to try and make these coincide, but it may be hoped that with the new Government plans for the regions there will be an increased awareness of the importance of presenting official statistics covering such matters as incomes, prices and production for economically meaningful regional units.

The region adopted for investigation is basically that which can be regarded as a catchment area for the Lower Swansea Valley. West South Wales, as referred to in this chapter, consists of the following local authority areas, and is shown in Figure 9.1.

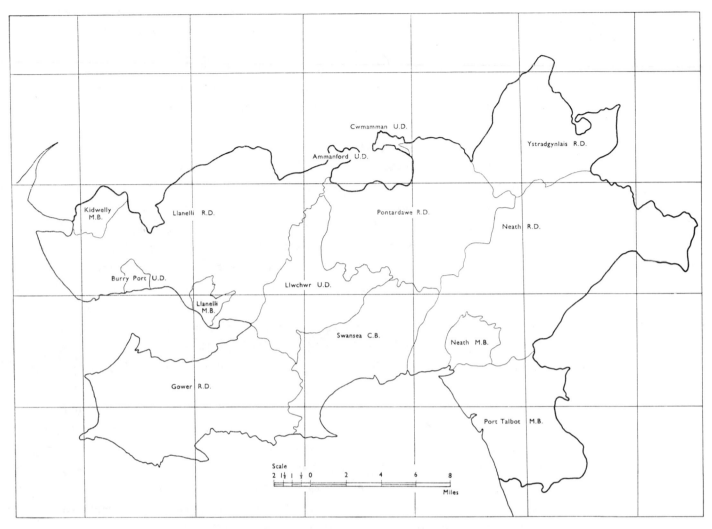

Figure 9.1 Local authority areas in the West South Wales Region

Ammanford Urban District	Llwchwr Urban District
Burry Port Urban District	Neath Municipal Borough
Cwmamman Urban District	Neath Rural District
Gower Rural District	Pontardawe Rural District
Kidwelly Municipal Borough	Port Talbot Municipal Borough
Llanelli Municipal Borough	Swansea County Borough
Llanelli Rural District	Ystradgynlais Rural District

The prospects for
industrial use:
a study of land use in a
regional context

With the postwar shift of Welsh industry to the southern coastal belt—despite Government efforts to halt the flow by inducing certain establishments into the valleys—there has been a tendency for the two main urban centres of South Wales, Swansea and Cardiff, to act as focal points for industrial, commercial and residential developments. Swansea County Borough contains almost 25 per cent of the total population of the West South Wales region and, with Port Talbot, is the only local authority area in the region to show substantial gains in population over the intercensal period 1951–61. The 1961 figures for the Swansea Employment Exchange area show that a very high proportion of Swansea's workers were engaged in service and distribution and relatively few in manufacturing. Many goods and services are distributed on a regional basis from Swansea and the area on the map is that taken by many wholesale and retail distributors as their 'sales area'. Furthermore, the Glamorgan County Council Survey of Journey to Work shows that in 1959, of the 21,639 persons engaged in Mining and Manufacturing Industry and resident in Swansea, 30 per cent travel daily out of the Borough to their place of work.[1]* This is relatively unusual for a town of the size of Swansea, and it seems that the net outflow of workers consists mainly of those in manufacturing industry while the net inflow of workers into the Exchange area is mainly accounted for by the pull of service industries. Further evidence about the interdependence within the region is contained in a study of the transportation network of the Swansea and West South Wales bus and train routes. The closure of certain railway lines under the Beeching proposals has tended to strengthen the position of Swansea as a regional transportation centre.

The region has a fairly distinctive tripartite character. Two of its areas (the Neath and Swansea Valleys, and Industrial Carmarthenshire) are characterized by declining populations in the inland areas and the third, the coastal belt from Swansea to Port Talbot, has a growing population and enjoys considerable prosperity. Taken as one unit, the region experienced some growth over the period 1951–61. In most instances this growth (in population, employment and economic activity) was fairly high along the coast, this being offset by very limited growth inland.

The population of the region

The South Wales background

The intercensal period 1951–61 has been taken for analysis largely because this gives a good base for projections, and also because this is the standard period used in other regional studies of this kind. However, some attempt is made to look at the changes up to 1963, using the Registrar-General's mid-year estimates of civilian home population. These differ somewhat from the estimates of home population published in the Registrar-General's *Annual Statistical Reviews* for England and Wales and the *Census of Population*, both of which include members of the British Commonwealth and foreign armed forces stationed in this country and also visitors to the region from abroad and elsewhere.

The three areas referred to above as subdivisions within the region are as follows:

* References are given on p. 229.

1 Coast (Swansea County Borough; Port Talbot Municipal Borough; Gower Rural District)
2 Neath and Swansea Valleys (Llwchwr Urban District; Neath Municipal Borough; Neath Rural District; Pontardawe Rural District; Ystradgynlais Rural District)
3 Industrial Carmarthenshire (Ammanford Urban District; Burry Port Urban District; Cwmamman Urban District; Kidwelly Municipal Borough; Llanelli Municipal Borough; Llanelli Rural District)

In 1961 the total civilian population of Wales was 2,620,650, of which two-thirds lived in industrial South Wales; of these, 456,210, or 25·3 per cent, lived in West South Wales as defined. In the whole of South Wales the population was almost equally distributed between the mining valleys and the coast. 896,000 persons lived in the valleys and Industrial Carmarthenshire, while 905,000 lived along the coastal belt extending from Swansea and Gower in the west to Chepstow in the east. Table 9.1 shows the essentially tripolar pull of population along the coast: with the 88,960 persons in Industrial Carmarthenshire added to the Swansea–Port Talbot area, the population of West South Wales is greater than that of the Newport area and more than half that of the Cardiff area.

Table 9.1   Civilian population of coastal areas and hinterland valleys in South Wales (excluding industrial Carmarthenshire) 1961

Swansea–Port Talbot	Bridgend	Cardiff	Newport
367,350	119,590	762,070	410,010

The geographical breakdown between valleys and coast in 1961 was similar in West South Wales to what it was in South Wales as a whole. This is shown in Table 9.2.

Table 9.2   Distribution of civilian population in West South Wales 1961

Areas	Estimated civilian population	Per cent of West South Wales
Coast	229,900	50·4
Neath and Swansea Valleys	137,350	30·1
Industrial Carmarthenshire	88,960	19·5
Total West South Wales	456,210	100·0

Natural change, 1951–61

Table 9.3 shows estimated civilian population changes in West South Wales from 1951 to 1961 by areas. It can be seen that the natural increase rate (i.e. the balance between births and deaths) for West South Wales was 2·6 per cent. This consisted of a fairly high natural increase rate for Swansea–Port Talbot (4·3 per cent) and low rates for the valleys and Industrial Carmarthenshire. Over the same period the rate for the whole of industrial South Wales was 4·1 per cent, while that for the United Kingdom was 4·6 per cent. The West South Wales rate was therefore little over half that of Britain as a whole. Furthermore, although the natural increase rate in the Swansea–Port Talbot area was high compared to the inland areas, it was the lowest of the coastal areas of South Wales. (For Bridgend the rate was 5·3 per cent, for Cardiff 6·5 per cent and for Newport 6·8 per cent). The Swansea and Neath Valleys and Industrial Carmarthenshire both had rates lower than that for Wales as a whole (3·3 per cent).

The prospects for
industrial use:
a study of land use in a
regional context

Table 9.3 Estimated civilian population change in West South Wales 1951–61

Area	Estimated mid-year civilian population		Total change		Natural change		Balance	
	1951	1961	No.	%	No.	%	No.	%
Coast	215,460	229,900	14,440	6·7	9,381	4·3	5,059	2·4
Valleys	142,600	137,350	−5,250	−3·7	2,067	1·5	−7,317	−3·2
Industrial Carmarthenshire	90,790	88,960	−1,830	−2·0	293	·3	−2,123	−2·3
Total	448,850	456,210	7,360	1·6	11,741	2·6	−4,381	−1·0

Migration

Migration statistics for regions are somewhat unsatisfactory since there is as yet no one source which supplies full data on movements of population within the United Kingdom. The Ministry of Labour publishes estimates of interregional movements of insured employees based on the exchange of National Insurance cards and deduced from a 1 per cent sample. The other main sources, and more satisfactory ones since they are more comprehensive, are the data on changes in the total population. However, the difference between the total and the natural change in the population only gives information about the total number of migrants: it tells nothing about the age or sex structure of migrants, nor where they go to or come from. Similarly, although this will show the extent of movement (i.e. the balance between total and natural change) in a region, there is no way of knowing whether the net outward movement from one part is in any sense a gain to another. In, for example, the case of West South Wales we can only assume that the gain in population along the coast, associated with a reduction in the population of the hinterland, is to some extent a result of the movement from the inland areas. A further complicating factor is the fact that during the period under review the civilian population increased due to a rundown in the armed forces. In order to achieve a more accurate assessment of population movement, the forces rundown has been deducted from the increase in total civilian population to obtain a migration figure. This figure is a useful guide to trends but, largely due to the fact that the forces rundown is not obtainable on a local authority basis, some adjustments have to be made and it should be treated with some caution when it refers to small areas.

Table 9.4 shows that the coastal belt is the only part of West South Wales to have experienced net immigration (of 1·6 per cent) during the period, while the net emigration (5·9 per cent) was greatest in the valleys. The net migration from West South Wales was −1·7 per cent. The gains along the coast were not sufficient to offset the losses in the valleys and Industrial Carmarthenshire, and the region as a whole lost 7,673 persons through migration.

Total change 1951–61

Total change in the population is made up of natural change and migration. The movement of young people away from the inland areas, with a resulting ageing population, leads to a close connection between migration and low natural increase rates so that the problems of the inland areas rapidly become self-perpetuating.

Tables 9.5a and 9.5b indicate that in the coastal area the proportion of the total population aged under five (8 per cent) approximated to that of England and Wales as a whole (7·9 per cent). The proportion of the total population aged under fifteen is somewhat higher

Table 9.4   Civilian population changes in West South Wales 1951–61*

		Coast	Valleys	Industrial Carmarthenshire	West South Wales
Mid-1951 population		215,460	142,600	90,790	448,850
Mid-1961 population		229,900	137,350	88,960	456,210
Total change	No.	14,440	−5,250	−1,830	7,360
	%	6·6	−3·7	−2·0	1·6
Natural change	No.	9,400	2,050	293	11,743
	%	4·3	1·5	0·3	2·6
Forces rundown	No.	1,600	1,050	650	3,300
	%	0·7	0·7	0·7	0·7
Migration	No.	3,450	−8,350	−2,773	−7,673
	%	1·6	−5·9	−3·1	−1·7

* Slight variations between this Table and Table 9.3 are due to rounding.

than that for England and Wales (15·7 per cent compared with 14·9 per cent). These figures reflect the relatively high natural increase rate. By contrast, in the valleys and Industrial Carmarthenshire the proportion of the population is lower than that of England and Wales as a whole, and considerably lower than that of the coastal belt. Industrial Carmarthenshire showed an older age distribution and also a higher female: male ratio than the valleys. There are, of course, more women in the older age groups so that these two factors are likely to correlate. The valleys area, though having a lower proportion than the coast in the under-fifteen age group, has a higher proportion in the fifteen to sixty-four age group, so that the over sixty-five group is only 0·4 per cent higher than the coast.

Table 9.5(a)   Distribution of the population of West South Wales by age, sex and area 1961*

		Age	0–4	5–14	15–64	65 and over	Total
Industrial Carmarthenshire							
Males							
	No.		3,106	6,323	29,608	4,470	43,507
	%		7·1	14·5	68·0	10·3	99·9
Females							
	No.		2,926	6,147	30,595	6,379	46,047
	%		6·4	13·3	66·4	13·9	100·0
Total							
	No.		6,032	12,470	60,203	10,849	89,554
	%		6·7	13·9	67·2	12·1	99·9
Neath and Swansea Valleys							
Males							
	No.		4,866	10,378	46,027	6,761	68,032
	%		7·2	15·3	67·7	9·9	100·1
Females							
	No.		4,675	9,773	46,829	9,151	70,428
	%		6·6	13·9	66·5	13·0	100·0
Total							
	No.		9,541	20,151	92,856	15,912	138,460
	%		6·9	14·6	67·1	11·5	100·1
Coast							
Males							
	No.		9,462	18,415	75,022	10,027	112,926
	%		8·4	16·3	66·4	8·9	100·0
Females							
	No.		9,148	17,807	75,893	15,546	118,394
	%		7·7	15·0	64·1	13·1	99·9
Total							
	No.		18,610	36,222	150,915	25,573	231,320
	%		8·0	15·7	65·2	11·1	100·0

* Tables 9.5(a) and (b) are extracted from the Census of Population 1961 and therefore include armed forces at home.

The prospects for
industrial use :
a study of land use in a
regional context

**Table 9.5(*b*) Age of the West South Wales population compared with England
and Wales 1961**

Figures in brackets show percentages in England and Wales

Age	Number	Percentage
0–4	34,183	7·4 (7·9)
5–14	68,843	15·0 (14·9)
15–64	303,954	66·2 (65·2)
65 and over	53,234	11·4 (12·0)
Total	459,314	100·0 (100·0)

West South Wales experienced a total increase in population between 1951 and 1961 of
7,360 persons, or 1·6 per cent of the population. Population losses in the Neath and Swansea Valleys were −3·7 per cent, while in Industrial Carmarthenshire they were —2·0 per
cent; the coastal gains were 6·6 per cent. (The rate of growth of this region in relation to
the rest of South Wales is illustrated by the fact that industrial South Wales as a whole increased its population by 2·8 per cent over the same period.)

Population changes 1956–63 and 1951–61 compared

In 1956 there began a marked rise in the birth rate of the United Kingdom which effectively
divided the intercensal trend into two parts. Table 9.6 illustrates this trend as it occurred
in West South Wales by showing the numerical increase in the average annual growth.

**Table 9.6 Comparison of average annual population change in West South Wales
1951–61 and 1956–63**

Area	Neath and Swansea Valleys	Industrial Carmarthenshire	Coastal Belt	West South Wales
Total change per annum				
1951–61	− 550	− 200	1,450	700
1956–63	− 550	− 300	2,000	1,150
Natural change per annum				
1951–61	200	50	950	1,200
1956–63	150	50	1,050	1,250
Forces rundown per annum				
1951–61	100	100	150	350
1956–63	100	100	200	400
Net migration per annum				
1951–61	−850	−350	350	−850
1956–63	−800	−450	750	−500

The natural increase in West South Wales was a little higher in 1956–63 than in 1951–61.
This was because a rise (of 100) in the average in the coastal area more than offset the fall
(of 50) in the Swansea and Neath Valleys. In the case of migration there was a fall (of 350) in
1956–63 compared with 1951–61 in the average net loss of people by migration from West
South Wales. This fall consisted of a rise of 400 in average annual inward migration to the

coastal area, a fall of 50 in the net migration from the valleys and a rise of 100 in net outward migration from Industrial Carmarthenshire.

The total population gain per annum in West South Wales was 450 per annum higher in 1956–63 than in 1951–61. This was due to an increase of 50 per annum from natural change, an increase of 50 due to armed forces rundown and a decrease of 350 in outward migration.

Population projections 1961–81

The projections of population presented in this section are based mainly on data supplied by the Welsh Office, certain adjustments having been made to allow for variations in geographical detail.

Reference was made earlier to the movement of young people away from the inland areas and the resulting ageing of the population in those areas. The assessment of future trends is based on the changes in population between 1956 and 1963, since it seems likely that the higher birth rate of those years will continue. Among other things, however, changes in government policy towards the regions might result in alterations to the migration rate which cannot be foreseen or taken into account. The projections assume that the 1956–63 trends will continue; it is, however, also assumed that Wales's share of the total natural increase for Wales and England, which has declined steadily from 1921 to 1963 (from 8·5 per cent to 4·0 per cent), will remain constant at 4·0 per cent.

The result of these projections, as shown in Table 9·7, gives the 1981 population of West South Wales as 485,360, an overall increase of 29,150 compared with 1961. The anticipated loss by migration of population from the inland areas would not be quite compensated for by the immigration to the Swansea–Port Talbot coastal belt. But the loss would be reduced to less than half its 1961 figure because the anticipated increase in migration into the coastal belt would be even greater than the considerably enlarged outward migration expected from the inland areas. Although outward migration from the inland areas is expected to increase considerably, it is not expected to increase as much as the migration into the coastal belt.

Table 9.7 Estimated civilian population changes 1961–81 West South Wales

Area	Estimated civilian population		Population change 1961–81					
	Mid-1961	Mid-1981	Total change		Natural change		Migration	
			No.	%	No.	%	No.	%
Coast	229,900	274,000	44,100	19·2	27,000	11·8	17,100	7·4
Neath and Swansea Valleys	137,350	126,800	−10,550	−7·7	3,700	2·7	−14,300	−10·4
Industrial Carmarthenshire	88,960	84,560	−4,400	−4·9	445	0·5	−4,845	−5·4
West South Wales	456,210	485,360	29,150	6·4	31,145	6·8	−2,045	−0·4

Though these figures only represent guesses, which may turn out to be wide of their respective marks, it appears that one can with some degree of confidence expect a growth of population along the coast, a loss of people from the valleys and a slightly smaller loss from Industrial Carmarthenshire. The rate of gain on the coastal belt between Swansea and

The prospects for
industrial use:
a study of land use in a
regional context

Port Talbot will, however, be lower than that for other coastal areas of industrial South Wales, indicating yet again that the West South Wales region has a slower growth rate than the region east of Port Talbot.

Conclusions

West South Wales has, and is likely to continue to have, a population consisting of two distinct parts. Along the coast there is a growing and comparatively young population which is attracting new migrants. In the inland areas the population is declining due to two connected reasons: low rates of natural increase and outward migration. The net result of these situations is that the total population of West South Wales is growing slowly. The population of the coastal belt is not growing as fast as that of the Bridgend, Cardiff or Newport areas but it is nevertheless growing sufficiently to outweigh the losses from the inland areas. It is considered likely that these trends of the recent past will continue to operate in the next decade or two.

The labour resources of the region

The period taken for study in this section is again 1951–61, and as stated above the analysis is based on statistics provided by the Ministry of Labour from their employment returns.[2] The following employment exchanges are covered by the analysis on a similar geographical breakdown to that used for the population study:

1 Coast (Swansea, including Gower; Port Talbot);

2 Neath and Swansea Valleys (Morriston; Neath; Resolven; Pontardawe; Ystalyfera; Gorseinon; Pontardulais);

3 Industrial Carmarthenshire (Ammanford; Burry Port; Garnant; Kidwelly; Llanelli; Tumble).

Although these employment exchange areas provide the most satisfactory coverage of the total working population of the region they include persons living outside but working in the region, and exclude those living in but working outside the region. The net result of this is to increase a little the total working population since the pull of the Steel Company of Wales's Port Talbot plant attracts rather more daily workers than leave the region for other works outside.

The change in the pattern of employment 1951–61, by geographical area

Table 9.8 shows that between 1951 and 1961 the total insured employee population in West South Wales rose by 2·5 per cent, or 4,602 persons. In 1951 the population was fairly evenly distributed between the three areas, the valleys, Industrial Carmarthenshire and the coastal belt. By 1961 the latter area had almost half the insured population: that is, the general shift towards the coast which was noted earlier was also reflected in the employment pattern.

Table 9.8   Distribution of employment in West South Wales by area

Area	1951		1961	
	No.	%	No.	%
Coast	70,988	39·1	85,502	45·9
Industrial Carmarthenshire	41,741	23·1	38,252	20·5
Neath and Swansea Valleys	68,963	37·8	62,540	33·6
West South Wales	181,692	100·0	186,294	100·0

Table 9.9 shows the differences in industrial structure between the three areas.[3] It can be seen that the coastal belt had in 1961 a rather more evenly distributed pattern of industry than the other areas. The largest single group is metal manufacture, which is of course weighted by the Port Talbot steelworks. Yet, despite the size of the steelworks, the spread through the other industry groups is considerable. The other major group, the distributive trades, tends as previously mentioned to reflect the importance of Swansea as a regional service and shopping centre. It is noticeable that employment in the coastal area is very much concentrated on service rather than manufacturing industry.

In the valleys and Industrial Carmarthenshire, however, the employment pattern is significantly different. Mining still occupies an important place in these areas, and although there is also considerable emphasis on the service industries, manufacturing industry is rather more fully represented, especially in the valleys, where there is considerably more employment in engineering.

Table 9.9   Distribution of insured employees in West South Wales by area and industry group 1961

S I C order		Neath and Swansea Valleys		Industrial Carmarthenshire		Coastal belt	
		No.	%	No.	%	No.	%
I	Agriculture, Forestry, Fishing	331	0·4	318	0·8	390	0·5
II	Mining and Quarrying	12,381	19·8	7,483	19·6	1,591	1·9
III	Food, Drink, Tobacco	945	1·5	574	1·5	1,209	1·4
IV	Chemicals and Allied Industries	2,918	4·7	1,100	2·9	2,311	2·7
V	Metal Manufacture	12,153	19·8	6,051	15·8	19,172	22·4
VI	Engineering and Electrical Goods	3,568	5·7	1,437	3·8	2,797	3·3
VII	Shipbuilding and Marine Engineering	—	—	1	—	555	0·6
VIII	Vehicles	1,382	2·0	2,390	6·2	826	1·0
IX	Metal Goods n.e.s.	4,408	7·0	1,533	4·0	2,617	3·1
X	Textiles	76	0·1	196	0·5	247	0·3
XI	Leather, Leather Goods, Fur	210	0·3	38	0·1	12	—
XII	Clothing and Footwear	280	0·4	1	—	1,115	1·3
XIII	Bricks, Pottery, Glass, Cement	403	0·6	360	0·9	207	0·2
XIV	Timber, Furniture	141	0·2	244	0·6	500	0·6
XV	Paper, Printing, Publishing	1,145	1·8	137	0·4	388	0·4
XVI	Other Manufacturing Industries	71	0·1	216	0·6	2,680	3·1
XVII	Construction	4,453	7·1	3,642	9·5	8,827	10·3
XVIII	Gas, Electricity, Water	783	1·3	987	2·6	1,798	2·1
XIX	Transport and Communications	3,482	5·6	2,220	5·8	8,361	9·8
XX	Distributive Trades	4,016	6·4	3,498	9·1	11,384	13·3
XXI	Insurance, Banking, Finance	489	0·8	378	1·0	1,507	1·8
XXII	Professional, Scientific Services	4,847	7·8	2,325	6·1	7,194	8·4
XXIII	Miscellaneous Services	2,588	4·1	1,426	3·7	5,962	7·0
XXIV	Public Administration and Defence	1,469	2·3	1,692	4·4	3,845	4·5
XS		1	—	5	—	7	—
	Total	62,540	99·9	38,252	99·9	85,502	100

The prospects for
industrial use:
a study of land use in a
regional context

The general change in employment 1951–61

Tables 9.10 and 9.11 show that the two other groups which have shown the largest percentage change in West South Wales over the ten-year period are those of Mining and Quarrying (Order II) and Distributive and Service Trades (Order XX). Between 1951 and 1961 the percentage of the insured employees of the region employed in mining declined by 2·9 per cent while in Great Britain as a whole over the same period the decline amounted to only 0·8 per cent: by 1961 the percentage of the region's workers employed in mining and quarrying was 11·5. Some of the decline was due to the difficulties of recruitment to the industry; but the concentration of activity in larger, more highly mechanized pits makes it likely that the number of workers engaged in coal-mining in the region will continue to fall.

The distributive trades and services increased their share of the total labour force in the region by 2·4 per cent, reflecting a change which took place in the country as a whole; the percentage increase for Great Britain over the same period was 2·3 per cent. There was also an increase of 2·2 per cent in those employed in professional and scientific services in the region, compared with 2·6 per cent for Great Britain as a whole. Significantly, in view of the importance of the building industry as a bottleneck to expansion over the decade, employment in construction industries in West South Wales declined by 0·1 per cent compared with an increase of 0·3 per cent in Great Britain. It is not, however, easy to draw any general conclusions about trends in the construction industry on a regional basis since much of the labour is highly mobile, entering the region for specific contracts and then moving out.

Table 9.10 shows also the change in employment by industry for the decade 1938 to 1948 in order to give some further information about the long-run changes that have taken place.

Table 9.10 Percentage distribution of employment in West South Wales by industry group 1938, 1948, 1951, 1961

Industry group	1938	1948[4]	1951	1961
Agriculture	2·0	1·5	1·1	0·6
Mining	26·0	19·0	14·4	11·5
Metal manufacture	25·5	22·5	21·0	20·0
Other manufacture	8·5	16·5	18·3	19·6
Distribution and services	38·0	40·5	45·3	48·3
Total	100·0	100·0	100·1	100·0

Table 9.11 West South Wales employment distribution by standard industrial classification 1951 and 1961

Figures in italics show percentage employment by industry for Great Britain

	S I C order	1951 No.	1951 %		1961 No.	1961 %	
I	Agriculture, Forestry, Fishing	1,949	1·1	4·0	1,036	0·6	2·7
II	Mining and Quarrying	26,221	14·4	4·1	21,455	11·5	3·3
III	Food, Drink and Tobacco	3,618	2·0	1·6	2,728	1·5	3·6
IV	Chemicals and Allied Industries	5,121	2·8	2·3	6,329	3·4	2·4
V	Metal Manufacture	37,922	21·0	2·7	37,376	20·0	2·8
VI	Engineering and Electrical Goods	7,320	4·0	8·1	7,802	4·2	9·5
VII	Shipbuilding and Marine Engineering	976	0·5	1·3	556	0·3	1·1
VIII	Vehicles	3,212	1·8	3·7	4,598	2·5	4·0

Table 9.11—*contd.*

S I C order		1951			1961		
		No.	%		No.	%	
IX	Metal Goods n.e.s.	7,506	4·1	2·5	8,558	4·6	2·5
X	Textiles	487	0·3	5·0	519	0·3	2·8
XI	Leather and Leather Goods	158	0·1	0·4	260	0·1	0·3
XII	Clothing and Footwear	2,311	1·3	3·1	1,396	0·7	2·5
XIII	Bricks, Pottery, Glass, Cement	1,889	1·0	3·9	970	0·5	1·5
XIV	Timber, Furniture, etc.	1,386	0·8	1·5	885	0·5	1·3
XV	Paper, Printing, Publishing	846	0·5	2·5	1,665	0·9	2·7
XVI	Other Manufacturing Industries	1,979	1·1	1·4	2,967	1·6	1·4
XVII	Construction	16,754	9·2	6·4	16,922	9·1	6·7
XVIII	Gas, Electricity, Water	2,757	1·5	1·8	3,570	1·9	1·7
XIX	Transport and Communications	17,114	9·4	8·3	14,063	7·5	7·4
XX	Distributive Trades	14,000	7·7	10·3	18,898	10·1	12·6
XXI	Insurance, Banking, Finance	1,606	0·9	2·1	2,374	1·3	2·5
XXII	Professional, Scientific Services	9,950	5·5	6·6	14,366	7·7	9·2
XXIII	Miscellaneous Services	9,304	5·1	7·1	9,976	5·4	8·9
XXIV	Public Administration	7,191	4·0	9·3	7,006	3·8	5·7
XS		110			19		
	Total	181,687	100·1		186,294	100·0	

The change in the sex structure of the labour force 1951–61

It has already been noted that total insured employment in the region grew by 2·5 per cent over the decade. This increase was mainly due to the fact that the increase in the female insured population more than offset the decline in the male insured population. The male insured employee population of West South Wales fell from 139,927 in 1951 to 139,160 in 1961 (a decline of 0·5 per cent) while the female labour force increased over the same period from 41,765 to 47,134 (an increase of 12·9 per cent). The decrease in the male labour force consisted of declines in the Neath and Swansea valleys and Industrial Carmarthenshire and an increase in the Swansea–Port Talbot coastal area. The female insured employee population increased in all three areas.

Table 9.12 Changes in male and female employment in West South Wales 1951–1961

	1951				1961			
	Male		Female		Male		Female	
	No.	%	No.	%	No.	%	No.	%
Valleys	55,783	39·9	13,180	31·6	47,310	34·0	15,104	32·0
Industrial Carmarthenshire	33,939	24·3	7,802	18·7	29,770	21·4	8,608	18·3
Coast	50,205	35·9	20,783	49·8	62,080	44·6	23,422	49·7
Total	139,927	100·1	41,765	100·1	139,160	100·0	47,134	100·0

These changes reflected a general trend in South Wales as a whole, where the total male insured employee population declined while the female increased by more than the same amount, and where also the losses of male employment were mainly concentrated on the valleys and inland areas while there were gains along the coast.

Unemployment in West South Wales 1951–61 and 1964

Unemployment in West South Wales in mid-June 1951 amounted to 2·2 per cent of the insured workers. In mid-June 1961 it amounted to 2·5 per cent. This was almost twice the

The prospects for
Industrial use:
a study of land use in a
regional context

British average (1·2 per cent in both years) and was about the same as the rate for Wales as a whole.

By June 1964 unemployment rates were higher than in 1961 and the West South Wales rate remained at twice the British average (3·2 per cent compared with 1·6 per cent). However, the West South Wales unemployment rate was by then higher than that for Wales as a whole (2·3 per cent). Table 9.13 indicates that the lowest unemployment rate in June 1964 was in Industrial Carmarthenshire. This was mainly the result of recently established industry in and around Llanelli which had to some extent the effect of anticipating future redundancies in declining works. The Industrial Carmarthenshire area includes the Llanelli Development District while the Neath and Swansea valleys includes the Pontardawe and Ystalyfera Development District.

Table 9.13   Unemployment rates by area, West South Wales, June 1964

	%
Neath and Swansea valleys	3·9
Industrial Carmarthenshire	2·6
Coast	3·0
West South Wales	3·2

Both numerically and proportionately the greatest unemployment tended to be in metal manufacture. This was generally due to short-time working or redundancy at one particular works or another, but there has probably also been a certain amount of residual labour from the old-type tinplate works and this is likely to continue for some time. The other major unemployment group was the construction industry, but as has been noted above this is a highly mobile labour force and the long-term effect on the region is unlikely to be very great.

Fluctuations in the unemployment rate since 1951 have tended to be associated with the closure of particular works which have thrown considerable numbers on to the labour market for short periods of time. Where these closures are part of the overall decline of an industry, such as the old steel and tinplate works, the long-term effect has been considerable, but in the case of individual establishments the surplus labour has been fairly rapidly reabsorbed. Similarly, the bad winter of 1963 brought high unemployment which had a sharp effect on the region, but this effect was of short duration. These are indications of a fairly resilient economy though it should be stressed that there are still small pockets of persistent high unemployment, such as occur in the northern part of the region around Ammanford and Garnant.

Although the unemployment rates of prewar years have been reduced to what would then have seemed negligible proportions, the region's unemployment rate was, in 1961, as high as the rates of those regions cited by the National Economic Development Council as 'less prosperous'.[5] That the rate remains high is due more to high unemployment levels in certain small areas than to a high rate in the region as a whole.

Activity rates in West South Wales and the future working population

'Activity rates' are useful indicators of the concealed labour reserve of a region—the activity rate being the number of insured employees as a proportion of the total population of working age.[6]

Since the insured employee statistics include employed and unemployed and since nearly all males register as unemployed when not working, it may be assumed that it is unlikely that significant variations occur in the male labour activity rates over a period. Women, however, tend not to register as unemployed but simply to take work when it is available, and because of this activity rates can be a useful guide to the female labour reserve.

Table 9.14 indicates a low activity rate for women, which is probably a reflection partly of social attitudes to women in employment in West South Wales, and partly of the fact that there are fewer jobs for women than women to fill them. The high male rate and the wide disparity between areas should be treated with caution. There is a considerable flow of workers between exchange areas and consequently the relationship between geographical areas may be misleading.

The male activity rate in the region in 1961 was 80·9, and since this was a year of low unemployment in the region (2·6 per cent) it may be reasonable to assume that if the level of demand for labour remains high over the next decade the male activity rate will remain around its 1961 level. On this basis and accepting the population projection of 485,360 for 1981 (Table 9.7) if the sex ratio and age distribution were to remain constant we can predict a male working population of 142,000 in 1981.

Although this is only a crude estimate which covers the total male population aged fifteen and over and applies the same activity rate to the entire group, it is likely that the trend towards a declining male employee population noted above (Table 9.12) will, if activity rates remain at 1961 levels, be checked by 1981.

The future female working population has been calculated on the assumption that the activity rate will rise to 30·0 over the next decade thus bringing it closer to the rates for the more prosperous regions, and following the trend towards increasing female employment.[7] On this basis the 1981 female working population would be in the region of 58,000.[8]

Table 9.14   West South Wales activity rates 1961

Area		Neath and Swansea Valleys	Industrial Carmarthenshire	Coast	Total— West South Wales
*Home population aged 15 and over**					
Male		52,788	34,078	85,049	171,915
Female		55,980	36,974	91,419	184,373
	Total	108,768	71,052	176,468	356,288
Insured employees†					
Male		47,310	29,770	62,080	139,160
Female		15,104	8,608	23,422	47,134
	Total	62,414	38,378	85,502	186,294
Activity rates					
Male		89·6	87·4	73·0	80·9
Female		27·0	23·3	25·6	25·6
	Total	57·7	54·1	48·5	52·4

* *Source:* Census of Population of England and Wales, 1961.
† *Source:* Ministry of Labour Insured Employee Statistics, 1961

The prospects for
industrial use:
a study of land use in a
regional context

Future employment prospects

It has already been noted that the two dominant industries in terms of regional employment are still metal manufacturing and mining. Although the steel industry's reorganization has re-employed many of the workers from the old works it seems likely that steel in West South Wales has already reached its employment peak. The effect of the increased substitution of capital for labour in the steel and coal industries is likely to be considerable, particularly in the inland areas. Employment in services and construction will probably continue to rise while incomes and the general level of demand continue to do so. The other industries which have attracted capital into the region in the past ten years have tended to be capital intensive, chemicals or petroleum products for example, and these have a relatively small effect on new employment other than the construction industry.

If these trends towards greater capital intensity continue in the region, as they are likely to do, employment particularly in the manufacturing and service sectors will have to increase somewhat faster than it has done in the past to keep pace with the anticipated increase in the population of working age. It is probable that some 10–15,000 new jobs will be needed in the next fifteen to twenty years simply to accommodate the anticipated future working population, which is likely to be in the region of 200,000. However, this estimate of the jobs required takes no account of any check on present migration trends nor of variations in the employment pattern of particular industries, and it may be that if there are great changes in the organization of labour at major local works the number of new jobs may need to be considerably greater than 15,000.

A sample survey of postwar manufacturing industry in West South Wales

In March 1963 a survey was undertaken in an attempt to find out as much as possible about firms in manufacturing industry which had set up works in the region since 1945. The main concern was to discover firms' motives for coming to the region, the nature of the firms and their subsequent experiences. A questionnaire was sent to 79 firms of which 44, or 55·7 per cent, replied. The most significant bias in the sample was the relatively high representation of larger employers; from this we can assume that although our information related to 55·7 per cent of establishments it probably related to a rather higher proportion of employment in postwar firms. The industry least adequately represented in the sample was clothing, which tends to be a large employer of female labour. However, the other industrial groups which employ women (mainly textiles and food) were well represented. Although, in the sample, engineering represented only 15·9 per cent of the firms whilst in the total population of postwar firms in the region they represent 21·5 per cent, this was mainly due to the fact that many small engineering works did not reply to the questionnaire.

The following paragraphs summarize the information which is more fully described in the Report on which this chapter is based.[9]

Area

Of the 44 establishments in the sample, 15 came from Swansea, 9 from Llanelli, 7 from Loughor, 7 from Port Talbot, 4 from the Neath Valley and 2 from the Swansea Valley.

A sample survey of
postwar manufacturing
industry in West South
Wales

Swansea not only had the highest number of establishments but, as might be expected, also had the most diversified industry. Most of the Swansea firms had come to the area in the immediate postwar period as a result partly of the high level of postwar demand and partly as the result of Government policy. However, the Llanelli area had a fairly high concentration (25 per cent) in engineering and also showed a more continuous rate of incoming firms. The Port Talbot area was fairly accurately represented by a high concentration of metal manufacture and chemicals. On the whole the survey showed that the valleys and the Loughor areas were not attracting new firms despite the existence of certain Development Districts.

Industry

By far the most highly represented industry was metal and metal manufacture, and 12 out of the 44 firms were in this group; 7 were in Engineering, 4 in Vehicles, 4 in Food, 4 in Chemicals, 4 in Textiles, Footwear and Clothing and the remainder were in a variety of other industries. It is obvious that West South Wales still attracts establishments in the field for which the region is known to have experienced labour and services. Despite the fact that many of the incoming metal works do not use local raw materials they are attracted by the resources of a specialized region.

Size of Establishments

Seventeen of the establishments employed 101–250 persons and twelve employed over 500 persons. Of the remainder five employed 1–25, three employed 26–50, two employed 51–100, and five employed 251–500. These figures confirm the point made above that the smaller establishments are least well represented in the sample.

Type of employment

The sex ratio in the sample was 5 male to 1 female. This compares with 2:1 for Britain and 3:1 for West South Wales in 1961. This is largely a reflection of the position of the steel industry in the region (metal manufacturing accounts for over 70 per cent of the employment in the sample) which employs mainly men. If the three major steel and tinplate works are excluded the ratio is reduced to 1·5:1. Of the females, most were unskilled workers and they mostly worked in Swansea. The Swansea Industrial Estate showed a very high employment of women, and it seems likely that, metal works apart, the postwar firms reflect a new development which has not yet made a major impression on the overall industrial structure of the region.[10] Certainly, as is mentioned further on, the presence of pools of female labour was a positive inducement to many firms in the postwar years.

Twenty-seven of the forty-four establishments brought key workers with them from outside, most of them also providing or getting local authorities to provide housing. Twenty-seven of the firms ran apprenticeship schemes, but most of these were of fairly recent origin so that there was little evidence for assessing their effectiveness. There was, however, among the employers a fairly widespread dissatisfaction with the present apprenticeship methods, largely because many apprentices leave on completion and go to other firms which have not trained their own skilled workers. In this sense some firms felt that

The prospects for
industrial use:
a study of land use in a
regional context

they were merely training men for the benefit of other firms. Only one firm stated that discouragement by a trade union had dissuaded them from pressing on with an apprenticeship scheme. There was a fairly general feeling that the five-year apprenticeship scheme needed revision in the light of modern requirements. Many firms were training semi-skilled workers 'on the job', thus reducing their dependence on skilled labour to a minimum.

There was a relatively low representation of technical staff and this was probably partly because few of the establishments were science based but also because many of them, being branches or subsidiaries, have their research or technical departments in other establishments outside the region. Both numerically and proportionately, the metal manufacturing and metal goods industries employed the highest ratio of technical to other staff.

Of the thirty-six firms willing to predict their future employment over the next five years, twenty-one predicted no increase, nine some increase, two a decrease and four were uncertain. The firms seemed to do remarkably little forward planning towards either expansion or contraction, but it would appear that some firms are unwilling to impart information about this lest future difficulties make them seem inefficient in forward planning. Many of the branch establishments had their questionnaires filled in at head office, and undoubtedly some of the local managers who answered the questionnaire genuinely did not know what the future policy was since decisions were taken elsewhere.

Status of the establishment

Of the forty-four establishments, fourteen were independent and thirty were branches or subsidiaries. Of the latter, most had head offices in London or South-East England. The degree of autonomy of the firms varied widely. Most of the branches had control over appointments of operatives and a number over appointments of staff. Production and buying also tended to be decentralized while sales and broad policy were more often controlled from head office.

Government aid

Twenty-nine of the forty-four establishments had received no positive financial inducement to come to West South Wales. (Of these some were simply refused permission to develop elsewhere without being positively encouraged to come to this region.) Of the rest, most had come to one of the factories managed by the Industrial Estates Management Corporation. Other forms of aid varied widely from Government advance factories to straight financial loans or subsidized rents. Only one establishment received a rating relief from the local authority.

The location decision

Thirty-seven of the forty-four establishments had not been refused permission to develop elsewhere, and this at first suggests that West South Wales was their first choice. It should, however, be borne in mind that at the time when many firms wanted to expand, between 1945 and 1950, there was such a rigid restriction on expansion in the congested areas that many firms, believing that they would be refused, probably never bothered to apply for Industrial Development Certificates in those areas. The three 'traditional' motives

A sample survey of
postwar manufacturing
industry in West South
Wales

for location of industry (availability of labour, proximity to raw materials and proximity to potential markets) figure high in firms' reasons for coming to the region. Another important factor in bringing firms into the region was the immediate availability of suitable premises, and it seems likely that it is in providing readily adaptable factory premises that a region is most likely to compete successfully with others for incoming industry, other things being equal.

In looking at reasons why firms had chosen their particular sites it was found that the immediate availability of premises was the most often cited reason. That is, even if a firm had decided to come to a region for some other reason, such as the proximity of markets, it may well be attracted to a particular site within the region by the availability of premises. The other two main reasons given for site choice were good access roads and proximity to another particular plant or factory. Importance is also attached to the need for adequate space for expansion of factory premises and for some degree of assurance that when additional space is necessary planning permission will be granted.

The advantages and disadvantages of West South Wales

In the main, the advantages of the region which the firms experienced were seen to be similar to the factors which attracted them in the first place. Apart from the points mentioned above, particular mention was made of the availability of female labour and the high visual amenity of the region.

The disadvantages consisted mainly of transport and labour problems. The first ranged over all the transport and communications problems, some specifically related to transport facilities and distance from head office and from the market, but mostly there was a general feeling of 'remoteness'. Overall, the impression was that the problems of being so far from the main centres were such as would only be partly met by any specific improvements in transport arrangements. The firms which had used initiative and skill in providing their own transport arrangements still found that the general difficulties of distance existed. This can probably be largely overcome only by the growth and development of the area, and also of the East South Wales area, so that services can be brought nearer. Nevertheless it seems likely that if a cost is put on managerial time and energy spent on getting round the communications problems in these regions away from the main centres, the figure of 4 per cent extra transport costs cited by W. Lutterell is likely to be an underestimate.[11]

Labour problems are closely related to the general problem of distance. Firms have found that there is a shortage of skilled and especially of managerial staff, and that distance from the main industrial centres makes it difficult to persuade skilled personnel to come into the region. West South Wales may not be at present as short of skilled workers as many other regions, but such a shortage would develop if there were to be much influx of new industry. At present many of the postwar firms are still 'pioneering', in that the particular skills of their industry are new to a region which is traditionally associated with heavy metal and coal. It is likely that skills in techniques new to the region will emerge—as indeed has been happening. Meanwhile some firms have been able to take advantage of the traditional specialized skills which are available.

The prospects for
industrial use:
a study of land use in a
regional context

Conclusions

For successful competition with certain other regions West South Wales needs to be able to offer some form of financial inducement to incoming industry. Once establishments have come here they seem, by and large, to operate successfully and to overcome most of the problems presented by their location. There was widespread satisfaction with labour relations and those firms with a large measure of ingenuity in their management seem able to cope with the remoteness of the region. Such positive advantages as there are, however, seem largely to be personal rather than business advantages and the region does not seem to have really succeeded in showing that it has any advantage over the other regions that also have surplus labour. More attention should be paid in the future to attracting firms which can exploit the particular skills which are still available in the region and which are not too heavily reliant on outside markets, head office links or outside labour.[12]

The Lower Swansea Valley as an industrial site

The previous chapters have shown that the Lower Swansea Valley is centrally located in a region of nearly half a million people. The northern part of the Project area is bordered by the east–west Neath Road, and it is well placed as a 'bridge' between the valleys which are losing population and the coastal belt which is relatively thriving. The provision of regional transportation as described in Chapter 7 would enable the northern part of the Lower Valley usefully to attract workers from the eastern part of Industrial Carmarthenshire and from the Neath and Swansea Valleys. At the same time the valley, if developed, would widen the area of influence of the coastal belt and is well placed as a centre for distribution of goods and services both east and west. The industrial development of the Project area would have two main effects on the region. First, it would provide immediate employment for the areas of high unemployment; secondly, because of the central position of the Project area, the development could make an important contribution to the economic growth of the region, and if the development were part of a long-term regional plan, many of the problems associated with providing future employment might be overcome.

The demand for industrial land in the Swansea area

The land mainly available for extensive industrial development consists of the Fforestfach Trading Estate, the rough grazing land on the perimeter of the County Borough boundary and the Lower Swansea Valley. There are also isolated sites, mainly in Cwmbwrla and along the North Dock and Jersey Marine. The fact that the rough grazing land is outside the County Borough boundary becomes significant when the rate revenue from any large-scale industrial undertaking is considered. Within the Borough boundary the Lower Swansea Valley is competing directly with the Fforestfach Trading Estate for incoming new industry on any large scale. Of the 47 acres of land currently developed on the Industrial Estate, 63 per cent was developed between 1946 and 1950; this was the period during which postwar expansion coincided with tight Government control over location of industry. Between 1951 and 1959 only a further 14·1 per cent of the 1963 acreage was brought into use—mostly by extensions to existing buildings. Between 1960 and 1963 much more development took place, but this was partly due to a change in Board of Trade policy towards the Estate. The Board began selling their land freehold and permitting non-manufacturing development there. It is this distribution and storage use which has dominated recent growth at the Estate, and if this trend continues, it would appear that the available prepared sites (23 acres in 1963) will have been used up by 1970.

Within the West South Wales region there is a considerable acreage of land either earmarked for industrial use in development plans or regarded by Planning Authorities as suitable for industrial use. This is summarized in Appendix I at the end of the chapter. An objective evaluation of this land using standard criteria could well strengthen the case for the development of the Swansea Valley's coastal sites as a growth area for the region.

The economic development of the Lower Swansea Valley

The sample survey described above showed that one of the main needs of incoming industrialists was for immediately available suitable premises. This is confirmed by the experience that Government financed factories built ahead of demand tend, if they are standardized, to be fairly readily leased. Businesses need to move quickly and with minimum disruption to production. This is exemplified by the occupation of a disused Ministry of Supply factory by Addis Ltd in 1964 and by the movement of Fords to the former Prestcold factory at Jersey Marine. This need is particularly marked in the case of small firms whose expansion may be related to a specific order or contract for which the delays involved in a long period of construction are not practical. Similarly, small but expanding firms are frequently reluctant to tie up capital, which is much needed for plant and equipment, in property. Such firms create demand for premises of 6–7,000 sq ft with space for expansion.[13]

The Lower Swansea Valley Project is considering how to regenerate the derelict land before it is economically ripe for development. It is directly concerned therefore not only with current demand, and it seems likely that within the next ten years or so there will be a demand for larger sites for manufacturing premises. This demand will of course be much influenced by Government plans for the region.

In the light of these considerations it is suggested that an industrial estate could be established in the Lower Valley, with premises constructed for letting. The area selected for such a development is the 'Duffryn Tip', Plots 19, 18 and 16. This consists of 41 acres of levelled tip, 17 acres of marshy land and 38 acres on part of which there stands the Wales Gas Board plant and buildings. The area was chosen because it is easily accessible from the existing main road (A48) and is already partly served by a 24-ft carriageway. It is also reasonably level and is served by an existing railway line; being close to the A48 means that cost of services into the site is likely to be lower than on some of the more central sites and gives it good interregional communications. Development of the site can be adapted to the long-term planning framework: so road and earthworks can be undertaken without jeopardizing a long-term plan. A further feature of the site is the existence to the north of at least a further 50 acres which could be brought into use if required. Although this area is separated from the Duffryn Tip by the main road, the proposed Morriston by-pass will relieve much of the congestion on this road so that the connection between the two sites need not be unduly interfered with, especially if the present A48 is regarded as a service road to the new industrial area.

The prospects for
industrial use:
a study of land use in a
regional context

Expenditure on reclamation

It should be emphasized that the cost data relating to the Duffryn Tip Site, although as accurate as could be obtained, is only an estimate. Acquisition costs, for example, are limited by the fact that little derelict land has been exchanged in recent years, and costs of services are difficult to estimate when the precise nature of the manufacturing industry which may use the premises is unknown; the nature of the demand for electricity, for example, will affect the cost of the installation of the service. However, generally the estimates of costs given are a useful indication of the nature of the investment problem.

Land acquisition

There is considerable variation in the value of the sites between those in the Lower Valley which have roads and services and those which do not. Values may vary between approximately £100 per acre for derelict land in the centre of the valley floor and approximately £3,000 per acre for land which, though it may have derelict buildings on it, has good foundations and a road access. The freehold interests of Plots 19 and 18 have been estimated at £250 per acre and that of Plot 16 (excluding buildings) at £1,000 per acre. These values are similar to those of such adjacent land as has been exchanged in recent years.

Earthworks

The report on *Soil Mechanics and Foundation Engineering*[14] suggests an average figure of 7s per cubic yard for conventional hardcore excavation with a digger, transport over an average haul of 1–1½ miles, and simple compaction. This figure is adopted in this chapter but the qualification should be made that where there are large fused boulders in the hardcore the cost might be up to 3s per cubic yard higher.

Roads

Road costs in this Chapter are based on the estimate given by Mr Worrall. That is, road surfacing costs are assumed to be £20 per foot for a 30-ft spine road and £12 per ft for a 24-ft estate road.[15]

Services

As stated above a figure for service costs is difficult to arrive at until the layout of an estate and the user industries are known. However, an overall estimate of £10,000 to cover installation of electricity, gas, water and foul water drainage has been made. This excludes possible trade effluent and assumes foul water drainage at a cost of £200 per acre. It cannot be sufficiently emphasized that these costs are in a sense hypothetical since they are based on a 'typical' pattern of industrial diversification on the estate.

The economics of establishing a ten-acre industrial estate

No attempt has been made to examine the possibilities of establishing industrial premises on the entire Duffryn Tip. Only ten factories of 7,000 sq ft each, containing a minimum of internal fittings, are envisaged; each factory would be located on one acre so that there would be room for expansion if necessary. Estimates are based on local costs excluding fees which suggest that each could be built at approximately £2 per sq ft, which is the figure adopted in this chapter.

A number of alternative reclamation schemes are possible for establishing ten factories on ten acres of the Duffryn Tip site.

Option 1   The whole of Plots 16, 18 and 19 (refer to base map) might be reclaimed, providing roads and levelling as proposed by Worrall in his Plan A.[16] This would involve the acquisition of 96 acres but provision of services for only 70,000 sq ft of factory space. That is the ten-acre development would be undertaken as part of an overall plan for the 96-acre site.

Table 9.15 shows the total capital cost of a development of this kind.

Table 9.15   Reclamation cost of 96 acres (Plots 16, 18, 19) with ten acres on Plot 19 serviced for industrial use

Earthworks: 500,000 yd³ at 7s		£170,000
Roads	(as estimated by Worrall on Plan A)	£70,000
Land	(at £1,000 per acre for Plot 16, and at £250 per acre for Plots 19 and 18)	£52,500
Services	(for 10 × 7,000 ft² factory premises)	£10,000
		£302,500

Option 2   Alternatively, only the necessary ten acres might be reclaimed leaving the rest of the site, that is the remainder of Plot 19 plus all of Plots 18 and 16, for future reclamation. Details of the levels in three possible alternative ways which this might be done are shown in Appendix 2 to this chapter. Basically the differences between the three alternatives for reclaiming the ten-acre site in isolation are as follows: first, to develop in such a way that the ultimate levels for Worrall's Plan A remain so that at some future date overall development could accord with that Plan; secondly, to develop in such a way that future development of the remaining 86 acres would be possible though different from those outlined by Worrall; thirdly, to develop in the centre of the tip, thus incurring minimum earth-moving costs in the short run but involving at least partial future wastage of roads when the remaining 86 acres are developed.

Table 9.16 (*a*), (*b*), and (*c*) indicates these different possibilities in terms of capital costs.

Table 9.16 (*a*)   Reclamation cost of ten acres on Plot 19 (to 30 ft a.o.d.)

Earthworks: 79,640 yd³ at 7s	£27,800
Roads—Embankment	£10,000
Surfacing (800 yd of 30 ft at £20 per ft)	£48,000
(300 yd of 24 ft at £12 per ft)	£10,800
Services	£10,000
Land: ten acres at £250 per acre	£2,500
	£109,100

(*b*)   Reclamation cost of ten acres on Plot 19 (to 40 ft a.o.d.)

Earthworks: 41,400 yd³ at 7s	£14,500
Roads—Embankment	£13,000
Surfacing (as in (*a*) above)	£58,800
Services	£10,000
Land	£2,500
	£98,800

The prospects for
industrial use:
a study of land use in a
regional context

(c) Reclamation cost of ten acres on Plot 19 with minimum levelling but disregarding all future developments

Earthworks: 2,800 yd^3 at 7s	£1,000
Roads—Embankment	£13,000
Surfacing (as in (a) above)	£58,800
Services	£10,000
Land	£2,500
	£85,300

Feasibility of the investment

The possibility of a developer investing the sums required for the various reclamation schemes outlined above depends largely on the value of the land after it has been reclaimed. There is no published data on this, but through interviews and knowledge of the local land market it is estimated that the land might be worth between £1,000 and £2,000 per acre freehold with roads but no services. This means that under the first alternative scheme, shown in Table 9.15, the real net cost of the ten-acre reclamation would be the difference between the £300,000 it would cost to reclaim the 96 acres and what the developer could obtain by selling the other 86 acres which are reclaimed with it. Thus, at reclaimed value of between £1,000 and £2,000 per acre, the net cost is between £214,000 and £128,000. This compares with figures of £109,100, £98,800 and £85,300 under three other alternatives shown in Tables 9.16 (a), (b) and (c).

The amount which a developer would consider it feasible to invest will depend on the amount he can charge for letting his buildings and on the rate of return which he expects or requires on his total investment. Table 9.17 shows, for example, that if the market is 4s per sq ft a developer who incurs building costs of £2 per sq ft and expects a return of 8 per cent would be prepared to invest up to £35,000 in ten acres of land. If, however, he expects only 6 per cent he would be prepared to invest up to £93,333 in the same amount of land. This table can be used to indicate how much developers could afford to invest if different amounts of rent are charged. For instance if the rent is 3s per sq ft a developer wanting an 8 per cent return would not undertake the development unless he was given the land and a subsidy of £8,750.

If, as local evidence would suggest, the market rent is in the region of 4s per sq ft, the investment shown in Table 9.16 (c) yields a net return of just over 6 per cent and those in Table 9.16 (a) and (b) a return of just under 6 per cent.

The investment described in Table 9.15 would yield a return of about 5½ per cent if the net cost was the minimum of £128,000, but if the net cost was as high as the assumed maximum of £214,000 the return would be just below 4 per cent. A developer wanting, for example, 8 per cent would not embark on the alternatives shown in Tables 9.16 (a), (b) and (c), unless the rent was between 5 and 6 shillings per sq ft, and in order to embark on the alternatives shown in Table 9.15 (at the assumed minimum net cost) the rent would have to be over 6 shillings per sq ft.

Finally it should be stressed that the real net cost of the ten acres chosen for development under the first alternative depends fundamentally on the value of the other 86 acres. If on the one hand the 86 acres proves to be in no demand at all, then the cost of the ten-acre estate will be the entire cost of approximately £300,000. But if the land after reclamation is found to be in particular demand, then the net cost of the ten acres could be lower than £128,000. Moreover if a developer embarked on reclaiming the whole 96 acres, his total costs of developing the land after the first ten acres will be lower since most of the roads and levelling will already have been provided.

Table 9.17   The amount which the developer could afford to pay for reclaiming land for a ten-acre industrial estate*

Expected rate of return %	3	4	5	6	8	10
Rent per sq ft (shillings)						
1	−33,333	−52,500	−70,000	−81,667	−96,250	−105,000
2	+93,333	+35,000	0	−23,333	−52,500	−70,000
3	+210,000	+122,500	+70,000	+35,000	−8,750	−35,000
4	+326,667	+210,000	+140,000	+93,333	+35,000	0
5	+443,333	+297,500	+210,000	+151,667	+78,750	+35,000
6	+560,000	+385,000	+280,000	+210,000	+122,500	+70,000
7	+676,667	+472,500	+350,000	+268,333	+166,250	+105,000
8	+793,333	+560,000	+420,000	+326,667	+210,000	+140,000

* Given 1 Cost of buildings (£140,000)
   2 Market rent of land and buildings
   3 Rate of return on investment

Conclusions

The adoption of the area between Llanelli and Port Talbot as a 'growth area' would help the development of the Lower Swansea Valley as part of an overall regional plan. West South Wales is a region which though not declining as fast as the eastern valleys of South Wales is not growing at the rate of the Cardiff and Newport region. The unemployment rate in West South Wales remains at twice the national average, indicating that there is need for further development in the region. Although the valleys, and parts of Carmarthenshire, clearly are communities which have an important part to play in the economic life of the region, the wisdom of past policy of trying to preserve the older valley communities as industrial as well as residential areas needs to be re-examined.

The new legislation introduced in the Government White Paper *Investment Incentives* (Cmnd 2874) replaces the development districts with new development areas. The whole of the West South Wales region is included in the Welsh development area, and this recognition of the relevant economic circumstances which combine to create regional economic units should improve economic expansion in the area. However, the selection of certain 'growth areas' within the overall development area remains desirable.

West South Wales needs better employment opportunities for two reasons: first to prevent further outward migration which is only just being compensated for by natural increase; secondly to stimulate growth and encourage inward migration and greater expansion of current economic activity. For this to happen a deliberate policy for growth is needed. In the main, firms coming into the region should be labour intensive as far as possible, with a high potential for growth on a national level; similarly they should take account of the considerable pool of female labour available. It is desirable that firms should

The prospects for
industrial use:
a study of land use in a
regional context

be encouraged to develop their central organization here so that the heavy reliance on communications with head office can be removed. If West South Wales is to compete successfully for new industry with other areas, certain specifically local advantages should be exploited, particularly local skills and raw materials. The establishment of a specialized complex of firms with linked processes, such as those dependent on steel sheet, would meet several of these requirements. Already in parts of the region small industrial complexes are developing, such as the petrochemical works around the Llandarcy oil refinery and the engineering works in Llanelli.[17]

If urgent action is taken to improve the infrastructure of the region, such as its communications and its docks, and if the industrial development of part of the Lower Swansea Valley is included in future proposals for the economic growth of South-West Wales, there is every chance that the comprehensive development proposals suggested in Chapter 11 will be carried through. Previous experience has shown that Government has not shrunk from providing very high cost employment. It is suggested here that if the overall pattern of regional growth is considered somewhat more carefully than it has been in the past, the development of the Lower Swansea Valley might not be such a costly operation as it has been considered in the past.

Appendix I

Potential Industrial Land in West South Wales in 1966 (acres)

Local Authority Areas (West South Wales)	Category A*	Category B†	Class 1	Class 2
Ammanford Urban District	—	86	46	40
Burry Port Urban District	—	46	46	—
Cwmamman Urban District	9	11	0	11
Gower Rural District	—	26	—	—
Kidwelly Municipal Borough	—	60	60	—
Llanelli Municipal Borough	—	318	318	—
Llanelli Rural District	—	1,066	550	516
Llwchwr Urban District	92	—	—	—
Neath Municipal Borough	78	307	—	—
Neath Rural District	786	311	—	—
Pontardawe Rural District	75	26	—	—
Port Talbot Municipal Borough	584	—	—	—
Swansea County Borough	1,040	1,490	—	—
Ystradgynlais Rural District	—	70	14	56
Total acres	2,664	3,817	1,034	623

* Category A. Land allocated and/or approved for industrial use but not developed.
† Category B. Land considered suitable for industrial use but not allocated or approved.
      Class 1   Land in Category B with roads and services suitable for immediate industrial use.
      Class 2   Land in Category B requiring preparation to make it suitable for industrial use.

Appendix 2   Levels for alternative sites

Alternative I

The site would be levelled to the levels recommended by Worrall in Plan A. That is in a plateau rising from the Neath Road (A48) to 30 ft a.o.d. on the Duffryn Tip.

Alternative 2

(*a*) Ten acres of Duffryn Tip would be levelled to 30 ft a.o.d. in accordance with Worrall's Plan A. This would mean that even though the overall development of the 96-acre site might not be undertaken until some future date, the ultimate levels could remain and the estate would accord with an overall plan.

(*b*) The estate would be located at the point on the Duffryn Tip close to the terminal point of the proposed new road. The ten-acre site would be levelled to 40 ft a.o.d., which is approximately the present level. This would involve extra embankment costs but lower earth-moving costs than (*a*). However, future development of the 100-acre site might then have to take account of different levels from those planned for by Worrall.

(*c*) It would be possible to locate the estate centrally on the tip for minimum earth-moving costs. This would be at approximately present levels but future development would involve wastage of much of the roads located in this way.

References

1. See Glamorgan County Council Industrial Survey, 1959 (unpublished).
2. These data refer only to insured employees in firms employing more than five persons and do not include self-employed persons.
3. The industrial classification is that used by the Ministry of Labour Standard Industrial Classification, 1958 (revised). Since the S I C was changed in the middle 1950s, some adjustments have been made to the 1951 figures, but these do not make any significant difference.
4. 1938 and 1948 figures are derived from T. Brennan, E. W. Cooney and H. Pollins, *Social Change in South West Wales*, Watts, 1954, pp. 34–5.
5. See National Economic Development Council, *Conditions Favourable to Faster Growth*, H.M.S.O., 1963, pp. 16–17.
6. Four important qualifications about activity rates must be made: (1) The student population of an area acts to increase the home population of an area but is not reflected in the insured employee data. Hence a university town will have a relatively lower activity rate than one with no student population. (2) The age structure of the population affects the activity rate, so that estimates of future population of work age should be related to prospective changes in the age distribution. (3) Since insured employee statistics do not include self-employed persons, areas having a high proportion of self-employed persons are likely to show a relatively lower activity rate. (4) The figures, of necessity, compare civilian employees to total population including the armed forces, because civilian population is not available by local authority area and age. For all these reasons care must be taken in drawing conclusions based on interregional and intraregional variations in activity rates.
7. See *Ministry of Labour Gazette*, October 1963, p. 389, and N.E.D.C., *Conditions Favourable to Faster Growth*, p. 16.
8. The assumptions were as follows:
    1. 1981 total population: 485,000.
    2. Sex ratio: 1,047 females per 1,000 males.
    3. Age distribution: males, 75 per cent aged fifteen and over; females, 78 per cent aged fifteen and over.
    4. Activity rates: 80·9 males = 142,000; 30·0 females = 58,000.
9. For more detailed information see S. H. Spence, *The Prospects for Industrial Use of the Lower Swansea Valley* (Study Report 6).

The prospects for
industrial use:
a study of land use in a
regional context

10. In 1963 the Swansea Industrial Estate at Fforestfach employed 37·5 per cent males, 62·5 per cent females, whilst the Swansea Employment Exchange (including the Industrial Estate) showed a ratio of 65·8 per cent males and 34·2 per cent females. This would imply that the newer firms, located on the Estate, have a quite different employment pattern from the longer-established firms.

11. See in particular W. Luttrell, *Factory Location and Industrial Movement*, National Institute of Economic and Social Research, 1962, Vol. I, p. 322.

12. For further details on the relationship between managerial efficiency and decentralization, see R. B. Heflebower, 'Decentralization in large enterprises', *Journal of Industrial Economics*, Vol. IV, pp. 7–23.

13. I am grateful to the managers of the Penclawdd Industrial Estate for their helpfulness in answering my enquiries and giving information.

14. H. G. Clapham, H. E. Evans and F. E. Weare, *The Soil Mechanics and Foundation Engineering Survey of the Lower Swansea Valley Project Area* (Study Report 5).

15. It is likely that roadway costs which include also footway foundation and surfacing, kerbing, lighting and surface water drainage, will amount to £17 per lin. ft over 50 ft overall, and £15 per lin. ft over 40 ft overall.

16. See R. D. Worrall, *Report on Transportation and Physical Planning in the Lower Swansea Valley* (Study Report 2), 1963, also Chapter 7 of this book.

17. See S. H. Spence, 'Toward a new regional policy for South West Wales' in *South Wales in the Sixties*, ed. G. Manners, Pergamon Press, 1964, pp. 185–98.

18. *Investment Incentives*, Cmd 2874, January 1966.

Authorship

This chapter was written by Susanne H. Spence.

The author acknowledges the debt of gratitude she owes to Professor E. Victor Morgan, R. O. Roberts and D. E. L. Thomas of the Department of Economics, University College of Swansea. They have given much time and patience in assisting the research which went into this chapter: Mr R. O. Roberts, in particular, read the various drafts of the Study Report of which this chapter is a summary.

The author also acknowledges the advice and encouragement received from K. J. Hilton, Director of the Lower Swansea Valley Project, and the assistance of Mrs Cross and Mrs Nuttall, the Project's secretarial staff.

Help has been received from too many local and central Government officials, private individuals and local industrialists for these to be listed individually. To all those who patiently answered inquiries, filled in questionnaires and offered advice, warm thanks are extended.

10 Visual improvement

In the past it has been the ugliness of the eastern approaches to Swansea that has prompted schemes for its redevelopment. Residential land in the County Borough has not been in short supply and unemployment has not been high enough to attract Government help to provide sites for new industry. Up to the present, as we saw in Chapter 3, statutory provision for dealing with derelict land has been rigidly related to the criterion of the relief of unemployment. The ugliness of the land has not so far been sufficient to justify its redemption and yet until it is visually redeemed it will remain unwanted. Ugly land is repulsive, it is avoided and neglected and this encourages further neglect. Rubbish is dumped on it, and because it is unwanted it can be had cheaply, and therefore tends to be used by small insubstantial enterprises—the car stripper and cement block maker—whose failures leave the land more unsightly still. It is a vicious circle.

The Project has devoted a considerable effort in an attempt to break this circle. Our resources have been small compared with those that will ultimately be needed to deal with the whole area and so we have confined ourselves to demonstrations which have tried to illustrate the importance of improving the visual quality of the landscape. Some of these have grown larger than we had originally intended. They are concerned with two aspects of ugliness, derelict buildings and bare land.

The demolition of derelict buildings

In 1961 a visitor to the Lower Swansea Valley would have noticed a succession of abandoned and derelict stone and brick buildings, strung out for some two miles on either side of the main railway approach to Swansea. During the last war it is said that people took these to be part of the bomb damage to the town centre; they were, in fact, the 'natural remains' of old copper and zinc smelting works which had closed in the thirties. They had a sad if not savage appearance which was made more striking by their desolate surroundings. (Most of the sites are shown on the base map in the end pocket.)

The removal of these structures, which occupied about 14 acres altogether, required bulldozers and other mechanical plant which the Project did not possess. Fortunately Swansea was then the Headquarters of the 53rd Divisional Engineers (T.A.). Good training areas especially for the handling of mechanical plant and for demolitions were not easy to find and the Unit's Commanding Officer appreciated that not only could the Regiment obtain valuable training close to its headquarters, but this could make an important contribution towards the Project's efforts and ultimately to the redevelopment of the whole Lower Swansea Valley. In this he was supported by the Chief Engineer, Western Command, and by the Divisional Commander.

The Regiment was first deployed on demolition tasks in February 1962, and has been involved since that time. Buildings have been levelled by bulldozer and winch and stacks demolished with explosives. Weekend camps were arranged and later other engineer units, both Territorial and Regular, were brought in for training periods in the valley. In this way, during the past four years, the standing buildings have been removed on five sites. For their part, the owners of the land helped with their own plant where this was available. A note explaining the operations on these sites is to be found at the end of the chapter (p. 236).

The most complete demonstration of the visual effect of site clearance is provided by Site 3. The *before* and *after* photographs included here show what it has been possible to achieve (Plates 10 and 11).

This site is now four acres of gently sloping meadow, with a copse of young birch trees on a hillock at one end and a hedge on two sides of hawthorn and lodgepole pine. It merges naturally with the future parkland and lake which is a feature of the plan discussed in Chapter 11.

About this time a number of railway buildings, mainly signal boxes, became redundant and were soon reduced by vandals to a ruinous state. With the cooperation of British Rail all these structures were removed. Also during the last four years four sites occupied by obsolete steel and tube works have been cleared by their owners so that the cumulative effect of all this effort by the Project and by private owners together is considerable.

In carrying out this demolition programme we were aware that some of the buildings were of interest particularly to the industrial archaeologist. Care was therefore taken to make a photographic record of the sites before demolition began.

In this unorthodox way it has been possible to make a considerable impression, though the full extent of the change is not easily appreciated. It is difficult without the help of photographs taken before the sites were cleared to realize now how depressing the railway approach to Swansea was in 1962. There are many ruinous industrial buildings scattered throughout Great Britain and it seems that there is nothing to prevent them remaining indefinitely, or indeed to prevent works which are active today from deteriorating and becoming eyesores once they have finally closed down. The Local Planning Authority is powerless to deal with such a situation except by the purchase of the site and the demolition of its buildings. There should, it is felt, be some sanction, whether financial or mandatory, which would oblige the owner of land either to remove or else adequately to maintain the structures on it.

Afforestation

Apart from its derelict buildings, the landscape of the valley was marked by an almost complete absence of trees; its undeveloped sides bore a sparse cover of hardy but visually unattractive grasses which were not wintergreen. It was therefore decided to carry out a demonstration programme of tree planting and grassland improvement which would have a visual effect complementary to the clearance of sites.

The biological nature of this work is fully covered in Chapter 5; here we are primarily concerned with it as a potential catalyst of opinion and of action. Before the smelters arrived, there is evidence from old books, prints and from Welsh place-names themselves that the valley was well wooded. Acorns have been found in profusion in the peat of Llansamlet and there is an old poem which describes the sylvan charms of Hafod, one of the village suburbs on the west bank of the Tawe.[1] [References are given on p. 238.] Heavy and continuous air pollution had destroyed much of this but it seemed that with the closure of the old-type smelting industry, and the consequent lowering of pollution levels in the valley, there was a good chance of re-establishing forest trees in it.

The Project therefore appointed a Conservator to be responsible for planning and carrying out, in association with the Forestry Commission, a considerable but nevertheless largely experimental programme of tree planting. An initial survey revealed that there were large areas of poor quality soil, together with widely scattered smaller areas where soil conditions appeared favourable. Miss Sylvia Crowe was consulted in the early stages and a planting scheme was prepared based on a hypothetical land use plan.

At this stage we could not be sure that some of the planted areas would not eventually be built over, but this risk was reduced as far as possible by choosing the steeper slopes where development would be expensive and therefore be likely to be deferred until the easier sites had been taken up. Even so, as long as there is no comprehensive plan for the valley, the future of all the planting which the Project has initiated must remain uncertain.

As the land to be planted was owned privately, it was felt that the owners should, on principle, bear the cost of labour and materials. The scheme for each site was costed and the owners were asked to cooperate by underwriting the proposals for their own land. Altogether, over £1,500 was subscribed in this way. In view of the experimental nature of the work, the services of the Conservator were not charged for.

The principal areas which have been planted with trees are shown in Figure 5.1. At the time of writing over 100,000 trees have been established on some sixteen sites, totalling over fifty acres. The work has been shared between the Forestry Commission, acting as the Project's Agent, and the Project's Conservator; the former dealing with the large areas of moraine on Plots 36–38 and on Plot 31 (see base map), and the latter with numerous smaller areas which could not be ploughed and were thus unsuitable for large-scale planting techniques. In addition to the trees, the grass on two two-acre plots on the infertile eastern slopes of the valley was developed and improved by cultivation, fertilization and reseeding. This work was carried out by the National Agricultural Advisory Service and is described more fully in Chapter 5. Although it was primarily experimental, the two areas were large enough to be visually effective and were sited with this subsidiary purpose in mind. There is often an advantage in making large-scale vegetation trials visible to the public.

The plough furrows of the Forestry Commission's plantation on the moraine made an early impression on the people who lived around the valley. It seemed to some that the countryside had suddenly returned and although there was little else to show at first, there was something to hope for. The risks were considerable. Apart from the poverty of the soil and the exposed nature of many of the sites, the valley was a wild playground for scores of children from the residential areas surrounding it.

Education

The ruins served as castles and dens, the tips as bicycle switchbacks and the canal was full of sticklebacks. It was a wild and free land where children could quite literally lose themselves. When we first examined the valley we found that the existing vegetation, alder, birch and willow, was being hacked indiscriminately by small boys, and that in the weeks before 5 November much green wood was dragged off for their bonfires.

It was obvious that there was a considerable risk that the new woodlands would be damaged, if not completely destroyed, by the very generation for whom they were planned unless something was done. Protective measures, such as fencing and patrolling, were expensive and because they would be regarded as restrictive they would be resented. The only way it seemed to us was to try to associate the children with what we were trying to do.

There are eight schools within the social survey area defined in Chapter I; four of these are primary schools where the ages of children range from five to eleven and four are secondary schools where the children start when they are eleven years old and leave when they are fifteen or sixteen. Over 2,000 children attend these schools and most of them live around the valley. Since 1962 the Conservator, with the cooperation of the Director of Education and of the head teachers of the schools, has helped to encourage in them a special interest in the Lower Swansea Valley. Illustrative talks and films in the classroom have made the children aware of the importance of afforestation and conservation, both at home and abroad. Out of school, four school forest plots have been started by the children themselves in the Project area and these are being maintained (Plate 12).

In addition, the open spaces on the floor of the valley have been used for field studies, and summer excursions have been organized by the Project to take school parties to Forestry Commission nurseries and forests and to nature reserves.

So far as can be judged, this effort has made the children aware of the purpose of the visual improvement scheme. They know where the trees have been planted, why they have been planted and of the threats to their survival. Losses through vandalism have been relatively small so far; less than 1,000 trees out of over 100,000 planted have been damaged. But constant vigilance is required. One small boy with a box of matches can nullify years of effort. As the trees grow taller the potential loss becomes greater and it will be necessary to arrange a system of voluntary wardens in 1967, especially between March and May and in the autumn when the old grass is dry. There is an agricultural tradition in Wales of burning the rough pastures on the hillsides in the spring, and against this background it is too much to expect boys to resist the temptation to fire the hillsides of the Lower Swansea Valley, even though they have not been grazed within living memory.

Apart from schools in the immediate area, the valley has been used in the teaching of geography, history and biology. A boys' secondary school has made a fibreglass model of it, the sixth forms of secondary schools have carried out a landuse survey of its urban areas and a primary school has prepared an excellent exhibition of its copper-smelting history. During the last four years numerous school and university parties from England and Scotland have included the valley on their itineraries, and students from the Swansea College of Art have used its landscape as a study theme.

For the past two summers, International Voluntary Service has arranged work camps in the Lower Valley in association with the Project. Students from Europe and other parts of the United Kingdom have joined with volunteers from Swansea in spending fourteen days digging planting pits, stone-picking grassed areas to facilitate their mowing, weeding and fertilizing young trees

The visual improvement brought about by all these various efforts has been substantial. They have done much more than demonstrate what is possible. A considerable part of the woodlands in the Land Use Plan which is illustrated in Figure 11.3 have actually been established (Plate 13). The Conservator will remain until 1968 to look after them with the help of volunteers, by which time it is hoped that a more permanent arrangement will have been made. Two things are required: first, the amenity areas proposed in the development plan must be acquired by the public authority that will be responsible for the redevelopment of the Lower Swansea Valley and a permanent warden/forester appointed to maintain them; second, the work with local schools must be continued beyond 1968. The importance of outdoor study areas for schools has recently been stressed by a study group set up by the Nature Conservancy[2] and more lately by a conference on education organized as part of the second Countryside in 1970 Conference.[3] The Lower Swansea Valley can provide its schools with a unique field study area and only by keeping up the education programme is it possible to envisage the new woodlands reaching maturity.

Rubbish dumping

It was mentioned at the beginning of the chapter that ugly land attracts ugliness. With the rundown of its industry the derelict sites, particularly those close to residential areas, became dumping grounds for a wide variety of urban and industrial rubbish; old cars, mattresses, builders' rubble and so on. This tipping tended to downgrade the valley whereas all our efforts have been in the other direction. It was pointless trying to remove the ugliness of the past if present-day rubbish was allowed to accumulate. We have therefore tried wherever possible to prevent largescale tipping in the valley by restricting vehicle access through the erection of bollards. This was done with the cooperation of certain landowners and has certainly checked dumping in the controlled areas. Elsewhere tipping has continued but only extreme vigilance has kept it within bounds and the situation will deteriorate quickly with the termination of the Project unless steps are taken to prevent it.

The accumulation of rubbish seems to have been caused partly by the increasing difficulty of disposing of certain industrial and domestic waste materials and partly by the absence of responsibility for keeping the land clean. The Litter Act was not designed to deal with this problem. There appears to be a need for a more effective instrument together with better arrangements for the disposal of rubbish, possibly organized on a Regional scale. It is obvious that during the next decade the quantity of domestic and industrial waste will increase tremendously and unless long-term plans are laid for dealing with it the countryside will be despoiled.

Summary and conclusions

The visual improvement of derelict industrial land is an essential first step in its eventual reclamation for amenity, housing or industry. Such improvement can be made at comparatively small cost as the Project has shown, but the effort made must be sustained and the work done maintained. It therefore needs to be undertaken by a public authority. Amenity organizations such as the Civic Trust should, however, be actively associated with visual improvement schemes; much more can be achieved if public action is supplemented by voluntary help.

Schools and young people should also be involved. There are many ways in which they can take part in a programme of visual reclamation. If the afforestation of derelict land in urban areas is to be successful, vandalism must be defeated. This is a long and difficult task, requiring enthusiasm and patience, and unless children are made partners in such schemes at an early age, the work done will almost certainly be wasted. The education programme and the maintenance of afforested areas in the Lower Swansea Valley therefore need to be continued on a more permanent basis.

The owners of unused buildings should be obliged either to maintain them or to de-molish them. Royal Engineers units can obtain useful training and perform a public service if they are deployed on demolition tasks. The total impression of dereliction is often as much an aggregate of a large number of small eyesores, such as broken fences, the unplanned routeing of overhead lines, untidy verges and unnecessary signs, as a single tip or a derelict building. Owners of land, including public authorities, should be obliged to keep their land in a reasonably tidy condition and sanctions should be imposed, not necessarily by the Courts, to make these effective.

The uncontrolled dumping of rubbish must be stopped. Consideration should be given to replacing or supplementing the Litter Act with more comprehensive legislation. Regional surveys of the arrangements for the collection and disposal of industrial waste products should also be considered.

A note on the clearance of derelict buildings in the Lower Swansea Valley

Site 1

This consisted of three acres adjoining the main London railway line east of the formal Pro-ject boundary, and contained the ruins of the Llansamlet Chemical Works which in 1961 consisted of standing stone and brick walls and a reinforced concrete bunker. After an initial survey of the site by the 53rd (Welsh) Div. R.E. (T.A.), field and plant troops of the Regiment began work on 4 February 1962 and continued at weekends until 25 March. During this period, most of the old structures were removed and the bunker partially collapsed. Owing to the proximity of houses, a series of small explosive charges had to be used which provided useful training but prolonged the operation. The owners of the land intend to complete the clearance themselves.

Site 2

(Plot 28 on the base map.) This consisted of seven acres of the ruins of the Dillwyn Spelter Works. Regimental week-end camps were arranged on 11 and 12 August and one Field Park Squadron demolished the standing walls. The landowners followed up the operation with their own plant and levelled the site.

A note on the clearance
of derelict buildings in
the Lower Swansea
Valley

Site 3

This was a four-acre site, formerly occupied by the Llansamlet Copper and Arsenic Works (Plot 33 on the base map). Here a complete facelift operation was carried through, starting with the demolition of walls and stacks, followed by grading and finally by spreading soil, cultivating, fertilizing, grassing and fencing. To facilitate this complete operation, the owner of the land generously presented the site to the University College of Swansea.

The bulk of the site clearing was carried out by the Western Command Plant Troop under the command of Major T. Goodman, M.B.E., who was also in charge of a training camp on the site for 42 Lancs. Div. District R.E. (T.A.). Demolition, grading and soil spreading was carried out between 12 May and 17 June 1964. In the course of this operation the unit built a short connecting road to the site from the Jersey Road at Cwm to enable subsoil to be brought in from a nearby housing development. This came from the excavation of foundations and was transported to the site by the contractors without charge. In the spring of 1965 the site was cultivated and sown with a mixture of clover and grass. Details of the treatment are given in Chapter 5. In the summer of 1965 the four acres were carefully picked clean of stones to facilitate mechanical cutting. This was done by the members of an International Voluntary Service Work Camp as one of the camp tasks. The site was fenced by the College and, in the winter of 1965/6, a copse of young birch, *Ailanthus* and *Sophora* was planted on it. It is intended that the site should eventually form part of the new woodland park which it is proposed should be developed on Plots 35, 36 and 37 and which is described in Chapter 11.

Site 4

(Plot 24 on the base map.) On the west side of the valley the ruins of the former Morriston Spelter Works were partially cleared in May 1963 by one troop of 48 Squadron Royal Engineers, but the use of explosives in this area had to be discontinued owing to the damage caused to the windows of neighbouring houses.

Site 5

(Plot 59 on the base map.) The ruins of the White Rock Copper, Silver and Lead Works stand on the bend of the river (see Plate 6). Although with some exceptions the buildings were not of great importance, the site was one of the oldest industrial sites in the area and had been occupied more or less continuously since 1737 until the Works closed about 1930. By 1963 the structure had deteriorated badly and there was unfortunately little prospect of its being protected from further spoliation. Many of the old flues had been ripped out and a considerable amount of rubbish had been allowed to accumulate around the walls. After a preliminary inspection of the site by staff of the Royal Commission on Ancient Monuments, it was decided to photograph the buildings and then to demolish them. Preliminary work was carried out in 1963, again by 48 Squadron R.E. but the main clearance was undertaken by 291 Plant Squadron R.E. (T.A.). This Squadron, with its headquarters in Walsall, held a Training Camp in Swansea in May and June 1965, during which the remaining walls were demolished.

In addition to the above five sites, four further sites comprising some thirty acres have been cleared by their owners between 1957 and 1962.

References

1. G. Grant-Francis, *The Smelting of Copper in the Swansea District*, 2nd edition, London, 1881, p. 139.
2. *Science Out of Doors*. Report on the Study Group on Education and Field Biology, Longmans, 1963.
3. The Countryside in 1970 (Second Conference), *Proceedings of the Conference on Education*, The Nature Conservancy, London, 1965. See also Conference Paper No. 5, '*Tree Planting on Derelict Land*'—*an experiment in conservation in the Lower Swansea Valley.*

Authorship and acknowledgements

This chapter was written by K. J. Hilton and B. R. Salter. The authors wish to acknowledge the help given by J. T. Fitzherbert and the Divisional Staff of the Forestry Commission, the Nature Conservancy, International Voluntary Service and the staff of all the schools who are taking part in the scheme.

The Project is also indebted to the Chief Engineer Western Command and to the Commanding Officers and men of the 53rd (Welsh) Division R.E. (T.A.) and the other units mentioned, for making the demolition programme possible and to Colonel R. I. Nicholl of Merthyr Mawr who gave Plot 33 to the College.

11 The use of derelict land in the Lower Swansea Valley

In the preceding chapters we have been concerned with a physical, social and economic study of the valley floor and of its hinterland. This is intended to provide sufficient information on which to base proposals for the future development of the area and in this chapter we attempt to bring together the conclusions reached in these studies in the form of a Land Use Plan. We do this because considerable changes have taken place since 1955 when the Borough Development Plan was prepared. Heavy industry has continued to decline and it is no longer realistic to consider the valley only as an industrial site as that plan proposed. The time has come to take fresh stock of the situation and to suggest what changes in the original scheme are called for. We therefore make a new allocation of the land in the Project area in the hope that this will at least stimulate thought and discussion about the area and eventually assist its redevelopment. In time, at the development stage, detailed architectural and landscape designs will be required, the quality of which will have an important influence on the character of the valley. We naturally hope that when that time comes the best advice possible will be obtained.

Before discussing our proposals we consider that it is necessary to emphasize that the redevelopment of the 650 acres or so of derelict* land in the Project area, and the renewal of the urban fabric around it, cannot be considered in isolation. The valley is not an island, its future depends on the economic health of South-West Wales and especially on Government policies for this region, on the supply and demand for land within the County Borough of Swansea and finally upon the physical condition of the land in the valley itself.

Aspects of the regional situation have been discussed in Chapter 9. It is worth while to remember that in 1964 the unemployment rate for the region was higher than that for Wales as a whole and that its insured male population actually declined. This is significant and is a trend which seems likely to increase in the future, having regard to recent pit closures and to the prospect of redundancy in the steel industry. A White Paper on *Investment Incentives*[1] [references are given on p. 256] makes it clear that the Government is aware of the need to stimulate industrial growth in South-West Wales, and this is to be welcomed. For the first time, selective inducements are proposed. It is too early to judge how effective these will be but there are certain points which should be noted. It is likely that the existing preference of industry to locate in the coastal areas of the region will continue owing to the advantages of labour, services and communications which are to be found there. This being so, the Lower Swansea Valley will have to compete as an

---

* The term 'derelict' used in this chapter means (*a*) land that is so damaged by industrial or other development as to be incapable of beneficial use without treatment; (*b*) land on which development has not been completed, e.g., tipping sites; (*c*) land which may be regarded as derelict from natural causes, e.g., marshland.

The use of derelict land
in the Lower Swansea
Valley

industrial site with other coastal locations where sites are also available and where the local authorities are willing on their own initiative to make them attractive for new industry. (In the boroughs of Port Talbot and Llanelli there are at least 900 acres of land available for industrial development in large and small sites.* Llanelli Borough Council has already purchased, cleared and laid out sites and carried out exploratory borings on potential sites.) Until location policy becomes more selective, not by area as hitherto, but also by industry,[2] such competition must limit the chances of new industrial use of the derelict land in the Lower Swansea Valley.

Situated as it is close to trunk roads and to docks, the valley would benefit from policies aimed at improving the regional road network on the lines suggested in Chapter 7 and from the development of the port as part of the economic plan for the region. Swansea Docks is a regional capital asset of considerable proportions which is certainly underemployed at the present time. (Tonnage handled in 1965 was 79 per cent of the tonnage handled in 1964.)

In the Government's programme for Regional development in the North-East and Central Scotland,[3, 4] emphasis is laid on the selection of growth points within the Regions. It is assumed that in the economic plan for Wales now being prepared there will be a similar emphasis. A planning study for Glamorgan, recently completed by the County Planning Officer, suggests that the Swansea area is a logical growth point for South-West Wales.[5] It is unnecessary here to restate the arguments which lead to this conclusion which we endorse, not because we are concerned with an area within the County Borough but because our own studies lead us in the same direction. It is therefore to be hoped that in the Welsh plan emphasis will be given to industrial location and growth in the Swansea area. The proposals which we make for the use of the Lower Swansea Valley assume that this will be so.

The Project area lies wholly within the Swansea County Borough, and for this reason some attention must also be given to the situation within it. Swansea, with 7·8 persons to the acre, is in area one of the largest County Boroughs in Great Britain. Although much of its 21,600 acres is taken up by commons, cliff land and foreshore, there are still about 2,500 acres of virgin land which is suitable for development. Even if allowance is made for the fact that site development costs in the valley are likely to be less than similar costs on hilly land outside it, there is still no economic pressure to build on derelict land in the valley and no obligation to do so. Furthermore, there are in the County Borough at least 540 acres of land outside the valley which are suitable for industry (and so allocated in the Borough Development Plan), including about 60 acres with services in the industrial estate at Fforestfach. Swansea is a service centre for South-West Wales,[6] and in 1964 three times as many people were employed in service industry in the Borough as were employed in manufacturing industry. Local demand for industrial sites comes from the service sector and is mainly for storage and for distribution. Recent population projections for the County Borough and for the Gower Rural District indicate that between 1961 and 2001 the civilian population will increase by 40,000 with service industry providing most of the new jobs required.[5] The implications of this situation are discussed in Chapter 12.

Finally, the state of the land itself is a serious inhibitor of its use. Most of the components have already been noted in previous chapters, but before we consider the development plan it will be helpful to restate them briefly. They are:

---

* See Appendix I, p. 228.

The use of derelict land in the Lower Swansea Valley

1 Multiple ownership, diversity of use, the production of industrial waste.
2 Lack of roads.
3 Flooding in certain areas.
4 Division into isolated zones.
5 Lack of services.
6 Large deposits of industrial waste, some of which are being excavated.
7 Absence of vegetation.
8 Large numbers of old houses.

All these combined make the redevelopment of the area expensive. They have an important bearing on the administrative method for dealing with the situation which we consider later.

The land-use plan

In this discussion, we shall refer to the research studies in Chapters 4 to 9 but we do not restate their conclusions. They provide the basis for the proposals which are developed in this chapter. We are primarily concerned with the formal Project area described in Chapter 1 and make detailed recommendations for this. In addition, there is a considerable acreage of old housing, especially in the Hafod and Brynhfryd suburbs, which is included in the social hinterland of the valley shown in Figure 1.1. Because of the relationship of the uninhabited valley floor and its residential sides which was noted in Chapter 8, it is necessary to consider these areas also.

On the floor of the valley we are primarily concerned with the redevelopment of all land that is not at present being used by industry. To avoid creating small islands we have, however, included in the development area a small amount of existing industry chiefly situated on Plots 11, 12, 13, 16, 29 and 48. The boundaries of this area are shown in Figure 11.1. It includes land which has been reserved for the tipping of industrial waste and tips which are at present being excavated for hardcore. It is not wholly 'derelict' in the sense in which this term has already been defined, although much of it would fall into this category. Most of it consists of used and unused tip land, infertile slopes, marsh and cleared sites previously occupied by industry. All of it is in our opinion land which has a development potential. In some of it this potential is more immediate than in others, for example where land cannot be built on until the completion of programmes for tipping industrial waste.

There are in all 642 acres of this land on the valley floor which is available for some future use. This we consider should eventually be apportioned in the following way:

Industry and Commerce			407 acres
Industrial area	1	232	
Industrial area	2	34	
Industrial area	B	50	
Commercial area	4	91	
		407	
Amenity—Area 3			120 acres
Housing—Area 5			115 acres
		Total	642 acres

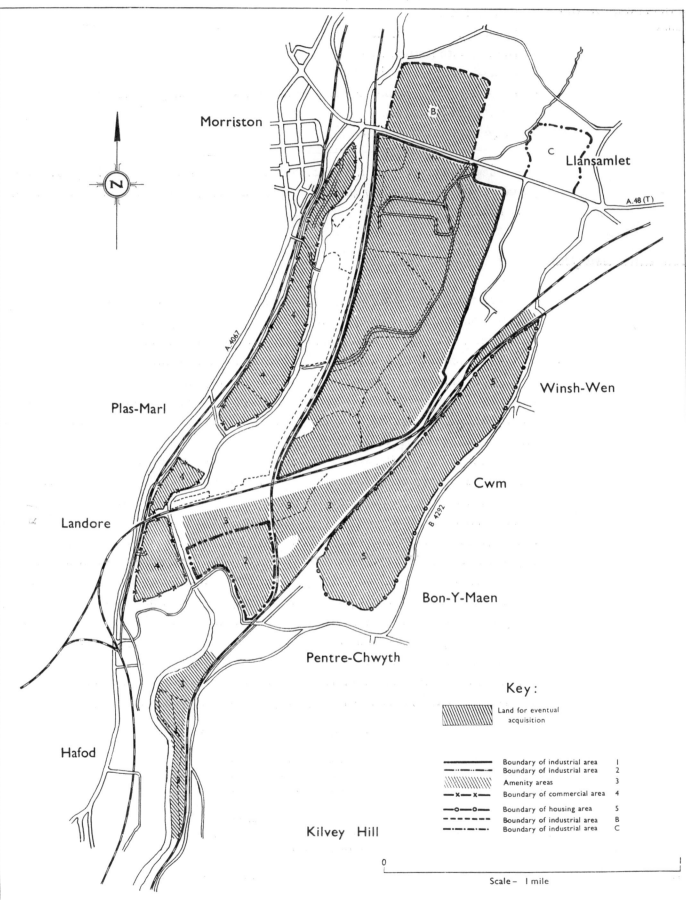

Figure 11.1 Land assembly

Morriston

Llansamlet

A.48 (T)

Plas-Marl

Winsh-Wen

Cwm

Landore

Bon-Y-Maen

Pentre-Chwyth

Hafod

Kilvey Hill

Key:

| | Land for eventual acquisition |

	Boundary of industrial area	1
	Boundary of industrial area	2
	Amenity areas	3
	Boundary of commercial area	4
	Boundary of housing area	5
	Boundary of industrial area	B
	Boundary of industrial area	C

0

Scale – 1 mile

The land-use plan   This provides for the eventual *maximum* use of developable land. It is, of course, possible to alter the emphasis between the three principal uses by taking up more acreage for amenity and less for industry and possible variations are discussed at the end of the chapter. A certain flexibility is desirable in the early stages, especially if the industrial growth of South-West Wales is likely to be slower initially than the South-East. In the long term, however, we are convinced that the valley has a considerable potential.

Industry

We begin by considering the land as an industrial site and here it is relevant to note that the Borough Development Plan, which is based on a survey completed in 1950, allocates the whole of the formal Project area for the use of heavy or 'dirty' industry, reserving the industrial estate at Fforestfach for light, or 'clean', industry. Since the Development Plan was published in 1955 heavy industry in the valley has declined and has not been replaced, whereas such new industry as has located itself in the area has been either of the service type or of the kind for which the industrial estate was considered appropriate, e.g. plastics.* It is therefore apparent that the land use allocation made in the Plan needs to be revised. In the minds of local people the valley's industrial history has made it a 'natural' location for modern industry. This ignores the fact that the locational advantages which were once suitable for heavy industry do not apply today. The river, as Chapter 6 shows, is not capable of meeting a heavy demand for water although the barrage which is discussed later could provide cooling water. Industry is no longer dependent upon coal or even upon rail communications and whereas, when William Siemens developed his steelworks, a site of 35 acres was adequate, a modern steelworks would require ten times as much, a petrochemical complex up to 350 acres, an oil refinery up to 500 acres. The valley cannot offer sites of this magnitude. Nevertheless, the area still has certain important advantages as an industrial site: (a) it is close to a large service centre and to labour supplies from Swansea and its hinterland; (b) it is close to a large port, to a main-line railway and to a proposed liner train terminus; (c) it lies across the main A48 South Wales road from which there are good road links to the M5 and to the M4 when this is extended into Wales; (d) it is close to an oil refinery and to petrochemical and vehicle manufacturing plants; (e) it is close to attractive sea and country for recreation.

Its principal disadvantages are mainly due to the physical state of the site itself. These can be overcome without difficulty provided that requisite capital is invested in the area.

Assuming that this will be done over a period of years and that the valley is developed in a comprehensive way,† we suggest that industry should be located in a principal Area 1 situated between the A48 and the main-line railway from the east (Figure 11.1). Here there is a potential area of 232 acres of which about 100 acres with access to the A48 could be prepared fairly quickly. A secondary area B of 50 acres exists north of the A48 on the site of the former Upper Forest and Worcester Steel and Tinplate Works. This site is, in the long term, capable of being very greatly extended both in depth and frontage once the

---

* Changes in industrial use since 1961 are summarized in the Appendix, p. 255
† The term 'comprehensive' is used here in the sense that is employed in Section 4 (4) of the Town and Country Planning Act, 1962 This does not imply that the procedure of the Act should be followed. The means by which comprehensive redevelopment is to be achieved are considered in Chapter 12.

The use of derelict land in the Lower Swansea Valley

measures to prevent flooding which were suggested in Chapter 6 are taken, and is capable of providing over 300 acres suitable for a single large industry. A third and smaller Area 2 of 34 acres is situated near existing roads and, although access and services to the site are not satisfactory at present, these could be developed quickly.

In addition, there are certain areas suited to the needs of commerce and of service industry. These are situated west of the river where a considerable amount of this develop-

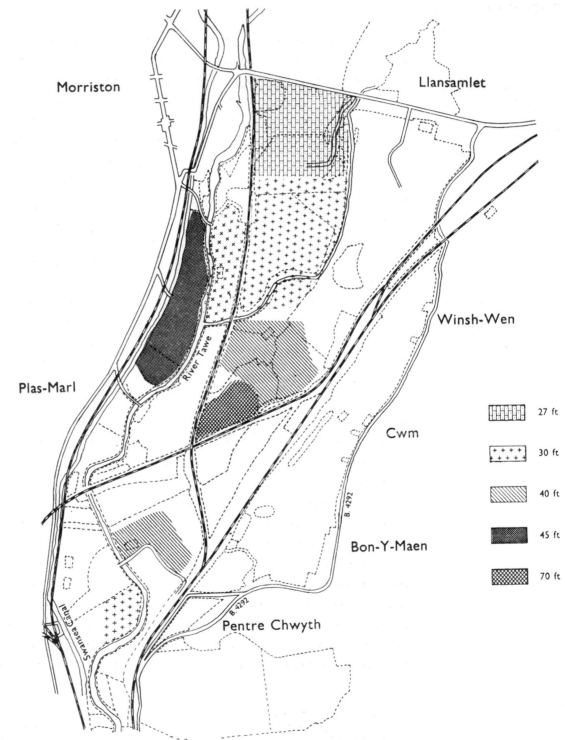

Figure 11.2 Development levels

ment is already located (see Figure 11.3). Altogether, there are 91 acres here of which 45 acres in Plots 21 and 22 are covered with industrial debris. The present levels of these plots are not satisfactory and since a considerable earth-moving programme would be necessary to prepare the sites, they find a later place in the development plan.

Proposed levels

Some idea of the diversity of levels in the valley can be obtained from the base map at the back of the report where the contours represent the state of the land in January 1962. It is essential to rationalize these levels in areas which are to be developed ultimately. In some cases, as for instance in industrial Area 1, the final level ought to be high enough to protect the development from the hazards of periodic flooding, in others the levels will be fixed in relation to neighbouring development. The levels which we propose should be adopted are illustrated in Figure 11.2. Briefly these suggest that the existing situation in Area 1 should be replaced by a series of plateaux rising from the existing level at the A48 to the existing level of the former Mannesman works on Plot 25. Between these, there would be new intermediate levels of 30 ft and 40 ft above Ordnance Datum (a.o.d.).

On Plots 21 and 22, a final level of 45 ft a.o.d. has been fixed in relation to the level of the Swansea Canal which it is assumed will eventually have to be filled in with possible culverting to receive surface water. We consider the future of the canal more fully later.

The amount of earth-moving which will be required to achieve these levels will depend on timing and on control. Many of the sites are at present covered with large tips of industrial waste, some of which are being dug out for hardcore and general fill by a number of haulage firms.[7] In some cases these operations have resulted in levels lower than those we recommend, while in others the operations are helping in the removal of large quantities which are surplus to the final levels of the site. While the levels of new tips can be fixed by the Planning Authority, there is apparently no control over the final levels of these excavations. There have been as many as six firms working in twelve separate areas with the result that the valley floor is in a continual state of disturbance, a situation which threatens by the very nature of its instability the efforts made by the Project to improve the visual appearance of the area. Properly coordinated, the working of the tips could greatly assist the redevelopment of the valley and we shall consider later how this coordination might be secured.

Climate and air pollution

A valley is unsuitable for the location of industry producing smoke and fume.[8] However strictly the creation of pollution might be controlled, the tendency towards temperature inversions in a valley increases the duration of smog conditions. We do not consider therefore that smoke and fume-producing industry should be located in any part of it. (See Appendix on 'Climatology and Air Pollution', p. 292.)

Foundations

In Chapter 4 the problems of building in the area, and particularly on made-up land, were considered. Although heavy structures can be erected more cheaply on some parts of the valley than in others, there are no insuperable problems to be overcome. There is no evi-evidence of mining subsidence or even of settlement, and provided that care is taken with foundations there appear to be no abnormal difficulties in the erection of ordinary industrial buildings. Where the loadings are extreme, as in the case of very heavy presses, it would be necessary to make careful site investigations, but these would be done as a matter of course in any event.

With modern earth-moving equipment, the preparation of sites presents no problems. We estimate that the whole of Industrial Area I west of the proposed north–south spine road could be prepared by movements of cut and fill within the site itself, thus saving on transport costs. Provided that industrial development is phased and hardcore working coordinated, the same economy could be achieved in other industrial areas except area 'B', where any extension of the present site would require levels to be made up by about 5 ft.

We conclude that the Lower Swansea Valley is suitable for both manufacturing and service industry provided that fume-producing industry is avoided. We consider that the sites can be cleared without difficulty and that the area has important locational advantages which merit attention being given to it as part of a regional plan for industrial growth.

Housing

Few houses were ever built on the floor of the valley; the few that were were built for key workers close to the works that employed them. Air pollution and industrial tipping combined with the low-lying nature of the land made the floor unsuitable for human habitation. But now the situation has changed; tipping has raised the levels and with the reduction in air pollution it is possible to envisage parts of the floor being used for housing in the future if services and amenities are available. This means that in the Land-Use Plan housing on the valley floor can be included in a later stage of the scheme, provided attention is paid to the climatic factors discussed in the Appendix to the report. It might, for example, be necessary to restrict pollution by designating the housing area as a smokeless zone.

In Chapter 8 a movement towards the east of Swansea was identified. This is important because if it is encouraged in the future housing policy of the local authority it can do as much to redress the environmental balance between east and west of Swansea as the location of new industry. Residential areas generate a need for schools, shops and places for recreation, and thus a considerable need for land.

Since 1945 there has been considerable urban development on the eastern valley slopes between Bonymaen and Llansamlet. Something like 2,110 houses have been built here of which 1,240 are owned by the Corporation. This trend is continuing but at present the communities are cut off from Swansea by the valley and their services are deficient.[9] Up to the present time, all the new housing has extended eastwards from the Jersey Road leaving a large expanse of 125 acres between it and the railway undeveloped, mainly because, as the base map shows, the slopes here are steeper.

We consider that this eastern valley slope (Area 5) is primarily suitable for terraced housing, and provided that this is developed with imagination it could make a substantial improvement to the appearance of the valley. This flank is part of the main railway approach

Housing

to the town and might provide a 'shop window' for imaginative lowcost private or municipal housing using methods of industrialized building. Costs would be further reduced if the
scheme was integrated with industrial development on the valley floor, otherwise drainage
and sewerage arrangements for housing alone would be excessive. It would be sensible to
relate housing growth here with the development in the valley industrial estate.

Urban renewal

On the other side of the valley there are large areas of old housing built before 1875 which
grew up with heavy industry on the valley floor, some of which are still associated with
what remains (see Figure 2.4). Much of this is deficient in structure and services and should
be replaced. Much again is capable of being improved. A structural survey is required in
order to identify the *areas* which are ripe for renewal, rather than the individual houses
which fall into the category of slums.[10, 11] Area redevelopment of the order indicated by the
conclusions reached in Chapter 8 would provide an opportunity for a new urban environment on this side of the valley, an environment in which the surroundings of a house are as
important as its interior design, in which environment is regarded as the living space of the
community as a whole. We have in mind a scheme similar to that recently approved for
revitalizing the Rye Hill area in Newcastle. This concept enlarges the planning area to
sizeable proportions; it approaches the social survey area whose boundaries are reproduced
for convenience on the Land-Use Plan between pages 248 and 249.

Urban renewal is a national problem of great complexity and dimensions and, with the
traffic problem to which it is closely related, it is probably the most important planning
task which this country has to face in this century.[12, 13] The problems in Swansea are not as
acute as they are in the larger centres of population but in proportion to available resources
they seem intractable enough.[14] It appears to us that the solution is as much a question of
method as it is of cost, and we suggest later how the situation that we find in the Lower
Swansea Valley might be tackled.

Schools

The accommodation and other facilities of schools on the western side of the valley are
deficient. Buildings are old and playing fields few. In the plan for the development of
education in Swansea it is proposed that a new comprehensive school be located in this area.
The present visual improvement of the land south of the main-line railway, together with
the Project's proposals for the development of housing and of amenity here, suggest that the
location of this school in this part of the Lower Swansea Valley is worthy of consideration.

Amenity

The Lower Swansea Valley has been an industrial site and rubbish dump for so long that it is
difficult to imagine it as anything else. Yet it is still a river valley, and underneath the skin of
its desolation there are the bones of which scenic beauty is made—sweeps and curves, high

The use of derelict land
in the Lower Swansea
Valley

bluffs and the twisting river. We have tried to show in Chapter 10 that its ugliness is really only skin deep and that the image of 'Landore' can be changed into 'something rich and strange'.

During the last four years as described in Chapter 10 we have prepared the framework for the amenity proposals which form an important part of our scheme for the valley. If the working and residential population of the valley area is to grow, then the case for providing space for recreation on this side of Swansea becomes overwhelming. The question is, what kind of facilities are required?

One of the attractions of the valley, even in its present state, is its remoteness, almost its wildness. This is a rare quality to have so close to built-up areas and is something that we feel ought to be preserved somewhere when other parts of it are developed. What we have in mind is an area of natural woodland with some water which may be used for boating and fishing, especially by schools and youth clubs. Fortunately the basis for such an area exists in the centre of the valley where there is a pond of about two acres which is capable of being enlarged by excavation to ten acres.[15] Two streams which at present bypass the pond could be diverted into it to maintain its level in summer. A surrounding woodland of over twenty acres was planted by the Project in 1962/3 and is now established. This woodland and lake extends to over fifty acres and forms a bridge between the residential areas east and west of the river and is linked to them by footpaths. It is associated also with our proposals for developing the river.

Proposed Boating Lake and Woodland Park on Plots 35 and 36

We further suggest that the new residential Area 5 should be linked to this parkland by a strip of amenity woodland extending from a disused colliery behind Cwm school. This would enable people living east of the river to move across the valley by footpaths through a continuous strip of woodland free of traffic.

Kilvey Hill

Although it is outside the Project area, the natural feature of Kilvey Hill rising to over 600 ft at its southern end so dominates the landscape that it cannot be ignored. We propose that about 200 acres of the northern slopes of the hill should be planted with trees. Initially these would have to be mainly conifers but as they developed they could be underplanted with suitable hardwoods to provide a mixed woodland. Schools and youth clubs would take part in establishing and maintaining this area along the lines already described in Chapter 10. In time it would become a second woodland park available for amenity as well as for its timber which would be extracted by selective felling. The southern and south-eastern slopes of the hill provide excellent views of the coastline and these ought to be preserved but the planting of the northern slopes would considerably soften the bleak aspect of the valley as similar planting has done higher up towards Pontardawe. This operation could, we suggest, be carried out by the Forestry Commission in association with the local authority.

There is a shortage of formal playing fields in Swansea East both for schools and clubs. It is considered that a twenty-acre site should be developed north of the A48, preferably east of Church Road, Llansamlet, where there is plenty of low-lying land the level of which could be made up. We have in mind a development comparable to the King George V Playing Fields on the west side of the town.

The river Tawe

Apart from Kilvey Hill, the other important natural feature of the valley is the river Tawe. For over 200 years it has provided industry with water and has received its effluent. In its $3\frac{1}{2}$-mile course through the Project area, its banks are crowded with tips and industrial buildings. Recent legislation [Rivers (Prevention of Pollution) Act, 1961], however, has already resulted in a considerable improvement in the quality of its water and this trend is likely to continue. Sea trout and even an occasional salmon have been caught in stretches of the river where ten years ago no fish could live. As the tips are cleared new possibilities are opened up of being able to enjoy the river once more.

Swansea as a seaside town is fortunate in being able to provide facilities for sailing and boating in the summer months. During the winter much of this activity is curtailed owing to the weather, as there is little sheltered water which can safely be used all the year round. Such a facility would be invaluable and there is ample evidence of a very great increase in water-linked activities such as swimming, boating, fishing, etc.[16, 18] We have therefore considered whether the river might be used to provide special water facilities in Swansea.

The river is tidal as far as the Beaufort Bridge. At low tide, banks of mud littered with debris are exposed (Plate 14), but at high tide the situation is transformed (Plate 15). If then the river could be permanently maintained at high tide level, a long, wide stretch of safe water would be available for a variety of amenity uses. The problem is how to maintain this level of water without causing the river bed to silt up and by doing so increase the risk of flooding north of Morriston.

The solution proposed is the erection of a self-regulating weir in the vicinity of the New Cut Bridge. A relatively inexpensive solution would be of a type developed by the Firestone Tyre and Rubber Company under the trade name of 'Fabridam', which is in essence a large fabric tube filled with water. This can be deflated automatically when flood conditions

The use of derelict land
in the Lower Swansea
Valley

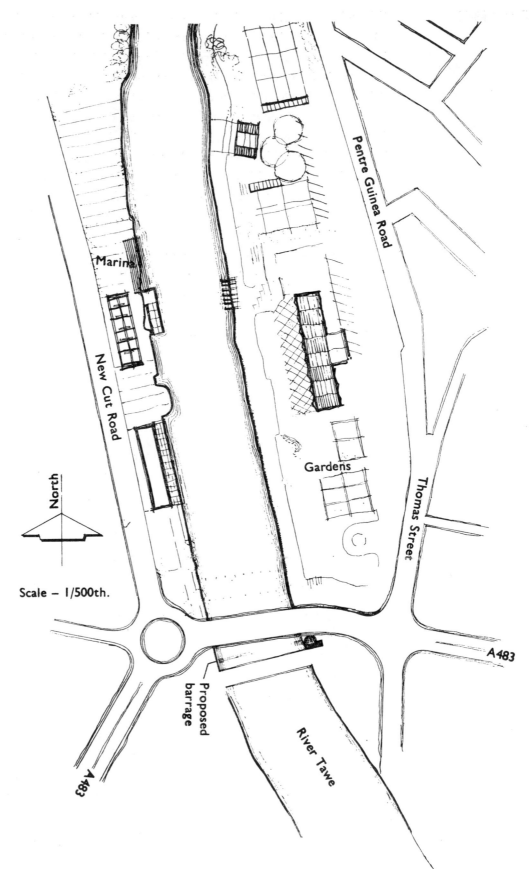

North

Scale – 1/500th.

Marina

New Cut Road

Pentre Guinea Road

Thomas Street

Gardens

A 483

Proposed
barrage

A 483

River Tawe

Sketch plan showing the location of the proposed Fabridam barrage, boating marina and riverside gardens

occur allowing the river to follow almost its existing gradient and in doing so to scour out accumulated silt. The weir would include a salmon leap and could also incorporate regulating sluices if required. Other types of movable barrage capable of achieving similar ends such as flat gates, drum gates or roller gates are available.

A structure of this kind for the Tawe would cost about £120,000. It would transform the river between the weir and the Landore viaduct into a narrow lake 1½ miles long and about 200 ft wide. This would be available for rowing and for small pleasure craft almost all the year. Such a development would also provide a safe winter anchorage for small craft which could be brought to their moorings over the deflated envelope. If required a lock could be incorporated at one side of the barrage to enable small craft to move up and down the river at most states of the tide. (A proposal along these lines has been made for the River Ouse.[17])

The Fabridam Barrage on the River Tawe

As part of the improvement of the river, a serious attempt would be made to clean up the banks and to provide a riverside walk from Morriston along the western bank of the river to the New Tawe Bridge and from there along the eastern bank to the New Cut Bridge. Already the whole of Plot 66 has been planted by the Project and several of the firms with river frontages are improving them. These efforts need to be coordinated within an overall landscape design.[20] Similarly the landscaping of the industrial and residential areas would need to be coordinated and here the biological work described in Chapter 5 could make an important contribution.

Roads

The deficiencies of the regional road system as well as the Valley's perimeter roads have been fully examined in Chapter 7. Also in that chapter, road systems for the valley floor based on three alternative land use plans were suggested. Of these, Plan 'B' most nearly corresponds to the land use proposals made here and therefore it follows that the road plan for the valley which has been adopted corresponds closely to the road plan for Plan 'B'.

We propose that the various sectors in the valley now separated from each other by river or railway should be brought together by two primary road systems:

(a) A north–south spine road from the A48 to Plot 52.
(b) An east–west link crossing the Tawe by a new bridge south of the Landore railway viaduct.

In addition, there would be two further roads, one west of the river along the line of the Swansea Canal providing access to the new commercial or residential areas located there, and the other west of the residential area on Plot 31. This road would bypass Bonymaen, Cwm and Winsh Wen and would provide a new alignment for the B4292 from Llansamlet to the Docks, leaving the existing road to serve as an estate road for the enlarged residential area. These proposals are illustrated in Figure 11.3. The design standards are those adopted for Plan 'B' in Chapter 7. The main road system would be supplemented where necessary by smaller spur roads serving housing and industry. It must be stressed that the road proposals for the valley floor, for its perimeters and for the regional network are related and should be considered as a whole.

The Tawe Bridge

There is a long history of attempts to link the settlements east of the river with those of the west beginning with the Hafod Bridge scheme in 1889. A new bridge over the Tawe cannot at present be entirely justified by traffic demand although once installed it would undoubtedly generate its own traffic. As the report on the human ecology of the valley[19] showed, there is evidence of the need for a bridge on social grounds. The location of the bridge is shown on Figure 11.3. This may have to be adjusted when the Borough road development pattern is finally developed. As a purely temporary measure which would provide immediate temporary access across the valley, the present wood and steel truss bridge north of the Addis factory could be strengthened and approaches provided at a cost of about £23,000. Such a bridge would be capable of carrying limited loads as a temporary measure. It is not possible to consider this as a permanent solution to the need for a cross-river link, and it would therefore be necessary to consider the proposal from the point of view of its cost in relation to its benefits to industry and to the public.

Services

At present gas, water, electricity and services are available on the perimeters of the valley. These would have to be extended if the central areas are to be developed as proposed. In particular, a new trunk sewer would have to be built running approximately north–south along the line of the spine road with pumping stations in the area of Plot 25 and near the

Addis factory on Plot 52. A scheme on these lines would also meet the needs of housing development on Plot 31.

The canal and the Nant-y-Fendrod

The site of the canal south of the A48 is virtually all within the Project area, and once the industrial water usage ceases, or is dealt with in another way, then it should be drained and filled. There is likely to be some surface water draining into the canal, but apart from some land drainage arrangements in the old course it is unrealistic to envisage that the whole waterway will need to be culverted. It is understood that it is practicable to terminate the present canal at the Mond Nickel Works at Clydach. Within the Project area much of the canal site can be used as the route of future roads to serve the Project area, and to connect it to the existing street system to the west. The Nant-y-Fendrod can remain an open channel until a large part of Industrial Area 1 is used.

Some alternative proposals

The main proposals we have made are summarized in the plan shown in Figure 11.3. There are certain alternatives which should be noted briefly.

Housing

West of the river there are 45 acres in Plots 21 and 22 where we have considered that service industry might be located when the tips have been worked out to the proposed levels. It is, however, feasible also to consider the site for new housing to accommodate some of those who will be affected by the redevelopment of the areas of old housing further south. At present the main disadvantage of this site as a residential area is that it is too close to heavy industry and to the river. If, however, there is change in the industrial use of Plot 24 the situation would be worth reconsidering. A properly designed river walk could act as a protective barrier between the residential area and the river.

Hitherto, industry has either occupied or tipped over the whole of the valley floor. It is considered that an attempt should now be made to bring housing and amenity on to the valley floor so that the sharp division between floor and sides may be blurred and the residential areas east and west of the river linked with one another. To this end, we suggest that the southern end of Industrial Area 1, where the levels proposed are 40 ft and 70 ft a.o.d. respectively, could become a housing area linked with Area 5 and to the amenity lake and woodland immediately south of it. Before a decision is taken on either of these proposals, the climate and air pollution characteristics of both areas should be investigated.

Sports stadium and recreation centre

Finally, as part of the scheme for the river, a site of about ten acres with a river frontage north of the river bridge would be suitable for multi-amenity use. The kind of development that we have in mind is a covered games stadium with running track and ice rink together

The use of derelict
land in the Lower
Swansea Valley

with a river esplanade as a terminus point for river activities—races, etc. This would also be a suitable location for Swansea's future zoological gardens and an aquarium. The whole would form a small version of the South Bank development and would serve the needs of the Region. Adequate car parking facilities would be available with easy access to the site by road or by river. If there is a pressure on land in the valley for industrial use, then this type of land use could be planned on Plots 58 and 59 linked with Plot 66 where altogether there are about seventeen acres.

The phasing of development

It is obvious that a comprehensive development scheme of the kind that we have outlined, and which is illustrated in Figure 11.3, would have to be achieved in stages and would be spread over a number of years. Twenty years is not too long a time to envisage being required for the development. It is therefore necessary to consider the order in which the proposals we have made could be carried out.

At present most of the land which has a development potential is owned privately. This fragmentation makes comprehensive development impossible. Planning powers are already inadequate to regulate tip working and, since investment in derelict land has to be made to some extent on social grounds, then this investment is properly made by society. The first stage therefore is the assembly under public ownership of all the land shown in Figure 11.1. This could be either the local authority, the Land Commission or a statutory body such as a new town corporation. The subsidiary stages might be as follows:

Stage I

Once acquired, final development levels for the land would be fixed and hardcore abstraction and tipping arranged so as to assist rather than hinder their achievement. The order in which the sites would be prepared would depend on the need for sites, on their present state and on the demands for hardcore. The development of the area should be coordinated with regional public works so that large Government contracts requiring bulk fill, e.g. the Morriston bypass, would give priority to debris from site-clearing operations in the Lower Swansea Valley. Structural surveys of old housing would be made and work started in the first urban renewal area. As the 27 ft and 30 ft a.o.d. plateaux on Industrial Area 1 are most easily prepared, those could be made ready first. The first section of the spine road would be laid from the A48 to the end of the 30 ft plateau and the first part of the main sewer with its pumping station would be completed. This would provide one large industrial site of about 80 acres on the 30 ft plateau with a further 40 acres of smaller sites on the 27 ft plateau. At the same time the approaches to the existing bridge between Plots 50 and 52 would be prepared and the bridge strengthened. Tips in Industrial Area 2 would be removed and the site made ready for industry or amenity. Housing development would be started on Area 5 together with its associated parkland.

Stage II

The levée would be built and Industrial Area 'B' prepared. Playing fields in the vicinity of

Church Road, Llansamlet, would be laid out. The realignment of the B4292 would be completed. The clearance of the old housing areas on the side of the valley would be continued. Plots 21 and 22 would be levelled and prepared for commercial development, together with Plots 40 and 49.

Stage III

Tipping by the National Smelting Company Ltd in the Fendrod Valley would be so arranged as to permit the spine road to be extended to the Tawe Bridge, which would also be built. The canal would be filled in and the western service road built. This stage sees the completion of the valley road network, by which time it would be expected that the new Morriston bypass would have been built and the A4067 improved. The housing development on Plot 31 (Area 5) would be completed and work started on the lake and forest park on Plot 35. The second stage of the main sewer with its pumping station would be started and the industrial development started on Plot 52.

Stage IV

In this last stage the Tawe weir and the multipurpose river amenity centre would be built. If required the Industrial Area 1 would be extended to the 40 ft and 70 ft plateaux or else housing would be developed in this area.

These four stages can be adjusted in their emphasis to suit the rate at which development takes place. The divisions between them are by no means clear cut. They are merely suggested here to show how the redevelopment of the Lower Swansea Valley might be phased. The important thing is to see the area as a whole and to avoid allowing what is at present a fairly flexible situation to become fixed by piecemeal development.

From the beginning, an effort should be made to upgrade the appearance of the valley along the lines that the Project has initiated. Areas like the steel waste heaps on Plots 26 and 27 which are unlikely to be developed for housing or industry at an early stage and where the 'soil' conditions are favourable should be temporarily screened with suitable trees and shrubs. The vegetation so established should be maintained by whatever body is responsible for the area, as suggested in Chapter 5.

While the plan presented in this chapter is designed to meet the needs of the area in an economical way it should be emphasized that these needs could undoubtedly be provided by alternative plans. It is, however, important to stress that whatever final plan is adopted, it should be comprehensive and should follow broadly the lines which we have described.

Appendix

The following principal changes in land use have taken place since January 1961:

Plot No.	Use in January 1961	Present use
5	Derelict	Site cleared—to be developed for storage
7	Steel and tinplate works	Unused
15	Disused brickworks	Scrapyard
25	Tube works—being demolished	Unused—cleared site
29	Storage	Scrapyard

The use of derelict land in the Lower Swansea Valley	Plot No.	Use in January 1961	Present use
	48	Light engineering	Vehicle—storage and repair
	52	Empty wartime factory	Manufacture of plastic consumer goods
	62	Sheet metal and insulating works	As in 1961 but with new administrative and works buildings
	63	Disused	Brewery storage

References

1. *Investment Incentives*, H.M.S.O., January 1966. Cmnd 2874.
2. G. Manners, et al., *South Wales in the Sixties*, Pergamon Press, 1964, Chapter 7.
3. *Central Scotland—A Programme for development and growth*, Cmnd 2188, H.M.S.O., November 1963.
4. *The North East—A Programme for regional development and growth*, Cmnd 2206, H.M.S.O., November 1963.
5. E. John Powell, *Glamorgan—A Planning Study*, Glamorgan County Council, 1965.
6. See L. S. Frame, 'The Functions of Swansea as a Regional Centre', University of Wales B.Sc. dissertation, June 1961, and P. R. Strawbridge, 'The Character, Location and Contribution of Services in Swansea', University of Wales B.Sc. dissertation, June 1964.
7. G. Holt, *Tips and Tip Working in the Lower Swansea Valley* (Study Report 12).
8. G. Howes, 'Location, health and planning', University of Manchester Town and Country Planning School Paper, March 1960.
9. Margaret Stacey, *The Human Ecology of the Lower Swansea Valley* (Study Report 1), together with a land-use survey of the residential areas east and west of the river by senior forms of Secondary schools in Swansea in 1963.
10. Ministry of Housing and Local Government, *Planning Bulletin 1—Town Centres, The Approach to Renewal*, H.M.S.O., 1962.
11. *Planning Bulletin 3—Town Centres, The Cost and Control of Redevelopment*, H.M.S.O., 1963.
12. Civic Trust, London. *Urban Redevelopment*, London, 1962.
13. J. Barry Cullingworth, *New Towns for Old—The Problem of Urban Renewal*, Fabian Research Series No. 229, May 1962.
14. See Margaret Stacey, *Lower Swansea Valley: Housing Report* (Study Report 7), Chapters 1 and 2.
15. R. E. Davies, *Report on a preliminary investigation to determine the feasibility of creating an artificial lake in the Lower Swansea Valley Project Area* (Study Report 12).
16. John Barr, 'Free time in Britain', *New Society*, 15 April 1965.
17. H. F. Clark and D. Sampson, *The River Ouse Survey Report*, York Civic Trust, 1964.
18. Michael Dower, 'The fourth wave', *Architects' Journal*, 20 January 1965.
19. See Margaret Stacey, *The Human Ecology of the Lower Swansea Valley*, Chapter 7 (Study Report 1).
20. I. C. Laurie, 'The Tyne Landscape', May 1965 (A comprehensive landscape study of the River Tyne, unpublished).

Authorship

This chapter was written by K. J. Hilton with the cooperation of the Land-Use Sub-Committee.

An economic assessment of the land-use proposals

The background   An economic assessment of the proposals contained in Chapter 11 must be made against the background of the development needs of South-West Wales. The coastal belt of South Wales from Port Talbot to Newport has had a history of rapid and vigorous industrial growth during the past twenty years, but the western end of the coastal strip, and the valleys spreading northward from it, have been much less fortunate. This can be seen clearly in Chapter 9, though the picture would have been even darker had Port Talbot been omitted.

Between 1951 and 1961 there was a slight fall in the population of the area studied in Chapter 9, as a result of a low rate of natural increase combined with net outward migration. The growth of the insured population can be seen from the following figures:

	Male		Female		Total	
	1952	1962	1952	1962	1952	1962
Swansea–Port Talbot coastal area	53·0	62·8	19·8	25·0	72·8	87·8
Industrial Carmarthenshire	34·0	28·8	8·4	9·2	42·4	38·0
Neath and Swansea Valleys	56·5	46·7	14·6	15·2	71·1	62·0
	143·5	138·3	42·8	49·4	186·3	187·8

Source: Figures provided for Mrs S. H. Spence by the Welsh Office and the Ministry of Housing and Local Government. There are minor differences in coverage from the area discussed in Chapter 9.

The net increase in the total insured population was only 1,500, an increase in the number of women being almost offset by a decline in the number of men, and a rise in the Swansea–Port Talbot area being offset by a fall in the valleys and in Industrial Carmarthen. By contrast, there was an increase of over 15,000 in the insured population of the Cardiff area and 14,000 in the Newport area during the same period.

Unemployment in South-West Wales has been consistently higher than the regional average. Activity rates have been fairly high for men but very low for women. The male rate is rather above the average for Great Britain in Industrial Carmarthenshire, and the Neath and Swansea Valleys, but rather below in the coastal strip from Swansea to Port Talbot. For women the rate is only about two-thirds of the national average.

The slow growth of the area has been mainly due to the big decline in manpower in coal-mining. As shown in Chapter 9, the proportion of the employed labour force engaged in mining fell from 24·0 per cent in 1938 to 11·5 per cent in 1961. A large part of the growth which has taken place elsewhere has been in 'service' industries (a broad group defined so as to include distribution and construction as well as personal services). The proportion employed in 'service' industries rose from 38·0 per cent in 1938 to 48·3 per cent in 1961. Though this figure is a little below the national average, it is high for a locality which contains no important organs of the central Government, and very few head offices of large

An economic
assessment of the
land-use proposals

firms. Moreover, it is expected that, if there are no active policy measures to stimulate industrial development, most of the prospective growth in the next fifteen years will be in services.

One thing which the service industries have in common is that—apart from services performed for tourists—they sell only to residents in their own immediate locality. They amount to 'taking in one another's washing', and no community can live and grow entirely on this time-honoured process. By contrast the extractive and manufacturing industries sell a high proportion of their products outside their own locality, they are the local equivalent of the export industries of a country and localities, like countries, must have healthy export industries in order to grow. The basic reason is simple—no community is self-supporting, and all have to purchase a high proportion of their requirements from outside. Money spent in this way, however, creates income not for local residents, but for outsiders. In a sense it represents a seepage of purchasing power away from a community to its neighbours. If this is offset by an adequate return flow, in the shape of outside purchases of local 'exports', there is no problem. If, however, it is not, the community will suffer a chronic tendency to a shortage of purchasing power—trade will be slack, and growth, unless stimulated from outside, will be slow. For this reason further developments in manufacturing are necessary to the economic health of South-West Wales.

These developments are especially necessary at the present time because of the prospect of large-scale redundancy in coal and steel. A number of mines are scheduled for closure in the Coal Board's recent reorganization scheme. The plants of the Steel Company of Wales employ far more labour in relation to their output than do their competitors in America and Japan, and a big reduction in their labour force is likely. These two developments could affect as many as 10,000 people—almost all men—in the area.

A rough estimate of the number of jobs that will be needed during the next fifteen years is as follows:

	Male	Female
To meet projected population growth with existing activity rates	8,000	2,000
To offset redundancies	10,000	
To raise female activity rates to 32 per cent		12,000
Total	18,000	14,000

The assumed rise in the female activity rates would still leave it well below the national average of about 38 per cent. To attain this figure would require about 11,000 further jobs for women. The area will need between 30,000 and 40,000 new jobs between now and 1981; at least half of these will need to be in manufacturing, and most of them are likely to be created in the coastal strip between Llanelli and Port Talbot. It is against the background of the demand for industrial sites implied in these figures that the proposals for the valley must be considered.

Comparing costs and benefits

The main objective of this chapter is to compare the prospective costs of the project with its prospective benefits, but first it is necessary to distinguish between costs and benefits from the point of view of the community, and from that of the institution undertaking clearance and development.

The problem of the developer is less complex. The general principles are that a developer should count as costs all the net payments that he would have to make as a result of undertaking a project, but which he would not have to make otherwise, and that he should count as benefits the net increase in revenue that he would receive as a result of the project, and which he would not receive otherwise. Thus a developer must count the cost of buying derelict land though, as will be argued later, this is not a cost to the community, and he must deduct from his gross payments any Government grants for which he may be eligible, though these do not reduce costs from the point of view of the community. A developer should not, however, count costs which he would incur independently of a project, e.g. a local authority acting as a developer should count the cost of building a road specifically for a particular development, but not the cost of a road which it would have built in any case. The extension of this principle to the benefits side implies that, for example, a local authority developer should not count increases in rateable values arising from the project if they are diverted from other parts of its own area; it should, however, count the whole of its net increase in rateable value, even though some of this may have arisen from diverting industry and trade from neighbouring authorities.

From the point of view of the community, the costs of a project should be compared with:

(a) The capitalized value of the net increase in real national income which it may be expected to yield, and

(b) An estimate, made in money terms where possible, of other benefits of a kind not included in the national income accounts.

In calculating (a), any loss of income resulting from a project must be brought in either as a deduction from gross return or as a cost. Consider, for example, an industrial development using agricultural land. The market value of agricultural land represents a capitalization of the income stream it is expected to produce in agriculture. Similarly, the market value of land developed for industrial purposes represents a capitalization of the income stream which it is expected to produce in industry. Our rule, therefore, could be met by counting the purchase price of agricultural land as a cost, adding the cost of development and comparing the total with the market value of developed land. In the case of derelict land, however, there is by definition no income stream accruing to the community and there can, therefore, be no loss to offset against the gain from development. Any price which it may be necessary to pay to owners of such land is compensation not for the loss of present income, but for giving up the possibility of income from future development. The purchase price of such land should not, therefore, be counted as a cost from the point of view of the community.

The increase in land values brought about by a development is the best starting point for a comparison of costs and benefits, but it needs to be supplemented in two ways:

(i) The development of a particular area of land may either have beneficial or harmful, effects on surrounding land, e.g. the introduction of industry creating noxious fumes would depress the value of nearby property, while the creation of a pleasant recreational area on formerly derelict land would enhance the value of nearby properties. Such changes of value should be taken into account as far as possible.

An economic
assessment of the
land-use proposals

(ii) Where a development brings new industry into areas where resources are unemployed it has what economists call 'multiplier' effects. The income earned by people in the new industry creates additional spending which provides employment and income for others who would otherwise remain unemployed. There is thus a secondary increase in output in addition to that initially created by the new industry, and the total increase in income is a multiple of the original one. Unfortunately it is impossible to put a value on the amount of this additional income for a small region, but in view of what has been said of the economic situation of South-West Wales, it is an important consideration.

In considering benefits under (b) account should be taken of anything which can reasonably be attributed to a project, and which cannot be measured fully under (a). Four such benefits will be considered in relation to the valley:

The value of open space for amenity and recreation.
The saving in travel to work and traffic congestion.
The improvement to social life from better communications, especially the new river crossing, and
The possible effect on industry and the tourist trade of removing this 'black spot' from the approaches to the town.

Since both costs and benefits are spread over a considerable time, it is desirable to compare the present values of the streams of receipts and payments discounted at an appropriate rate of interest. In the present case, however, we have only very imperfect knowledge of the 'time shape' of either stream. Moreover, the question of what is an appropriate rate of interest is controversial. No attempt at discounting has therefore been made.

The nature of the proposals

The costs and benefits which have been examined are those associated with the proposals which have been described in Chapter 11. Ideally, it would have been desirable to compare a number of plans for the valley area, both with one another and with alternative developments elsewhere, but this would not have been possible with the time and resources available.

The proposals studied involve the acquisition of some 642 acres of derelict land, and its development so as to provide 407 acres for industrial and commercial use, 115 acres for housing and about 120 acres of parks, lake, playing fields and woodlands.

The main works, the cost of which has been studied, are:

A levée to prevent flooding and a barrage to maintain the level of the Tawe at low tide and so add to its amenity value.
The construction of the two north–south roads, the east–west road and the realignment of B4292, as described in Chapter 11, together with housing roads in Area 5.
The construction of a new bridge across the Tawe.
The construction of sewers as deemed necessary by the Borough Engineer.
The levelling of sites.

The cost of providing gas, electricity and water, has not been included for two reasons. It is virtually impossible to obtain an accurate estimate of cost without detailed site plans, and the authorities concerned will presumably put in these services and charge the users on a commercial basis. This must, of course, be borne in mind when considering the value of the developed land.

Some other minor works have not been included because they are not essential parts of the plan. The most important of these are the possible culverting of the river Fendrod and of the canal. If the latter is eventually to be considered, the relevant costs will include those of providing alternative water supplies for the three firms now drawing water from the canal.

In the following sections costs and benefits are looked at from the point of view of the community, and also of the local authority on the assumption that it acquired the land and acted as developer.

The costs

The cost of the proposed development is shown in Table 12.1. The figures are estimates derived on assumptions explained below, and after consultation with engineers, both in the College and outside. Though they are given to the nearest thousand, they do not, of course, have that degree of accuracy and should be regarded only as indications of the broad orders of magnitude involved.

The figure of flood control is the estimate of the cost of the complete scheme, recommended in Chapter 6. The cost of the barrage was provisionally estimated by the manufacturers (Firestone) at £72,700, exclusive of the pump house and concrete work. On the basis of this figure and advice from civil engineers, the total cost is put at £120,000.

For reasons shown on page 259, no account has been taken of the cost of improvements to A48 or A4067, or of the Morriston bypass, since these will all be necessary regardless of what happens in the valley. The recommended realignment of B4292 has been included, together with that of the valley floor roads and 4,260 linear yards of housing roads in Area 5. The cost of these is estimated at £835,000 including excavation and filling that may be needed on sloping ground in Area 5. It will also be necessary to provide a new bridge to carry the main-line railway over the north–south spine road, at a cost of £60,000. The provision for sewerage includes the cost of two pumping stations, one near the south-east corner of Industrial Area 1, and the other north of the Addis factory (Industrial Area 2). The total cost of sewers and pumping stations is estimated at £267,000.

The cost of a new bridge over the Tawe is estimated at £300,000. The transportation studies, the results of which appear in Chapter 7, show that this expenditure is difficult to justify on strictly economic grounds. It would, however, bring the eastern outskirts closer to the town centre and, for this reason, a strong plea is made for it on social grounds in Chapters 8 and 11. This kind of social benefit is one which may be very significant but which cannot possibly be measured in money. An alternative scheme for the time being would be to strengthen the wood and steel truss bridge near the Addis works and improve the approaches to it. This could be done at an estimated cost of only £23,000, but it provides at best a temporary expedient.

An economic
assessment of the
land-use proposals

Table 12.1   The costs of the Project

	£'000
The River	
Flood control	105
River barrage (Fabridam)	120
Roads	
Road construction	835
Railway bridge over spine road	60
Sewers	267
River crossing	
New bridge	300
Temporary scheme	23
Clearing and levelling	800
Playing fields	
Soiling and seeding	30
Footpaths in amenity area	45
Total cost from point of view of community:	
With new bridge	2,562
Without	2,285
Land purchase	400
Gross cost to local authority developer:	
With bridge	2,962
Without bridge	2,685

The tips which are a feature of the area are as shown in Chapter 11, being worked by contractors for hardcore. It is assumed that this working will continue for some time and that it will lead to the removal of tips in Area 3 (amenity) and to the removal of 500,000 cubic yards from Industrial Area 1. The remaining tips would then provide approximately enough material to raise low-lying areas to the planned levels, though about 780,000 cubic yards would have to be moved. If hardcore working proceeds more slowly or development more quickly than has been assumed, the amount of earth-moving would, of course, be greater. In principle, account should also be taken of the loss of revenue from hardcore, though this is small in relation to the other costs involved. The cost of earth-moving has been put at 10s a ton. Total costs of earth-moving, compacting and levelling, including a 25 per cent contingency allowance, are estimated at £800,000.

The costs of roads, sewers and earth-moving do not include Industrial Areas 'B' and 'C', adjacent to and immediately north of the A48 road (Figure 11.1). Both areas were formerly occupied by industry. Area 'B' (50 acres) requires little site preparation. The main obstacle to its re-use is the risk of flooding and this could be eliminated by the building of the proposed levée. Area 'C' (20 acres) is already being developed privately and has, therefore, been withdrawn from the proposals.

It is suggested that the amenities of the area should include twenty acres of playing fields to be laid out on low-lying land levelled by tipping. No cost has been included for tipping as the Corporation is in need of tipping space anyway, but £30,000 has been allowed for laying the soil and seeding.

These costs have not been allocated between different parts of the project since roads, sewers and pumping stations serve more than one area and their apportionment would have to be arbitrary. However, Industrial Area 2 is bound to cost much more than other parts of the project as it requires a large amount of earth-moving and a considerable length of access road for only 34 acres.

The costs   Finally, the cost of acquiring the derelict land which it is suggested should be brought under the control of the local authority is estimated at £400,000, an average value of about £600 per acre.

The total cost of the proposals from the point of view of the community would be £2,562,000 with the new bridge and £2,285,000 without it. Adding the cost of land, the gross cost to the local authority would be £2,962,000 with the bridge and £2,685,000 without it. From this it is necessary to deduct, of course, any grants which may be obtainable.

Benefits from the point of view of the community

These benefits would consist of:

1   The value of the redeveloped land for industrial, commercial and residential purposes.
2   The enhanced value of adjacent and nearby land, both within and around the Project area.
3   The value of new amenities, and
4   The saving of travelling time and relief of congestion that might result from an improved balance between residential and industrial development in the town as a whole.

1   As stated earlier in this chapter, the value of reclaimed land should represent a capitalization of the additional stream of real income that its reclamation is expected to yield. However, in a free market the value of reclaimed land is also influenced by the price of alternative sites. No one will pay more for reclaimed land than for any other land except in so far as it is superior in nearness to a town centre, accessibility to transport or in some other way. Hence the free market value of reclaimed land also represents the 'opportunity cost' which a community saves by developing derelict land rather than diverting other land from some alternative use.

Ideally, it would be desirable to put a value on reclaimed land in the valley which could be compared with the costs of reclamation. However, discussions with a number of professional valuers have convinced me that this would be more likely to mislead than to help, for several reasons. There is at present a great disparity between land values in different parts of the Project area. While land on the valley floor has very little value, commercial sites on the periphery of the Project area, with access to main roads, are already valued at as much as £5,000 an acre.

It would, however, be very wrong to suppose that, in the present state of demand, much of the land which it is proposed to reclaim could be sold at this price. Sites on the Fforestfach Trading Estate, valued at about £3,500 an acre, are at present vacant and there are other sites, outside the borough, in the Gorseinon Clydach–Pontardawe and Neath areas, which are relatively very cheap though lacking some of the advantages which the valley enjoys by virtue of its central position. The prospects of the valley sites acquiring a value commensurate with the cost of reclamation depends, therefore, on the introduction of a substantial amount of new industry in South-West Wales. It has already been shown that this is essential to the economic health of the area, and presumably this was the intention of the Government in making it a Development District under the Local Employment Acts.

An economic
assessment of the
land-use proposals

A final difficulty is that, with interest rates at their present level, the length of time for which both costs and benefits are deferred makes a big difference to their present value. The timing, both of the redevelopment of the valley and of the introduction of new industry, is very uncertain, and changes in either could make any estimate of value very wide of the mark.

Land for residential purposes varies greatly in value between different parts of the town. In Bonymaen it is as low as £1,000 an acre, and at Birchgrove about £1,700. Values at Morriston, Cockett and Killay are about £2,000, while in the fashionable Sketty Green area they are as much as £6,800, even without services.

At present the valley sides are unpopular for residential purposes, but the proposed development should make them vastly more attractive and should raise land values to around the middle of the above price range.

2   The proposed developments within the valley will have a beneficial effect on the value of nearby land. There are about 500 acres within the Project area which are already in use and which have not, therefore, been included in the development proposals. These are used mainly for industrial and commercial purposes, where amenity is not very important, so that the effect on their value would be only modest. There are, however, large residential areas—especially those immediately to the west of A4067—which overlook the valley and for which the valley forms a natural source of open space and recreational facilities. As shown in Chapter 8, much of this property is old and out of date, and will have to be renewed during the next few years. The prospects for redeveloping this area would be radically altered by the proposals for the valley. Once again, consultations with professional valuers have shown that, while this fact is fully recognized, it is impossible to put a satisfactory figure on the prospective rise in land values.

3   The proposed additions to amenities include areas of park and woodland, playing fields, a lake, and a barrage which would both greatly improve the appearance of the river and also make it suitable for rowing, sailing and fishing. Presumably these facilities would be made available, as in other municipal parks, either 'free' or at a nominal charge. It is impossible, therefore, to ascertain how much the public would be willing to pay for them. Under our present system the amount which a community is willing to spend on amenities is essentially a political rather than an economic decision. It is relevant to note, however, that Swansea Corporation retains parkland in parts of the town which are well provided with open space, even though it could be sold for development at up to £6,000 an acre. It would seem, therefore, that they should not be unwilling to spend similar sums for providing new facilities in areas where, as shown in Chapter 8, they are sadly deficient.

4   A full assessment of the effect of the proposals on travel to work and traffic congestion would require a very detailed and costly study. It has been shown in Chapters 7 and 8 that there is already a substantial movement both into and out of the borough to work. This includes travel from the western residential districts such as Killay, Sketty, Mumbles and Langland Bay to the eastern part of the borough, travel from these places to factories outside the borough in Jersey Marine, Neath and Port Talbot, and travel across the borough from places outside to the west such as Bishopston and Pennard. All the traffic has to come through the town centre where it adds significantly to congestion. Two points about the proposed developments in the valley should help with this problem. First (with the Morris-

Benefits from the
point of view of the
community

ton bypass), industries located in the valley would be accessible from a wide area extending from Llanelli in the west, to the Amman, Dulais, Swansea and Neath valleys without this industrial generated traffic passing through the centre of Swansea or the heavily congested areas of Morriston. Secondly, industrial development, whether in the valley or outside, is likely to be mainly to the north and east of Swansea. Further residential development to the west is, therefore, likely to increase the average length of journeys to work and the degree of congestion in the town centre, while residential development in the east is likely to reduce both. The proposed development would provide for about 1,100 houses on the eastern slope of the valley but road improvements would improve communications with the town centre and facilitate further residential development in the Winsh Wen, Bonymaen and Pentrechwyth areas, while the proposed new amenities in the valley would, as already noted, make a big difference to the problem of renewal of old property to the Project area.

Benefits from the point of view of the local authority

Looking at the matter from the point of view of the local authority acting as developer, it is necessary to add land acquisition to costs and to deduct any grants which may be available. Account should also be taken of any set additions to rateable value created by developments in the valley and of the indirect effect in making the town as a whole more attractive to new industry and to tourists.

The position with regard to grants is complex, as there are several Acts under which a case might be made for grants in aid of one or more of the recommended developments. Moreover, there is a possibility of changes in the not too distant future for the recent White Paper, *Local Government Finance in England and Wales* (Cmnd 2923) contains the statement that 'a new grant of this type (i.e. specific as distinct from general) will be introduced to assist urban redevelopment, the reclamation of derelict land and the acquisition of public open space'.

The following possibilities appear to be available under present (March 1966) legislation:

1 *The Local Employment Acts*

The provisions of these Acts are administered in Wales by the Welsh Office in consultation with the Board of Trade. Before a grant can be made these authorities must be satisfied that a development is expedient for the provision of long-term employment in a development district.

Section 5 of the Local Employment Act, 1960, refers to derelict land and empowers the making of grants up to 85 per cent of the cost of land acquisition, exploratory work and legal fees and approved costs of reclamation, but excluding roads, main drainage and site development. In calculating costs to rank for grant, the value of reclaimed land is deducted from total costs. If the scheme were approved the costs of land (£400,000) and earth-moving (£800,000) would seem clearly to qualify, and it is possible that the levée (£105,000) would also be eligible for grant. A problem might arise in connection with the valuation of reclaimed land since a large part of the value would arise from improved access and drainage. As the costs of roads and sewers do not rank for grant, it would be inequitable that the

An economic
assessment of the
land-use proposals

value they create should be taken into account. It is understood that valuation would be made by reference to other level sites without access or services, so that the value imputed for this purpose would be less than market value.

Section 7 of the 1960 Act refers to basic services (including transport facilities, power, lighting, heating, water and sewerage) and to the making of grants or loans towards the cost of improvements. It is uncertain which of the proposed developments might qualify for grants and at what rates, but it seems that some assistance towards the cost of sewers, at least, might be available.

The Local Employment Acts also contain provision for financial assistance in respect of buildings, plant and machinery, and the movement of key workers, but these are not directly relevant. They may, however, enhance the value of cleared land indirectly by making the area more attractive to new industry.

2 Highway grants

These too are administered by the Welsh Office. Grants are given for improvements to 'classified' roads which are included in the Ministry's programme. The only classified road involved is B4292. If the proposed realignment were included in the road programme it would rank for grant at 60 per cent (estimated cost £170,000) but it would have to face stiff competition for a limited amount of money from other road projects all over Wales. A case could be made in due course by the Corporation for the classification of the north–south spine road and for the east–west road and river crossing as trunk roads. Access roads for industrial sites might be considered under Section 7 of the Local Employment Act, 1960.

3 Housing subsidies

Subsidies for building are not relevant here, since we have confined ourselves to the value of land before the erection of buildings. A subsidy is, however, available for site development on expensive sites. This is paid on costs (including roads, sewers and lighting) in excess of £4,000 per acre and is at the rate of £60 per acre per year for 60 years if the cost does not exceed £5,000 and a further £34 per acre per year for each £1,000 in excess of £5,000. It is doubtful whether costs in the proposed housing area would be high enough to attract this grant.

4 Forestry grants

Grants are available under the Forestry Act, 1919, for the planting and management of woodlands, but the small acreages of amenity woodland in the valley would not be eligible.

5 Rate deficiency grant

Any expenditure not covered by one of the grants listed above would attract rate deficiency grant. On present rateable value this would amount to rather more than 10 per cent. However, in so far as development added to rateable value, it would have the effect of reducing the amount of rate deficiency grant in the future.

The recommended developments would provide some 407 acres of land for industrial and commercial use. Assume, for the sake of illustration, that one-quarter of this is actually built on, leaving the rest for site roads, parking and loading facilities and open space between buildings, this would allow 4·4 million sq ft of buildings. If these were assessed at the very

Benefits from
the point of view of
the local authority

modest figure of 2s 6d a square foot they would add over £500,000 to the rateable value of the town. It must be emphasized, however, that this is a very large amount of building and, even on the assumptions with regard to growth and industrial development made earlier, it would have to be spread over at least fifteen to twenty years. Some of this might represent the diversion of development from other parts of the town, but most of it would be a net increase in rateable value. On the other hand, the residential development would be almost wholly in place of development in other areas, so that no account is taken of its rateable value here. (Some increase in rateable value might be obtained indirectly if building around the valley released sites in the County Borough for residential development which might otherwise take place outside it.)

Finally, the local authority should consider, as a benefit from development, the enhanced attractiveness of the town as a whole both to industrialists and visitors. It is quite impossible to put a monetary value on this but it is by no means negligible.

Conclusion

There are parts of the derelict area, near to roads and needing comparatively little clearing, which are already ripe for development in the sense that their value when prepared for use would cover their costs of acquisition and reclamation. Others are likely to become so in the near future, but this is not true of the sites which are inaccessible and difficult to clear. However, there are several reasons why piecemeal development is undesirable:

1   Roads, sewers, etc., need to be planned with regard to the area as a whole, and an individual developer considering only the best use of his own plot could easily hinder the development of other land, e.g. by placing a building astride the best line of an access road.

2   The reduction of the area to a series of usable levels involves a 'cut and fill' operation, removing material from tips in some areas to fill hollows elsewhere. The cost of this can only be minimized by planning the levels and the earth-moving operation as a whole. A series of piecemeal developments would be likely to add considerably to the cost of the whole operation.

3   As shown in the preceding pages the reclamation of the area would confer important indirect benefits on the community. These would not, however, accrue significantly to any one developer, so that each individual developer would have too little incentive to reclaim land.

These are important examples of what economists call differences between private and social costs and benefits. Further, under the present law, individual developers would not qualify for some of the grants which might be available to a public authority redeveloping the area as a whole.

It is essential, therefore, that the valley should be treated as a single project and developed by a single authority. A series of individual efforts would gradually bring into use land around the periphery of the area but at a cost of making development at the centre progressively more difficult. The result would be that some of the least accessible and most unsightly land would remain in its present state indefinitely.

An economic
assessment of the
land-use proposals

Considering the valley as a whole, on the basis of the present demand for land, it is unlikely that the total value of reclaimed land used for the purposes recommended would cover the full cost of the operation. This, however, would be to take a much too narrow view. There are important indirect benefits to the community as a whole in increased amenities and enhanced value of adjacent land, while a local authority developer could expect to benefit from a considerable increase in rateable value.

Finally, the Project needs to be considered not against the present demand for land, but against the demand that would be created by the introduction of new industries on the scale indicated at the beginning of this chapter. Considered against this background the indirect benefits which would accrue to the community create a strong case for the central Government assisting redevelopment by means of grants. Given the availability of such grants, and the prospective increase in rateable value, the local authority, if it purchased and redeveloped the whole area, would be likely to get a good return on its money, besides converting what has been for so long a blot on the landscape into a substantial amenity for the town.

Authorship

This chapter was written by Professor E. Victor Morgan of the Department of Economics, University College, Swansea.

The author gratefully acknowledges the assistance provided by G. S. Pollard, the Borough Treasurer, W. J. Anderson, the Chief Accountant, W. J. Ward, the Borough Engineer, and Bryn Jones, engineering assistant. He is also obliged to A. Tewdyr Watkins for discussing certain aspects of the chapter with him.

13   Land assembly and development agencies

Unification of land ownership

The proposals discussed in Chapter 11 are founded on the assumption that all the derelict land in the Lower Swansea Valley should be placed in the ownership of a single body. This does not necessarily mean public ownership and we suggest an alternative which, although private enterprise is involved, enables part of the increase in site values caused by development to be shared with the public who have helped to create it. But generally speaking, when we talk about ownership, it is public ownership that we have in mind. Under present conditions in the valley, the Local Planning Authority is largely powerless not only to prevent poor development but to encourage good development unless it owns the land. In some cases its inability to act is the result of legislation passed by Parliament. We begin therefore by cataloguing the reasons which make it necessary for the land to be acquired before development takes place.

1   The Lower Swansea Valley as it is today is the result of unplanned land use and, although planning legislation now goes some way towards preventing the same thing happening again, there are a number of gaps still to be closed. The excavation of nearly all the tips of industrial waste in the valley is not 'development' within the legal meaning of this term and therefore no planning permission is required for it. Although in the majority of cases the workings are subject to conditions imposed by the private owners of the land, in practice such conditions are not strictly enforced. Each owner is in any case concerned only with the working of his land to his own personal criteria. The result is a patchwork of excavations scattered throughout the valley with no coordination of levels or a planned working programme. If it had been possible to arrange such a programme immediately after the Second World War, some sites would today have been cleared completely, some would have remained untouched and could have been covered temporarily with vegetation; some sites would have been actively worked to rational levels. In short, the appearance of the valley would have been greatly improved without, it is believed, seriously affecting the rate of hardcore removal.

2   Between 3,000 and 4,000 tons of waste are produced monthly in the valley. Most of this is being tipped in accordance with conditions laid down by the Local Planning Authority. However, in certain areas, especially on Plots 26 and 27, this tipping is exempted from planning control by the Town and Country Planning (General Development) Order, 1963.*

---

* S.I. No. 709 of 1963. Class VIII (2), and Class XIX.

This means that the height and the superficial area of a tip already 60 ft above the valley floor is being increased without limit although there is adjacent land in other ownership which is below flood level and would be improved by tipping. Other areas in Great Britain have experienced similar difficulties from the application of this order to the Coal Board, and it would seem that a review of the exemptions provided by it is overdue. Until this is done, the difficulty that is created in the Swansea Valley is best overcome by the acquisition of the land both used for tipping and available for future tipping. This would enable a sensible long-term tipping plan to be arranged with all the firms concerned so that industrial waste is placed where it is required and in the way in which it can best assist the future use of the area.

3 In 1961 there were about twenty acres of derelict industrial buildings in the Project area. Although a local authority has adequate powers to remove derelict buildings, the cost has to be met by the authority unless the land happens to be either within a Development District, which until 1965 were restricted to small areas of high unemployment, or else in a National Park. Swansea was not made a Development District until October 1965 and it is not situated in a National Park, so unless the owners of the land could have been persuaded to remove the structures themselves the local authority would have been obliged either to clear the buildings at its own expense or to purchase the sites. This is an unsatisfactory situation and the question may be asked: How can buildings be prevented from being left in ruins or, having been permitted to become eyesores, how is it possible to remove them without a charge on the public? It is possible that buildings, particularly industrial or commercial buildings, can be prevented from becoming ruinous by making it expensive to keep them unoccupied. The proposal made in the White Paper on *Local Government Finance* (Cmnd 2923 of February 1966) for the payment of part-rates on unoccupied property could help in this direction. However, once a building is so ruinous that it is cheaper to demolish than to repair it then, as we have seen, the only practical remedy at present is for the local authority to acquire the land. A better solution might be to empower the appropriate Minister, after due inquiry, to make an order declaring that a ruinous building should be removed, with default powers vested in Local Planning Authorities to carry out the work and to charge the land with the cost.

4 The Lower Swansea Valley is a continuous triangular area roughly a mile wide at its base and three-and-a-half miles from base to apex. The undeveloped land provides a great opportunity for the comprehensive and imaginative development of recreational, residential and industrial areas. To avoid piecemeal development, there needs to be a degree of control higher than that provided by legislation at present. Already the road frontages of this triangle are being eroded by filling stations, garages, etc., whose *ad hoc* location is unrelated to a complete design. The fulfilment of such a design will, in the circumstances discussed in Chapter 11, necessarily be slow. It will be years before the jigsaw is complete, but unless the land is acquired it will be found that, because planning control is incomplete without land ownership, the pieces will never fit and the result will be as much a mess as it is now. In fact it will probably be worse, because then it will be a concrete sprawl which, unlike the tips, will not weather with age.

5 The need for a new road link to join the residential areas east and west of the river Tawe has been mentioned. This road would also, and quite incidentally, provide easy access to

unused land, thereby increasing its value considerably. It is logical that society which pays for the road should also share in the increase in site values which it creates.

These, then, are the main reasons which have led us to the conclusion that there must be a unification of the ownership of the derelict land in the Lower Swansea Valley. But if there is to be one owner, who should this owner be? It has been inferred that the public interest requires at least a share in the ownership and it now remains to consider ways in which this might be secured. There are three proposals which we suggest should be considered.

Proposed development agencies

Action by the local authority

As the whole of the Project area lies within the County Borough of Swansea where the local authority is also the Local Planning Authority, the most straightforward solution would be for the whole development area, that is to say both the valley floor and the urban areas requiring renewal on its sides (Figure 1.1), to be designated in the Development Plan as an area of comprehensive development to be acquired, replanned in detail and eventually redeveloped by the County Borough Council. This is the procedure that was followed in the redevelopment of Swansea's central shopping district, which was destroyed during the last war. The method has the advantage that the Council already possesses the power to act in this way. The main difficulty is finance. In a central shopping area, there is little risk of financial loss and good prospects of liquidating the capital debt and loan charges in a reasonably short time. The same situation does not exist in the valley but, provided that flexible and reasonably generous grant-aid for clearing derelict land is available, a start could be made. The redevelopment of old housing and the development of new council housing on marginal land on the valley sides would attract standard grants. If the Borough Council was so minded, it could, under the powers provided by the Local Authorities (Land) Act, 1963, develop its own light industrial estate as Caerphilly Urban District Council has done at Pontygwindy. This is not to say that all the conditions existing at Caerphilly which helped to make that particular venture a success are present in the Swansea situation, but there are few legal difficulties which prevent the Corporation from taking necessary action.

A consortium

An alternative method of developing the valley floor would be to form a consortium of the three principal interests concerned: (a) the owners of the land, (b) the local authority, and (c) the central Government acting through the Welsh Office. The proposal is that all the land would be valued on an appointed day and shares issued to the owners in proportion to the value of their interests (on the reversion of leases, the shares of a leaseholder would pass to the freeholder). The land would then be vested in a single company which could raise development capital and to whom the present income from the land, e.g. from hard-core working or from rents, would pass. The immediate income would facilitate preparatory planning and site clearing.

The Swansea Borough Council would participate in the equity[1] by the amount that the rate fund would normally be charged with the cost of roads and sewers. Its investment would also include the areas zoned for public use in the Development Plan, i.e. for schools and parks. The power to enable the Council to subscribe equity of this kind would have to be obtained by a private Bill. The Exchequer could either provide development capital on loan or on equity terms. A development board would be set up representing the shareholders.

During the last three years the Project's Committee has discussed this scheme with representatives of the landowners concerned, who have indicated their willingness to consider the proposal in detail. There are difficulties. The scheme is complicated; it envisages a compromise between public and private interests in the future development of land which may in practice be difficult but not impossible to obtain, and it would take time to complete the administrative arrangements. On the other hand it secures to the public a share in the increased land values, it makes the most productive land assist the development and maintenance of the least productive; it would maximize profits on the productive land, and would discourage land remaining unused, or even unsightly.

In this scheme only the valley floor, with its potential for future industrial and commercial use, could be considered. Urban renewal on the sides would still have to be the concern of the local authority which would separate responsibility for the two areas. To emphasize the demarcation of the areas in this way would be undesirable.

A development authority

The third alternative is to set up a small development authority to deal with the whole of the Lower Swansea Valley—both the floor and the sides together. This is not an original proposal but is an extension of the principle of the New Town Corporation specifically for dealing with urban renewal and industrial blight. It is an idea that has been discussed fairly widely during the last two years[2] and was especially commended by a Civic Trust Committee.[3] The authority that we have in mind would be financed by the Exchequer in the same way as a New Town Corporation, the extra cost of reclaiming derelict land being met by grant as in the case of Dawley New Town. In other respects, the authority would be expected to balance income and expenditure after allowing for standard grants for roads, for land reclamation, for slum clearance and for council housing.

An authority of this kind would, it is true, be an authority within an authority, and it may be questioned whether such an arrangement is necessary. We have, however, in mind that its membership should include members of the Swansea Borough Council in the same way that local councils are to be represented in the Peterborough, Ipswich and Northampton town development schemes. It would employ its own technical officers, and after completing the purpose for which it was created, namely the redevelopment of the floor and sides of the Lower Swansea Valley, it would be dissolved and responsibility for the developed area would revert to whatever local government body was then in existence. The life of the authority would be expected to last for the maximum development period envisaged in Chapter 11, namely for twenty years.

[1] References are given on p. 281.

It might be thought that we are proposing a sledgehammer to crack a walnut, but in putting forward this suggestion we are not thinking only or even primarily of the Lower Swansea Valley. There are urban regions where the combined problems of renewal and reclamation are far more acute than they are in Swansea. We do suggest, however, that it would be worth while to extend the New Town Corporation method experimentally to deal with this valley. It is a self-contained area and a considerable body of information about it has been built up by the project over the last four years. It would, we believe, be as good a place as any in which to run a pilot scheme of this kind.

In such an arrangement the closest possible cooperation would be necessary between the development agency and the local authority and it is reasonable to suggest that the former should only be set up by the Minister with the agreement of the Council concerned.

Of these three administrative arrangements, local authority, a consortium and a development authority, we conclude that in the context of Swansea alone the local authority could probably deal most effectively with the Lower Swansea Valley provided that a reasonable measure of financial help can be provided by the Exchequer, not only to prepare the area for re-use but to carry the Council over the early lean years when the return on its investment would be small. If, however, the need for an instrument to tackle urban renewal and industrial blight over large areas in Great Britain is considered, then we think that there is a case for setting up a pilot Development Authority in the valley where the basic research has already been completed.

However the development is carried out, the need for a high standard of design in what is for Swansea a strategic area cannot be sufficiently stressed. The site has immense possibilities and urban and landscape design of the first quality is needed. Otherwise, the area will become a mediocre hotch-potch which will be worse than the present varied and in parts striking landscape.

Derelict land in Great Britain

The 700 acres of derelict land in the Lower Swansea Valley is only a fraction of the total of such land in Great Britain. It may therefore be convenient in this report to consider quite briefly the extent of the national problem and the rate at which it is at present being dealt with. Unfortunately adequate information about the acreage, type and location of derelict land and the volume and type and distribution of the industrial waste is not available. As long ago as 1952, in a comprehensive paper on the subject of the restoration of derelict land,[4] J. R. Oxenham drew attention to this absence of essential statistics, and although the position has improved since, with the assembly of basic data by the Ministry of Housing and Local Government, this only began in 1964[5] and is confined to 'land so damaged by industrial or other development that it is incapable of beneficial use without treatment'. Thus land in current industrial use, such as present tipping sites and land which is derelict from natural causes (e.g. marshland), is excluded. In the Lower Swansea Valley out of a total of 1,174 acres, there are 346 acres of derelict land which come within the Ministry's definition and 803 acres which come within the definition we have used in Chapter 11. To provide the information that is needed, a detailed national survey of all derelict sites in Great Britain on the lines of the land utilization survey is essential.

On the basis of the latest information provided by the Ministry of Housing and Local Government (Appendix I) it will be seen that there is a total of 99,000 acres of derelict land in Great Britain of which 59,000 acres require treatment of some kind. It has been estimated that the national total is being increased annually at a net rate of 3,500 acres,[6] which means that the rate of reclamation is too low.

The number of acres of derelict land which have been reclaimed (including reclamation for building and restoration for amenity, such as playing fields and afforestation) can at the moment again only be estimated. This information should build up in the future as annual returns are made in accordance with the Ministry's Circular 65/64. All that is possible at the present time is to indicate the range of reclamation rates for different parts of Great Britain so as to provide some idea of how effective past efforts have been.

The highest rate of reclamation is achieved in thriving areas where the pressure of population creates a demand for housing, for industrial sites and for amenity. In the West Midlands, for example, the rate of reclamation since 1946 has been estimated at 600 acres a year,[7] of which 74 per cent is used for housing, and industry.[8] In the Potteries, out of 4,392 derelict acres in 1948, 332 acres had been reclaimed by 1952, an average of just over 80 acres a year.[4] In South Wales, between 1945 and 1963, about 500 acres had been reclaimed,[9] an average of 28 acres a year. Between December 1963 and December 1964, 405 acres were reclaimed or landscaped in South Wales and between December 1964 and December 1965 it is estimated that a further 507 acres will be dealt with. In the North-East Region the annual rate of reclamation from 1960 to 1965 was 72 acres and between 1965 and 1968 the average anticipated annual rate is 448 acres.[10] In Lancashire 1,000 acres had been reclaimed in the ten years before 1965, and in the North-West Region the local authorities are dealing with not less than 300 acres a year.[11]

Future needs

If a rate of 500 acres a year could be maintained it would take the Northern region at least twenty-five years to reclaim the worst of its derelict land, and if the same rate was applied to Wales it would take sixteen years. Obviously there is a need for a very great effort indeed if a problem which is partly illustrated by the Lower Swansea Valley is to be tackled within a reasonable time. The greatest difficulty in the past has been finance. This is illustrated by the fact that after the rate of grant was increased in April 1963 three times as many schemes for clearing derelict land were approved in Scotland in one year as in the previous three years.[12]

But finance has not been the only difficulty. Exchequer grants have been available to deal with land only in Development Districts, and even then only if the clearance was likely to promote employment. The first difficulty has now been largely overcome by including almost all the derelict land in Great Britain in new Development Areas,[13] but the second difficulty will remain until Section 5 of the Local Employment Act is replaced by less restrictive legislation which, it is hoped, will enable the local authorities to receive grant assistance for dealing with derelict land whether by landscaping or by clearance simply because the land is derelict. At the second Countryside in 1970 Conference, which was held in London between 10 and 12 November 1965, the Minister of Land and Natural Resources in a statement on 12 November 1965 said: 'The Government has in mind legislation—not necessarily part of the Countryside legislation—providing that expenditure by local authorities in England and Wales on the treatment of derelict land—that is land so damaged by industrial or other development that it must be treated before it can be restored to any useful purpose—should qualify for Exchequer aid.' This intention has been confirmed in a recent White Paper.[14] It is hoped that with the demise of the Ministry of Land and Natural Resources this legislation will not be forgotten and that the Ministry of Housing and Local Government and the Welsh Office will treat it as an essential and urgent inducement to the reclamation of derelict land in England and Wales.[26]

It is therefore to be hoped that both grants and powers will at last be combined to enable local authorities in England and Wales to begin to deal with the 59,000 acres of derelict land requiring early treatment. But this is only the end of an era of difficulty and frustration going back as we saw in Chapter 2 to the depression of the thirties. Grants and powers are not enough, the inadequacy of our present knowledge about the extent and character of derelict land has been mentioned. Statistics need to be refined. But there is a considerable body of other information which is lacking or which, if available, is not easily accessible.

A Land Research Unit

While considerable time and resources are spent on inquiring into the pollution of the air and of water, and rightly so, as yet the study of land pollution has not received very much attention. An Air Pollution Research Laboratory we have, a Water Pollution Research Laboratory we also have, but a Land Pollution Research Centre as yet we have not. What work that is being done, and much of it is of high quality, is being carried out by University and Government departments, by local authorities and by industry, on an *ad hoc* basis. There appears to be a need for some or all of the following:

1 An assembly of statistics and the preparation of a classified index of information relating to derelict land.
2 A national survey of derelict land on the lines of that carried out by the Lancashire County Council.
3 A review of legislation dealing with land reclamation and mineral working.
4 The development of ways of measuring costs and benefits of industrial tipping programmes and of reclamation schemes, including their social costs and benefits.
5 Research into the microbiology, ecology and chemistry of industrial wastes.
6 The assembly of information on (*a*) earth-moving equipment and its operating costs, (*b*) the cost of planting and the maintenance of vegetation, (*c*) the reclamation of derelict land in other parts of the world.
7 The application of methods of mapping and of measuring tip volumes using air photographs.
8 The application of computers for planning both mineral extraction and large-scale tipping programmes.
9 Research into the physiography, drainage, and settlement of waste heaps and of ways to stabilize them.
10 Research into the dispersal or treatment of wastes.
11 Research into the re-use of industrial waste.

The reality and extent of this need and the best way of meeting it should be properly assessed by an inquiry sponsored, it is suggested, by the Ministry of Housing and Local Government in association with the National Coal Board, the Central Electricity Generating Board and the Confederation of British Industry, who might also contribute towards its cost. The International Institute for Land Reclamation at Wageningen in Holland, valuable though it is, concentrates on the reclamation of poor-quality land for agricultural use. Research into industrial wastes has hitherto been primarily concerned with their revegetation,[15] but as was seen in Chapter 5 plant life is significantly affected by both chemical and physical circumstances while practical action is often limited by an imperfect understanding of the costs and benefits involved. A case for research into the 'built environment' was put to the Committee on Social Studies.[16] There is obviously an intimate relationship also between the 'built environment' and other uses of land, as the Heyworth Committee recognized, and the inquiry which we propose would need to take account of the recent proposal to set up a centre for environmental studies[17] as well as of the more obvious relationship between the pollution of land and the pollution of air and water. In the Lower Swansea Valley, for example, tips of industrial waste indirectly pollute the river and burning tips and heaps composed of fine particles, e.g. PFA or zinc residues, pollute the atmosphere.

It is not suggested that a large research establishment is required to deal with this subject. On the contrary, much of the work for which there appears to be a need might well be done in the universities and by industry itself, but it would seem that a measure of co-ordination and direction is needed which is now lacking. An inquiry on the lines we propose would clarify the position and enable policy decisions to be reached.

There are at least welcome signs of a wide interest in an awareness of the national problem of derelict land. For years, and especially since the Second World War, people like the late Sir Dudley Stamp, Professor S. H. Beaver, J. R. Oxenham, U. A. Coates, John Casson and many others, have been prophets in the wilderness and it must have seemed to them at times that their preaching was without effect. Fortunately slag heaps and the affluent society are not compatible. Probably more derelict land has been reclaimed for housing and industry since the last war than the total reclaimed for any other use before or since. Society today does not have to tolerate the conditions which George Orwell once described—'the frightful landscapes where your horizon is ringed completely round by jagged great mountains and under foot is mud and ashes and overhead steel cables where tubs of dirt travel slowly across miles of countryside'[18] and if it is properly informed it will be able to avoid replacing one kind of frightfulness with the twentieth-century kind so vividly described by Ian Nairn and Peter Blake.[19, 20]

In 1963 the Ministry of Housing and Local Government issued *New Life for Dead Lands*, a booklet dealing with a number of sites showing the 'before' and 'after' of reclamation schemes. This was followed by a Civic Trust study entitled *Derelict Land*, an original attempt to examine the scale of the problem and to estimate the cost of dealing with it. Meanwhile, a series of regional economic surveys were produced on Scotland, the North-East, the West Midlands and the North-West, in each of which the need for effective regional action to deal with derelict land was recognized. In June 1965 an excellent regional survey of derelict land in the North-East Region was carried out by a technical sub-committee of planning officers. The report which was prepared by the Durham County Council clearly states the difficulties and proposes both immediate and long-term action on a national basis. At the same time that this survey was being completed, preparations for the Duke of Edinburgh's Study Conference on the Countryside in 1970 included a Study Group (No. 12) on Derelict Land which also produced a useful memorandum.[21]

Assessment of the Project

It is against this background that the Lower Swansea Valley Project needs to be seen. Almost fortuitously, certainly without any clear appreciation of the extent and complexity of the national problem, a decision was taken in 1960 to investigate in depth what has proved to be as comprehensive an area of industrial waste land as any to be found in Britain. What is more, the value of the interdisciplinary approach has, we believe, been confirmed by the various studies we have mentioned. We are conscious of the Project's limitations but these have been partly due to a lack of basic economic and social statistics of a kind that is not easily assembled by local surveys.

Apart from the academic content of the work, the Project throughout has been an extremely valuable experiment in community relations. The firms and owners of the land in the valley have responded in cooperating with the scheme, and a basis of understanding and confidence between them and the Project has been created which will be essential in the later development of the area. The Royal Engineers, especially the 53rd (Welsh) Div. R.E., with its headquarters in Swansea, has come to regard the valley as its own training area. The Forestry Commission has acted as the scheme's unpaid consultants. The Corporation's officers and especially the Town Clerk have been continuously helpful. The schools have used the valley for field studies, and student volunteers, many from overseas, have helped dig and plant and clear the land.

It is natural that we, the Project's Committee and its sponsors, who have seen the proposal develop through the last five years, are concerned that these pages should not be its epitaph; and that others will carry forward where we have left off, not only in the Lower Swansea Valley but wherever derelict land and poor urban environment are found. In order that the scheme should not run down too quickly after the publication of this report, a Forester with special responsibility for the conservation of planted areas will be maintained until September 1968. The biological research into the problems of revegetating spoil heaps will also be continued, at least until 1968 with the help of a grant made by the Natural Environment Research Council. By 1968 it is hoped that a long-term policy for the area will have been settled. To assist this we suggest that, on the publication of this report, the Secretary of State for Wales in association with the Minister of Housing and Local Government should set up a technical working party to consider what action is required to bring about the comprehensive redevelopment of the Lower Swansea Valley on the lines we have proposed.

The vision of the future is of a valley in which people live and play as well as work, without these activities intruding much on each other; a valley which offers the seclusion of wooded slopes and quiet paths as well as the activity of its workshops; a valley where the sides and the floor are brought together, not only in the daily journey to work as in the past, but for shopping and for entertainment, for walks along the river bank, for games and for school; a valley which, instead of dividing the Borough, unites it in a new focus of landscape beauty, enjoyment and employment. This is a vision which is quite capable of becoming a reality with the local and regional resources which are available provided that a determined effort is made to achieve it.*

Note on powers and finance for the rehabilitation of derelict land

Powers

1 *The National Parks and Access to the Countryside Act, 1949,* as amended by the Local Authorities (Land) Act, 1963, enables local authorities to carry out such work as they consider expedient to bring into use or to improve the appearance of land which appears to them to be derelict, neglected or unsightly. These powers may be exercised by an authority either on land belonging to them or, with the consent of all persons interested, on other land. A local authority may acquire land compulsorily for these purposes.

2 *Section 36 of the Town and Country Planning Act, 1962,* provides that if a local planning authority considers that the condition of any garden, vacant site or other open land seriously injures the amenity of the locality, they may require the owner or occupier to abate the injury. A number of Court decisions have shown that this power is of limited scope and it appears that while the section is not completely ineffectual, the circumstances in which it could be invoked successfully are likely to be limited.

3 *Section 28 of the Town and Country Planning Act, 1962,* empowers the Local Planning Authority to serve an order requiring the discontinuance of the use of land or the alteration or removal of any buildings or works on it. This order is subject to confirmation by the Minister of Housing and Local Government but the Planning Authority must be prepared to pay compensation (open market value). These provisions do not bind the Crown.

4 *Under Section 58 of the Public Health Act, 1936,* a local authority can, if it appears to them that any building or structure is in such a condition that it is dangerous, apply to a court of summary jurisdiction for an order requiring the owner to execute such work as may be necessary to obviate the danger or, if he so elects, to demolish the building or structure. If the person on whom an order is made fails to comply with it in the time specified the local authority is empowered to execute the order and recover expenses reasonably incurred. Under Section 25 of the Public Health Act, 1961, a local authority may take any necessary steps to remove such danger without the need to obtain a court order.

5 *Section 27 of the Public Health Act, 1961,* empowers local authorities to deal with ruinous and dilapidated buildings and neglected sites. A survey carried out in May 1963 amongst some thirteen local authorities in South Wales indicates that the powers of the section are little used.

6 The experience of the Welsh Office is that derelict site clearance schemes by local authorities are usually carried out under the powers relating to the purpose for which the land is to be eventually used.

Finance

7 *Section 20 of the Industrial Development Act, 1966,*[26] empowers the Secretary of State to make grants to local authorities towards the cost of carrying out work on derelict, neglected

---

* A T.V.A. in miniature perhaps, see Ref. 22.

Note on powers
and finance for the
rehabilitation of
derelict land

or unsightly land situated in a development area. The work must enable the land to be brought into use or must be directed towards improving its appearance, and the power to make a grant can be exercised only where it appears to the Board of Trade that the work is expedient with a view to contributing to the development of industry in the development area. The rate of grant is 85 per cent of the approved estimated net cost in addition to any rate deficiency grant attracted by the expenditure subject to a maximum aggregate Exchequer assistance under both grants of 95 per cent.

8 Grants are also available under the *National Parks and Access to the Countryside Act, 1949*, towards schemes carried out under Section 89, but only where the land is in a National Park or an area of outstanding natural beauty. The rate of grant may be up to 75 per cent of the cost incurred by the local authority in carrying out the work.

9 Apart from these two sources of grant, local authorities have to rely on their own resources to meet the cost of clearance schemes. Loan sanction is usually available and this has the effect of spreading the rate burden over a period of years.

10 *Under section 52 of the Requisitioned Land and War Works Act, 1945*, owners may apply for reimbursement of the cost of the removal of war works from their land. Where the work is considered to be in the public interest, the total cost less the amount of compensation paid or payable under the Compensation (Defence) Act, 1939, is reimbursed.

11 *Derelict land of Service Departments.* Service Departments have no legal responsibility for rehabilitating land which they hold before disposing of it, and it has been the general policy to look to the owners of derequisitioned land to carry out any necessary rehabilitation works and to claim reimbursement of the cost. This policy, however, has rarely achieved the results hoped for, because most owners have preferred not to take the trouble.

The Service Departments have accordingly been considering alternative methods of dealing with their sites and whenever the Welsh Office learns that one of the Service Departments intends to dispose of land, representations are now made to try to secure clearance of the site *before* it is derequisitioned.

Appendix I

Derelict land in England and Wales at 31 December 1964

Region	Area of dereliction County	Acres	Total acres	Acreage justifying treatment	Type of dereliction justifying treatment Spoil heaps	Holes and pits	Other
Northern	Durham	8,710					
	Northumberland	7,431					
	Cumberland	2,317					
	Other	1,364					
			19,822	13,291	4,449	1,600	7,242

Appendix 1—*contd.*

Area of dereliction			Type of dereliction justifying treatment				
Region	County	Acres	Total acres	Acreage justifying treatment	Spoil heaps	Holes and pits	Other
Yorkshire and Humberside	East and West Ridings	6,870					
	Lincolnshire (Lindsey)	2,863					
			9,733	5,660	1,599	3,128	933
North-West	Lancashire	11,522					
	Cheshire	932					
	Other	330					
			12,784	9,453	3,132	2,007	4,314
East Midland	Derbyshire (excl. High Peak)	1,913					
	Notts	1,443					
	Leics	1,398					
	Lincs (excl. Lindsey)	1,026					
	Other	362					
			6,142	3,899	1,221	1,628	1,050
West Midland	Staffs	9,052					
	Salop	1,429					
	Warwicks	931					
	Worcs	862					
	Other	16					
			12,290	10,991	4,678	2,073	4,240
South-West	Cornwall	14,284					
	Somerset	1,034					
	Other	724					
			16,042	2,763	1,796	322	645
South-East England	Norfolk	1,739					
	Oxfordshire	1,749					
	Kent	1,023					
	Bucks	631					
	Other	2,945					
			8,087	5,134	58	3,267	1,809
Total for England			84,900	51,191	16,933	14,025	20,233
Wales	Monmouthshire	4,671					
	Glamorgan	2,560					
	Caernarvonshire	2,422					
	Denbighshire	1,642					
	Pembrokeshire	1,038					
	Carmarthenshire	764					
	Flintshire	643					
	Other	451					
			14,191	8,304	5,987	1,170	1,147
Total England and Wales			99,091	59,495	22,920	15,195	21,380

Source: Ministry of Housing and Local Government

References

1. See *The Times* of 18 April 1962, Dennis Pilcher in the *Chartered Surveyor*, December 1963, A. Samuels in the *Financial Times Survey of Building and Contracting*, 11 November 1963, and the proposals for the cooperative redevelopment of Slough.
2. *The Times*, 18 April 1962, *The Guardian*, 21 January 1964, *Estates Gazette*, vol. 195, no. 5221, 14 August 1965.
3. Civic Trust, *Urban redevelopment*. Report of a Committee appointed by the Civic Trust, June 1962, para. 133.
4. J. R. Oxenham, *The Restoration of Derelict Land*. Report: Public Works and Municipal Services Congress, 1952.
5. M.H.L.G. Circular 65/64.
6. *Derelict Land*. A study of industrial dereliction and how it may be redeemed by the Civic Trust, 1962. Includes a useful bibliography.
7. Department of Economic Affairs, *The West Midlands*: A Regional Study, H.M.S.O., 1965.
8. 'Reclamation of derelict land in the Midlands', unpublished study by the Birmingham School of Architecture, July 1963.
9. 'Derelict land in South Wales', unpublished report by the Welsh Office.
10. Durham County Council, 'Derelict land in the North-East', an unpublished report, June 1965.
11. Department of Economic Affairs, *The North-West*: A Regional Study, H.M.S.O., 1965.
12. Scottish Development Department, *Report for 1963*, Cmnd 2326, H.M.S.O., Edinburgh, 1964.
13. *Investment Incentives*, Cmnd 2874, H.M.S.O., 1966.
14. *Local Government Finance England and Wales*, Cmnd 2923, H.M.S.O., 1966.
15. G. T. Goodman et al., *Ecology and the Industrial Society*, Blackwell's Scientific Publications, Oxford, 1965.
16. *Report of the Committee on Social Studies*, Cmnd 2660, H.M.S.O., June 1965.
17. *The Times*, 12 March 1966.
18. George Orwell, *The Road to Wigan Pier*, Penguin Books.
19. Ian Nairn, 'Outrage', *Architectural Review*, 1955.
20. Peter Blake, *God's Own Junkyard*, Holt, Rinehart and Winston, New York, 1964.
21. The Countryside in 1970 (Study Group No. 12), 'The reclamation and clearance of derelict land', Royal Society of Arts.
22. Julian Huxley, *T.V.A.—Adventure in Planning*, The Architectural Press, London, 1963.
23. Ministry of Housing and Local Government, *New Life for Dead Lands*, H.M.S.O., 1963.
24. *The North-East: A Programme for Regional Development and Growth*, Cmnd 2206, H.M.S.O., 1963.
25. *Central Scotland: A Programme for Development and Growth*, Cmnd 2188, H.M.S.O., 1963.
26. Section 20 of the Industrial Development Act, 1966, replaced Section 5 of the Local Employment Act, 1960, after this chapter was completed; note 7 was modified in proof. It remains to be seen whether the rate of reclamation will be significantly increased.

Authorship

This chapter was written by K. J. Hilton.

Summary of the main conclusions and recommendations made in the Report

The following summary of the main conclusions and recommendations in the Report has been included to help the busy reader and to provide a convenient digest for the public authorities and private developers who will be concerned, at a later stage, with implementing some of them.

Chapter 4: Geology, soil mechanics and foundation engineering

Conclusions and recommendations

1 From existing records of previous investigations, together with work undertaken by the Project using seismic and gravimetric traverses, and by the drilling of new boreholes in the valley area, it has been possible to build up a comprehensive record of the sub-surface solid geology, particularly in relation to the coal seams. The extent and type of drift material found in the area have also been recorded.

2 Geophysical traverses across the valley floor have revealed the approximate shape of the north–south buried valley in the solid rock.

3 In certain areas, particularly Trewyddfa Road and Graig Road, quarrying and opencast mining have over-steepened the sides of the valley, thereby increasing the tendency for soil creep and land slip.

4 Extensive underground workings in the area give rise to two particular problems:

(a) The exact location of old adits, shafts and air vents prior to construction work.

(b) The possibility of subsidence if old flooded workings were to be pumped dry.

5 A comprehensive survey of existing buildings has failed to reveal any subsidence which can be directly attributed to mining.

6 The Project area is surrounded by and underlain at depth by a series of rocks which generally offer good engineering characteristics, but the Project area itself lies almost entirely on a flat marshy plain, consisting in parts of deep deposits of alluvium which have poor foundation properties.

7 The tipping of large quantities of waste material in depth within the Project area has served to reclaim large areas by improving the foundation conditions and to a large extent has reduced the foundation problems generally associated with soft alluvium.

8 The bearing capacity of the fill material which varies from $\frac{1}{2}$–2 tons per sq ft may, in

certain circumstances, be improved, where required, by the use of vibro-flotation or vibro-replacement.

9   At particular sites, detailed investigations will be required to detect the presence of chemicals, such as sulphates, which may have a detrimental effect on structural foundation materials.

10   On the basis of the contour map produced by the Project, the quantities of fill material existing in the northern part of the Project area have been estimated. This estimate has been presented on a mean height basis enabling rapid appreciation of the implications of proposed future levels to be made. A computer programme has been written enabling the quantities of fill in other parts of the Project area to be evaluated if and when required.

Chapter 5:   Revegetation techniques in the Lower Swansea Valley

Conclusions

1   The present study has confirmed that there are three principal types of derelict ground in the Lower Swansea Valley:

(i)   Infertile and largely non-toxic clay loams, badly eroded by former smelter smoke pollution.

(ii)   Tips of relatively innocuous waste materials, e.g. coal shale, foundry sand, furnace slag, domestic refuse.

(iii) Tips of waste poisonous to plant growth and derived from the smelting mainly of copper and/or zinc ores.

2   The successful establishment of forest trees (e.g. Japanese Larch, Lodgepole Pine, Birch, Corsican Pine, Alder, Norway Spruce, Scots Pine, Black Locust, and Silver Fir) using normal forestry techniques and the successful establishment of agricultural grass leys (e.g. mixtures of Red Fescue, Bent-grass, Cocksfoot, Timothy, Perennial Ryegrass, Red Clover and White Clover) using normal agricultural methods have proved possible on ground types (i) and (ii), provided adequate general NPK fertilizer is incorporated.

3   A further period of study of these tree and grass trials is needed to see whether their initial establishment success is followed by a satisfactory long-term performance.

4   The revegetation of the copper and more particularly the zinc tips (type iii) presents a far more difficult problem and so far two main lines of approach have proved very encouraging:

(a) The incorporation of lime, general NPK fertilizer and a cheap, readily available form of organic matter, e.g. domestic refuse or sewage sludge, allows the successful establishment of Common Bent-grass, an agricultural grass ley and certain shrubs, notably Privet, Buddleia and Gorse. Growth of the grasses and some of the shrubs falls off after two years and a further period of study is required to see whether these plants respond to further additions of NPK fertilizer or whether a metallic toxicity effect is slowly becoming manifest.

(b) It is possible to establish certain strains of grasses, especially Common Bent-grass and Creeping Bent-grass, which have been found growing on the spoil heaps of old lead/zinc or copper mines and have evolved a special degree of tolerance to these metallic poisons.

Summary of the main
conclusions and
recommendations made
in the Report

They grow well if a general NPK fertilizer is added to the tip material but much better if one of the organic amendments is also incorporated. A further study is needed to assess their long-term performance.

5   The micro-organisms in normal soils (which are responsible for releasing plant nutrients from old dead growth ready for use by the established plants during the following years) are present in the copper and zinc tips, but in very small numbers; soil animals are largely absent. This study indicates, however, that the bacteria are tolerant of the high levels of poisonous metal and their populations will quickly build up, given adequate supplies of nitrogen and organic matter, so as to initiate a normal cycle of nutrient release. However, it is not known at present whether they will, in doing so, release copper and zinc and hence create conditions toxic to plant growth.

6.   The study of the revegetation techniques on the copper and zinc tips carried out so far has raised questions of considerable biological interest, and it is felt that their follow-up would not only contribute materially to our knowledge of this field but also improve the general applicability of revegetation techniques to reclamation work elsewhere in Britain and in other parts of the world.

Recommendations

1   The exact way in which the future revegetation of the valley will be most effectively and economically achieved will depend on what suitable soil amendments are most available and can readily be transported to the tip sites. The following recommendations can be advanced:

(*a*) Ground types (i) and (ii) can be treated successfully without departing radically from accepted forestry and agricultural practices at a cost of not more than £35 per acre (exclusive of any site clearance, earth-moving, e.g. filling in erosion channels, and fencing).

(*b*) Ground type (iii) should as far as possible be cleared of its tip material by giving priority to hardcore extraction industries in these areas. The residual metallic contamination could then be best treated by burying it with a layer of more innocuous waste, e.g. direct dumping of a layer of domestic refuse up to about six feet thick, with the surface properly covered by a layer of suitable inert material such as spent foundry sand so as to avoid a possible risk of nuisance. This could be planted after two to three years; or by using spent foundry sand or steel slag at least 9 in thick set to grass. Direct dumping of domestic refuse may not cost more than normal refuse disposal and the resulting ground may be revegetated at the usual agricultural rates. The cost of using the sand or steel slag may be up to £400 per acre (excluding stone picking, cultivation and fencing).

Where for various reasons it is undesirable or impossible to remove and level the copper and zinc tips, it is suggested that a 1–3 in cover of organic amendment plus lime and fertilizer be sown to a tolerant strain of grass seed especially multiplied for this purpose. This procedure would probably not cost more than about £185 per acre (excluding stone picking, cultivation and fencing).

(*c*) Careful attention should be given to a maintenance programme of fertilizer application and on grassed areas of cutting and if possible controlled grazing.

2   It is recommended that a special advisory group be constituted not only to maintain the

existing tree plantations and grassed areas but also to provide continued technical information and advice to whatever authority is ultimately charged with revegetation under the land-use plan.

Chapter 6:   The river Tawe

Conclusions

1   The Tawe is a 'flashy river' with a rapid alternation of high and low flows.

2   Floods in the Lower Swansea Valley are caused by the overflow of the river into the Llansamlet marsh, and thence into the Project area.

3   Flooding is influenced by factors other than rainfall, e.g. by tide, by obstructions such as weirs, bridges and narrow culverts, and by the filling of flood storage space by tipping.

4   Evidence suggests that average flood levels in the Lower Swansea Project area have increased over the past fifty years.

5   The Tawe is only a limited water resource for industry in the absence of any form of water storage.

6   Pollution levels in the Tawe make it generally inimical to fish life, but the position is improving and can be expected to improve in the future.

Recommendations

1   The valley should be protected from flooding by a levée system.

2   At a later stage of development the Nant-y-Fendrod should be culverted.

3   The Tawe should be regarded in the long term primarily as an amenity. This use is not incompatible with its serving industry as a limited water resource for cooling water provided that the water abstracted is recirculated satisfactorily.

4   The Tawe is not suitable for navigation without considerable improvement to the existing river gradient. It is not considered that the cost of this would be justified. It is therefore recommended that the present tidal movement in the river be stabilized eventually, by means of a movable barrage located in the vicinity of the New Cut Bridge, at a cost of about £120,000. This would transform the appearance of the river and would provide Swansea with a valuable amenity on its eastern side.

Chapter 7:   Highway and transportation planning

Conclusions

1   The Lower Swansea Valley is advantageously situated relative to all major elements of the existing transportation network. This network is fast becoming inadequate to meet the needs of future road traffic. The A48 Swansea to Cardiff and the A465/A40 Swansea–Ross Spur roads require special attention.

2   The construction of the Morriston bypass should be expedited.

Summary of the main
conclusions and
recommendations made
in the Report

3 The peripheral roads around the valley, particularly the A4067 (the Neath Road) and B4292 (the Foxhole/Nant-y-Ffin Road), are inadequate and should be improved.

4 No further railway closures are envisaged. The Beeching Plan proposals for the Swansea area will, if implemented, greatly enhance the development potential of the Lower Swansea Valley.

5 The Swansea canal should eventually be filled in when alternative arrangements have been made to meet the needs of industrial water supply.

6 A complete and comprehensive new road network for the valley floor is essential.

7 There is no significant traffic demand for a new cross-river bridge link in the centre of the valley. Such a link is nevertheless most desirable in terms of the general development of the Borough.

8 A new network of pedestrian footpaths connecting surrounding residential areas with new open space and amenity areas on the valley floor is required.

Recommendations

1 The M4 'South Wales Motorway' should be extended westwards as far as Llanelli and the A465/A40 trunk road between Swansea and the Ross Spur should be improved to conventional dual carriageway standards.

2 No major improvements in rail and port facilities other than those recommended in the Beeching and Rochdale reports are considered necessary.

3 The A4067 (Neath Road) should be replaced by a two-lane dual carriageway connecting the town centre with the Morriston bypass.

4 The B4292 (Foxhole/Nant-y-Ffin Road) should be widened to a uniform three-lane standard with a realigned section bypassing the existing settlements of Cwm, Pentrechwyth and Bonymaen.

5 A new network for the valley floor together with a network of footpaths should be constructed along the lines recommended in Chapter 11. This involves a new railway bridge over a new north–south spine road, and a new road bridge across the river Tawe.

Chapter 8: The people, their environment and their houses

Conclusions

1 The population of the area of the Lower Swansea Valley is a normal cross-section of the County Borough of Swansea as measured by their distribution along indices of age, sex, marital status, occupation, status grading, educational attainment, income, receipt of free school meals, of children taken into care, of juvenile delinquency, except for some shortage of the most wealthy groups.

2 This 'normal' population is living in a substandard environment, judged by the standards of the Borough as a whole and of other and newer towns, and in ways enumerated below:

(a) The buildings are old and many are in need of replacement and renewal. These include:
  (i) public buildings, e.g. schools, (ii) residential buildings.

The people, their
environment and their
houses

(b) (i) There is a shortage of acres of open space per head of population. Provision at 2·44 acres per 1,000 persons in Swansea East is below the Swansea West level (7·32 acres per 1,000) and below the recommended national figure (6 acres for playing fields alone per 1,000). (ii) Such open space as is provided is of a lower standard than that in Swansea West.

3   The Valley offers possibilities because of its excellent road and rail position for the provision of recreational amenities for the sub-region as well as for the valley and the east side.

4   Despite 1 and 2 above, the people are not leaving the valley. Population is declining only in the older wards to the south of the area. East and north of the valley the population is increasing.

5   Building and improvement of buildings is being undertaken extensively in the valley area and on balance (up to 1963) by private individuals and companies slightly more than by the local authority.

6   There is a movement from Swansea West to Swansea East for persons in the income group up to and just above the national average wage and particularly of those working in the north, east, and south-east of and around the Borough.

7   The reasons which have taken people to the valley area have been mainly economic, principally cheap houses and reduced costs of travel.

8   Applicants for council houses do not always know well the geography of the whole Borough nor the respective merits in terms of their life situation of various house locations.

9   The Borough still needs to build (a) new houses to accommodate an expected population increase to 1981 (over 9,000 dwellings). (b) 2,700 new dwellings between 1961 and 1981 to reduce overcrowding and sharing; (c) new houses to replace those which are outworn; it needs also (d) to improve those that can be brought up to standard. (c) and (d) together make a total of 10,000.

10   The conception of the valley floor as a problem of industrial dereliction considered separately from the valley sides thought of principally as residential areas is artificial in terms of the present problem.

11   The weight of land development has shifted from industry to residential use.

Recommendations

1   Where parts of the valley sides need redeveloping, contiguous areas of the valley floor could be taken over for residential development, thus making houses available near to those being replaced. (This recommendation is subject to the findings of further microclimatological study—see page 292.)

2   It is suggested that sewers and services be provided and houses be built, suitably interspersed with open space and other relevant amenity such as primary schools, shops, meeting places, on undeveloped land:

(a) On the east side of the valley up to the railway.
(b) On the west side of the valley up to the Tawe.

3   In doing this, care should be taken to graft new settlements on to existing ones.

Summary of the main
conclusions and
recommendations made
in the Report

4   Housing can after this extend further into the central area of the valley if this is not allocated to or taken up by industry. (This is subject to the findings of further micro-climatological study—see page 292.)

5   Any such housing should be at a cost suitable for those with a weekly income (at 1963 rates) of £10–£20, i.e. total outgoings including rates should be in the maximum range of £2 10s.–£5 per week. Since the clustering is likely to be about £15, a maximum rent of £4 may be desirable (1963 prices).

6   The valley sides and the valley floor should be looked upon as one urban renewal exercise with a master plan, with detailed development of small areas by stages.

7   Occupants are most likely to be found among those who work to the north, east and south-east of the Borough, and in the town centre.

8   Since the number of low income receivers requiring rehousing is likely to increase as they are displaced by urban renewal, including those displaced from the valley sides, there is a case for siting here specially low cost dwellings for the lower income groups because proximity to the town centre will also (a) reduce their living costs and (b) make labour available in that area.

9   Attention must be paid in housing administration and housing management (a) to suiting houses in the valley to the clients; (b) to explaining the implications of locations to each in relation to his situation bearing in mind conclusion 8 above. It is noted that houses are likely to be more acceptable than flats or maisonettes.

10   The valley should be upgraded and developed to continue to house a quarter of the town's population, including the increases to 1981, i.e. there should be a net increase in the numbers of houses in the valley in order to retain the present proportion.

11   Part of the derelict areas of the valley should be developed as open space (in addition to the open space which should be a necessary part of the housing development). In particular:

12   Two parks are suggested, (a) on the east; (b) on the west.

In both cases these should run down from the hillside to the river. Park (a) should start in the old colliery tip behind Cwm school and run down to the river linking with Plot 33 and (b) on the common land of Graig Trewyddfa and run down to the Tawe's west bank.

13   A riverside walk should be planned, with which park 12 (b) above would link.

14   Certain tip areas could be used for such developments as adventure playgrounds and bicycle tracks.

15   Part of the area should be developed as free ranging open space.

16   Playing fields similar to the King George V playing fields should be developed in the north.

17   The recreational area should include an indoor recreation centre for winter recreation in particular, and its location in the Lower Swansea Valley should be considered as part of the regional plan for sport and recreation.

18   Any severe air pollution in the development of new industry in the valley should be avoided because of the already existing large increase in residential use.

19   Further research should be undertaken into (a) the physical structure of dwellings, and (b) the social fabric, to avoid unnecessary destruction of dwellings or of social life.

Chapter 9 : The prospects for industrial use

Conclusions and Recommendations

Population and employment trends

1   The total insured population of West South Wales is growing very slowly. The two industries dominating regional employment are still metal manufacturing and mining. The effect of the increased substitution of capital for labour in the steel and coal industries is likely to result in considerable future unemployment. The growth of employment in the region will have to be increased substantially to provide an extra 30–40,000 jobs by 1981.

Industrial location

2   Since the Second World War, a considerable number of new establishments have been set up in West South Wales. In the main they appear to have been successful. Information was gathered about the motives of an appreciable sample of the firms in setting up these establishments, and about their experience of operating in the region.

3   More effective inducements are required to attract manufacturing industry to locate in West South Wales. The recent proposals (Cmnd 2784, 1966) will help, but in the long term more selective inducements are required.

The Lower Swansea Valley as an industrial site

4   The Lower Swansea Valley is centrally located in a region of nearly half a million people and parts of it could provide valuable industrial sites.

A regional growth policy

5   The industrial land use of the valley depends on having an effective policy for industrial growth in West South Wales. In the absence of such a policy it is unlikely that the comprehensive redevelopment of the Lower Swansea Valley will be undertaken. Such redevelopment is essential if manufacturing industry is to be attracted to the area.

Chapter 10 : Visual improvement

Conclusions and recommendations

1   The visual improvement of derelict land is an essential first step towards its eventual redevelopment for industrial, residential and amenity use.

2   The cost of doing this is low in comparison with the long-term benefits to be obtained although at present many of these benefits cannot be adequately measured.

3   The total impression of dereliction and neglect is as much an aggregate of a large number of small eyesores such as fences, wirescape, untidy verges, etc., as a single tip or a derelict building.

4   Powers should be available to enable a Local Planning Authority to deal effectively with such eyesores. Early consideration should be given by the Minister of Housing and Local Government to replacing the Litter Act with more comprehensive legislation dealing with derelict buildings, industrial tipping as well as domestic litter, and as to whether legislation of this kind is best administered by the Courts.

Summary of the main
conclusions and
recommendations made
in the Report

5   There is some evidence that the indiscriminate dumping of industrial rubbish, as opposed to the waste from extractive industry, is the result of uncoordinated policy for its collection and disposal. A regional study of the situation in South Wales would be valuable.

6   Schools should be encouraged to take part in efforts to upgrade the environment of the community at large. In the Swansea Valley, vandalism has been reduced as a result of schools participation in tree planting and conservation. This kind of activity needs to be continued on a more permanent basis and it is suggested that Swansea County Borough Council might consider how this can be achieved.

7   The participation of voluntary bodies such as the Civic Trust and International Voluntary Service in civic schemes of visual improvement ought to be encouraged by local planning authorities, even though the help that such bodies can provide is necessarily limited. What seems to be required is an effective dialogue between bodies with statutory powers and responsibilities for planning and development and those voluntary associations of citizens who are actively interested in their civic environment.

8   The deployment of Royal Engineer plant units of the Territorial Army in the clearance of derelict sites in public ownership has already offered valuable training as well as performing a public service.

Chapter 11:   The use of derelict land

Conclusions and recommendations

1   The existing development plan for the Lower Swansea Valley should be revised.

2   The traditional industrial land use of the floor should be replaced by an integrated scheme for housing, amenity, and industry, with the following distribution:

Industrial and Commercial—407 acres
Housing—115 acres
Amenity—120 acres

Alternatively, the area designated for industrial and commercial use could be reduced by eighty acres to provide additional residential areas and by a further thirty acres to provide sites for a large sports centre and a school.

The provision of roads and services and the reorganization of certain tips to five principal levels are suggested in this chapter, and a proposed phasing of the above development is given on page 254.

3   New industry should not be fume-producing. Further climatological data are required before housing is developed on the valley floor.

4   The residential sides and the industrial floor of the valley should be treated together as an area of comprehensive redevelopment. There should be a structural survey of old housing areas.

5   Parts of the valley not scheduled for early development should be temporarily landscaped to provide a pleasant prospect at least for a number of years. Arrangements should be made to maintain areas already planted with trees and shrubs.

Chapter 12 : An economic assessment of the land-use proposals

Conclusions and recommendations

1 Further development in manufacturing industry is essential to the economic health of South-West Wales.

2 Part of this development could reasonably be located in the Lower Swansea Valley where over 400 acres are available for industrial and commercial use as in the Project's plan.

3 The cost of the development of roads, industrial and residential sites and amenity areas will be of the order of £3 million.

4 It is essential that the valley should be treated as a single project and developed by a single authority.

5 Although it is unlikely on the basis of the present demand that the total value of land that is reclaimed would cover the cost of reclamation, there would be an important indirect benefit to the community as a whole. In the long term an authority developing the whole area would be likely to get a good return on its investment.

6 There is a strong case for central Government grants towards the cost of reclamation.

Chapter 13 : Land assembly and development agencies

Conclusions and recommendations

1 It is essential that all land to be developed should be acquired by one (preferably a public) body.

2 The local authority already has adequate powers to enable it to carry out comprehensive development schemes. The main difficulty in dealing with areas like the Lower Swansea Valley has been finance, but recent Government proposals might make it possible for the authority to take a fresh initiative.

3 As an alternative, a small development authority set up in association with the Swansea County Borough Council should be considered.

4 Such an authority might have the structure and powers similar to those of Development Corporations established under the New Town legislation but it would be concerned only with urban renewal and the reclamation of derelict industrial land.

5 An authority on these lines could serve as a pilot authority for the development of other areas in Great Britain where the twin problems of obsolescence and industrial blight require urgent treatment.

6 It is recommended that the Secretary of State for Wales in association with the Minister of Housing and Local Government take further expert advice as to the financial and administrative feasibility of this proposal.

7 In the meantime, it is recommended that as much of the land as possible on the valley floor should be acquired by the local authority or by the Land Commission, and that a survey of the older housing on the valley sides be carried out by Swansea C.B.C. with the help of the Welsh Office, in order to define the boundaries of the future area of comprehensive redevelopment.

8 There is evidence of a need for research into the pollution of land. It is recommended that the Ministry of Housing and Local Government should sponsor an inquiry to establish the extent of this need and the most effective way of meeting it.

Appendix

The climatology and air pollution of the Lower Swansea Valley and respiratory symptoms and lung function in Llansamlet

---

I The climatology of the Lower Swansea Valley

J. Oliver, B.A., F.R.Met.S.

Climatology and planning

Climatic factors are often ignored or given only conventional and perfunctory attention in planning studies. Their relevance and significance varies. Whilst in many instances in dealing with small areas they have limited importance, and it may be justifiably felt that any adjustments which they require in day-to-day life have already been made, there are situations in which their effects can be more critical. The importance of topographically determined local climates has been demonstrated by several studies in Britain and elsewhere, and localities surrounded by marginal higher ground rising only a few hundreds of feet or less have been shown to be liable to quite drastic unfavourable climatic features. Most notable have been valleys in which atmospheric pollution has been greatly accentuated by unfavourable features of temperature and relatively calm air. In the final analysis the general pollution level is determined by the quantity of pollutants added to the atmosphere, but irregular variations in time and place may result in concentrations many times the anticipated normal. It was in the light of these facts that it was felt necessary to investigate whether the Lower Swansea Valley was likely to experience any such special local climatic qualities which could have a bearing upon the different possibilities of future land use in the area.

The general climate

The regional climate of the Swansea area is characterized by a general absence of extremes. The coastal situation of the town has an ameliorating influence so that neither very high nor low temperatures are experienced. At times of bitter cold Swansea avoids many of the rigours of frost and snow suffered by places more inland or farther east. Proximity to the coast combined with a sharp rise in height to the north of the town contribute to moderately high annual rainfall and to a relatively large average number of rain-days. (i.e. days with 0·01 in or more of rain). These features of rainfall and humidity mean that a moisture check to plants and a drying out of the upper layers of the soil, even in freely draining tip material, are less frequent problems than they would be in drier parts of Britain.

From the architectural point of view, one of the most significant climatic problems arises from the periods of inland-blowing south-westerly, humid, maritime airmasses with which high relative and absolute humidities are associated. Although not so favoured as the coastal fringes of the peninsulas of Gower and Pembrokeshire, Swansea enjoys a favourable average

The climatology and air pollution of the Lower Swansea Valley and respiratory symptoms and lung function in Llansamlet

Table A.I Climatic data for Swansea. Means for the period 1931–60

	Jan.	Feb.	Mar.	Apr.	May	June	July	Aug.	Sept.	Oct.	Nov.	Dec.	Year
Temperatures °C													
Maximum	7.7	7.9	10.2	12.9	16.0	18.9	20.0	20.3	18.1	14.6	11.0	8.9	13.9
Minimum	2.8	2.7	4.1	6.1	8.8	11.8	13.5	13.6	11.9	9.0	6.2	4.2	7.9
Mean	5.3	5.3	7.2	9.5	12.4	15.4	16.7	17.0	15.0	11.8	8.6	6.5	10.9
Rainfall: inches*	4.73	3.22	2.49	2.41	2.62	2.41	3.48	3.87	3.83	4.69	4.73	4.51	42.99
Rain-days*	21	16	15	16	15	13	17	17	17	19	19	20	205
Sunshine, hours	54	76	123	168	200	206	183	182	137	101	58	46	1,534
Fogs at 09 GMT	2.7	1.6	1.4	0.4	0.4	0.2	0.3	0.2	0.1	0.9	2.5	3.2	13.9
Snow or sleet days	2.5	1.7	0.8	0.1	0.1	—	—	—	—	—	0.1	0.7	6.0
Snow lying 09 GMT	1.8	1.4	0.5	—	—	—	—	—	—	—	0.1	0.5	4.3
Extremes													
Highest maximum temp.	13.9	14.4	19.4	22.2	27.8	29.4	31.1	30.6	25.6	23.9	16.1	13.9	31.1
Lowest minimum temp.	−10.0	−7.8	−6.7	−1.7	0.6	2.8	5.6	5.6	1.7	−1.7	−3.9	−5.6	−10.0
Heaviest rainfall in a day*	2.02	1.21	1.24	1.58	1.58	1.29	1.65	2.20	1.83	2.38	2.62	1.80	2.62

Source: The information in the table is published by permission of the Director-General, Meteorological Office (Copyright, Controller, Her Majesty's Stationery Office).

* Rainfall data refer to the period 1916–50. They have been adjusted to take into account changes in the site of the rain gauge.

sunshine duration, particularly in contrast with the upland areas further inland. A coastal situation implies rather more frequent strong winds and gales but, although open to the south and south-west, Swansea benefits from the shelter of the backing high ground and enjoys protection from colder winds from between north-west and east. Within the valley itself relief results in modifications in the general regional wind-flow so that the standard meteorological records are not entirely representative. Table AI summarizes the main features of the general climate of the area of which the valley is only a small part. In the context of this inquiry no more detailed analysis is needed.

The local climate of the valley

The question which requires an answer is whether or not the Lower Swansea Valley itself has any climatic peculiarities which will make it necessary to limit or modify suggestions for the future use of the area. Man's modification of the surface of the land by buildings and paved surfaces, together with the concentration of fume and dust-producing sources, have resulted in some towns having distinctive local climatic features which are grouped as a whole under the heading of 'urban climates'. In varying degrees the characteristics of the urban climate such as 'heat-islands', altered wind circulation, reduced incidence of frost and snow, poorer quality and less sunlight and, perhaps most drastic of all, atmospheric pollution are superimposed on the general climatic pattern. The Lower Swansea Valley, in this respect, is peripheral to the main built-up area of the town, and there is little reason to suppose that it suffers major climatic disabilities purely because of its urban situation. A firm statement of this sort, however, could only be made if an intensively instrumented inquiry could be carried out over several years for the whole Swansea area.

A local climate, however, may not depend for its production upon human disturbance of the natural conditions. The topography of an area may be especially conducive to the development over small distances of marked climatic contrasts. Such contrasts may result from well-developed variations in slope and altitude in an area. A valley situation is often characterized by nocturnal inversions and greater diurnal ranges of temperature, by site-to-site contrasts in the heating power of the sun as the orientation and gradients of slopes change, and by modifications of the direction and force of the wind.

Topographically the Lower Swansea Valley has a form which might be expected to produce some of these features of a valley climate. High ground rises on the west at Clase to 541 ft and on the east at Cefn-hengoed to 371 ft above sea level. The Pennant sandstone ridges of Kilvey Hill (663 ft) and Townhill (over 560 ft) constrict the southern exit of the valley, where the river Tawe cuts through to the sea. Not far to the north of the Project area, the Glais moraine helps to complete the rim of higher ground.

Temperature inversions

The instrumental recording upon which the subsequent discussion is based was mainly directed towards the evaluation of the importance of temperature inversions in the valley. In stable, relatively calm weather with clear skies, air cooled at night by radiation over the upper slopes of a valley drains downwards because of its higher density. This cooled air tends to accumulate in the lowest parts of a depression so that on the valley floor the temperatures fall to their lowest values. In the air above the valley and up the slopes,

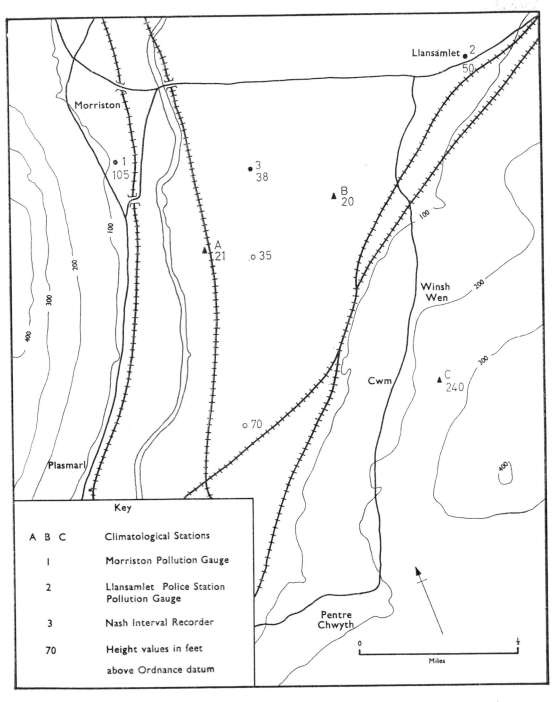

Figure A.1 Locations of the climatological stations and the sites of the pollution gauges. The gauge at Llansamlet Clinic is not shown on the map but is located at map ref. 695971. The heights shown against the pollution gauge sites are those at the gauges

temperatures rise in contrast with the normal pattern of decreasing temperatures with height. Under such circumstances mist, fog and frosts are more numerous and persistent on the valley floor. Shut in by the layer of warmer air above, smoke, fumes and dust cannot easily disperse and are, therefore, concentrated in the shallow pool of dense, cold, stagnant and often humid air. Ordinary condensation mist or fog can be tainted and thickened by atmospheric pollution to produce 'smog', of which the effects, for health, can be particularly harmful and in some cases lethal. The combination of a well-defined topographic hollow with sources of atmospheric pollution within it or on its slopes, and with particular weather situations can result, therefore, in a most unattractive local climatic phenomenon. So if the Project area is found to be subject in its lower parts to marked and frequent inversions, then such sites would be unfavourable for residential building, or for the location of industries producing large amounts of smoke or fumes. Frost-sensitive trees and plants would fare badly in such sites. If lower night temperatures, perhaps persisting into the early hours of daylight, were a common occurrence on the valley floor, additional heating costs for buildings would arise.

Recording stations were operated for almost a year at three stations. There were two stations (A and B) on the valley floor at about 20 ft above sea level and a third station (C) on the eastern slope at 240 ft above sea level. The three stations are distributed from west to east across the valley. Their locations are shown in Figure A.1.

The data collected are summarized in Table A.2. It is apparent that nocturnal inversions of temperature (when the valley floor stations are colder than the site on the slope) occur frequently. Some of these inversions develop in the early evening hours of one day and last well into the morning hours of the next day. Without much more elaborate instrumentation than was possible in this particular investigation, it was impossible to determine the depth of the temperature inversion and to assess the thickness of the polluted air layer likely to accumulate during a long period of night cooling and, therefore, the height of places up the valley slopes which would be affected. There were relatively few inversions during the recording year when there was a very large temperature difference between the stations B and C. In a shallow depression, such as the Lower Swansea Valley, particularly near the sea, one would not expect spectacular inversions.

Table A.2 provides considerable evidence of the frequency and duration of inversions of temperature. If the level of pollution were to be increased, either from domestic or industrial sources, then clearly the meteorological conditions which can aggravate the pollution dangers are shown to exist.

It should be noted that the normal temperature lapse with height, equivalent to the difference between the valley floor and slope stations, would be 0.4°C (0.7° F). Thus where an inversion occurs not only is the normal decline of temperature with height prevented but also the cooling is sufficient to make the lower areas cooler than the upper parts of the valley. Over the year period covered by the investigation there were 239 days on which measurable inversions occurred, whilst the valley floor was colder than the station C, 220 ft above it, for 23 per cent of the duration of the period. A comparison of the daily minimum temperatures of stations B and C (not necessarily the times when the inversions were most marked) showed that only 9.8 per cent of the days experienced inversions of 2°C (3.6° F) or over. The greatest recorded difference between the minima was 5.2° C (9.4° F). There were some occasions when the valley floor remained colder than the slopes for much of the day, and in one case in November, apart from a brief gap of $2\frac{1}{2}$ hours, the valley floor was cooler for a spell of 86$\frac{1}{2}$ hours. During the recording period there were 46 night-time inversions which extended beyond 10 a.m. (local time) on the next day.

Table A.2 Temperature inversions at station B compared with station C

					1964					1965		
	May	June	July	Aug.	Sept.	Oct.	Nov.	Dec.	Jan.	Feb.	Mar.	Apr.
Occasions when minimum at B>0.5°C below C	9	6	6	18	19	21	15	11	9	11	8	11
Occasions when minimum at B>2.0°C below C	2	0	0	2	8	7	6	0	2	1	3	4
Max. diff. between minima at B and C, °C	3.3	1.6	1.6	2.8	3.2	2.8	5.2	1.8	2.8	2.3	4.0	3.1
Max. inversions from thermograph charts, °C	4.1	2.1	1.8	4.6	3.8	3.2	5.6	3.7	3.1	2.3	5.8	4.2
Total duration of inversion from thermographic charts, hours	$59\frac{1}{4}$	$55\frac{1}{2}$	$174\frac{3}{4}$	$243\frac{1}{2}$	$180\frac{1}{4}$	229	$263\frac{1}{4}$	$197\frac{1}{4}$	209	$135\frac{1}{4}$	$115\frac{1}{4}$	$138\frac{3}{4}$
Percentage of month with inversions	12.3	7.7	23.5	32.7	25.0	30.8	36.6	26.5	28.1	20.1	15.5	19.3
Maximum duration of any single inversion, hours	$13\frac{3}{4}$	$11\frac{1}{4}$	$22\frac{1}{4}$	$19\frac{1}{4}$	$14\frac{1}{4}$	$18\frac{1}{4}$	$50\frac{1}{4}$	$19\frac{3}{4}$	$20\frac{3}{4}$	23	$20\frac{1}{4}$	$21\frac{3}{4}$
Number of days with inversions from thermograph charts	16	12	20	24	24	26	25	23	20	14	15	20
Number of inversion periods from thermograph charts	14	11	17	29	21	33	30	28	26	17	17	17

Largely as a result of the colder nights, but at times also because of higher maximum temperatures on the sheltered valley floor, the average diurnal range of temperature of station B was consistently greater than that of the valley side station C (Table A.3). Though this means that the lower parts of the valley have more extreme thermal conditions, this is a rather academic point with limited practical significance. The occasions of frost and fog at the three stations were recorded, but the data were insufficient to express the difference in quantitative terms. It was apparent, however, that frosts, mists and industrial haze were more frequent in the lower parts of the valley than on the slopes. Sheltered hollows below the general level of the valley floor, or between the tip heaps, can be expected to experience even greater 'frost-hollow' conditions. Station A, for example, which was in a sheltered site, experienced greater extremes than the better-exposed station B which has been used for the main comparisons.

Table A.3 Diurnal range of temperature derived from maxima and minima

	1964								1965			
	May	June	July	Aug.	Sept.	Oct.	Nov.	Dec.	Jan.	Feb.	Mar.	Apr.
Station B	8·4	7·1	7·5	9·0	9·1	8·4	6·6	6·1	5·2	6·2	7·4	8·0°C
Station C	7·6	6·6	6·9	7·7	7·6	6·8	4·9	5·5	4·2	5·9	6·6	7·1

It must be appreciated that the data presented can be considered strictly representative only of the weather conditions experienced over the recording period. Sufficient evidence has been accumulated, however, to suggest that it would be very desirable to avoid the establishment, either on the valley floor or the sides, of any large sources of atmospheric pollution. From the climatic viewpoint the lower parts of the valley are less attractive for residential use. As well as the concentration of sulphur dioxide, particulate acids, and other harmful atmospheric constituents, the greater frequency and longer duration of wet mists and periods of high relative humidity would make droplet inhalation more harmful. The duration on the valley floor of periods with over 90 per cent relative humidity is shown in Table A.4 to be considerable.

Table A.4 Percentage duration of relative humidity over 90 per cent at station B

1964								1965			
May	June	July	Aug.	Sept.	Oct.	Nov.	Dec.	Jan.	Feb.	Mar.	Apr.
35	43	43	43	41	42	46	53	31	18	23	20

Wind directions

Valleys introduce into the general surface wind pattern distinct local features. The prevailing wind which would be indicated from the records of a well-exposed meteorological station, such as that at Victoria Park, Swansea, may bear little similarity to the conditions experienced within the valley. Air is channelled so that winds blowing at an angle to the valley, provided they are not entirely transverse, tend to be diverted to flow along the axis of the valley. As well as directional changes, wind velocities may well be increased by this channelling, but, in the case of the Lower Swansea Valley, Kilvey Hill and Townhill afford a considerable degree of shelter from the south and south-west. The valley floor also enjoys some shelter from winds from east or west, more or less transverse to the valley. No anemometer readings are available, however, to provide a measure of these shelter effects. Eddying and turbulence disturb the general wind flow in the valley so that considerable

The climatology and air
pollution of the lower
Swansea Valley and
respiratory symptoms
and lung function in
Llansamlet

directional differences exist between one site and another. This is readily apparent from the fluctuating directions of chimney smoke, but it was shown more specifically by the data derived from the wind-vanes operated at the three recording stations. Wind directions were noted at each morning observation and, although they suffered from the disadvantage that the vanes were only 6 ft above ground level, they indicated clearly the different responses at each station to a particular general wind direction. These special circumstances of wind circulation in the valley would need to be considered where smoke or fume dispersal from any source in or around the area is involved.

The main impression gained was that there were very few wind patterns which were frequently repeated. Only 8·9 per cent of all the observations showed the same direction at each of the three stations at the recording times. Most of these instances occurred when the general wind direction agreed with, or was close to, the south-west to north-east trend of the valley. The more central station B often had a wind direction which was the same as that of the regional wind but near or on the valley slope winds tend to be diverted up-slope. Figure A.2 shows a limited selection of the more frequent wind patterns which were observed. Too much must not be read into these directional associations, since horizontal eddying produces a great complexity of different patterns, and other sites, with contrasted exposure characteristics, might well show other assemblages of wind directions. Vertical wind eddies must also be reckoned with, but the instruments available did not permit these to be recorded. Taking both the horizontal and vertical disturbances into account, it is clear that care must be exercised in the location of any major sources of atmospheric pollution. Without a detailed prior investigation, it would be dangerous to assume from any of the standard meteorological data which are available that smoke and fumes would be dispersed and mixed with the atmosphere, or carried out of the valley by the prevailing winds, without causing any harmful effects. The point needing emphasis is that in such a valley situation freedom from atmospheric pollution is much more difficult to forecast. The value of different forms of dispersal by hot, forced blast and high chimneys is much harder to assess.

Aspect

With the more or less south to north orientation of the valley slopes, there should be little significant difference in sunshine duration between the east and west facing slopes. Whilst in theory the slope angle of the valley sides should give them some advantage at all times of the year over the floor in the intensity of the solar radiation, it is improbable that the significance of these differences would be worth considering in relation to the other factors which affect sunshine intensity and soil heating. At the beginning and end of the day, when the altitude of the sun is low, and particularly in winter, there would be some shadowing effect from higher ground to the east or west. The losses of sunlight would be only a small proportion of the average total. These problems could be resolved only by measurements of solar radiation intensity on a detailed basis. This, unfortunately, was out of the question in the particular circumstances of this climatic enquiry.

Conclusion

Whilst it would be unrealistic to claim that climatic factors would be a major determinant

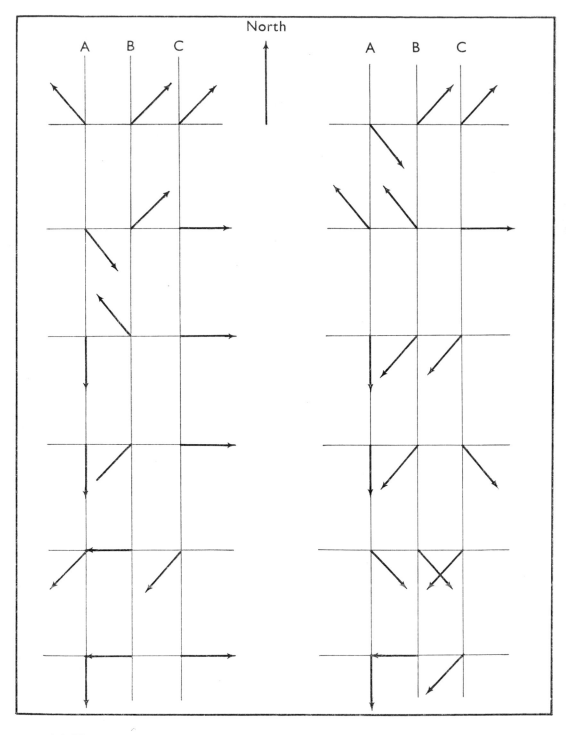

Figure A.2 The most common wind patterns in the Lower Swansea Valley at the recording stations A, B and C

of the different ways in which the valley might be used in the future, it would be fair to say that there are elements of the local climate which should not be complacently dismissed. There is already enough evidence to indicate that caution is necessary in using some of the lower parts of the valley floor. The present information on the intensity of pollution within the valley indicates that, at the recording gauge sites, the values of sulphur dioxide and of

The climatology and air
pollution of the Lower
Swansea Valley and
respiratory symptoms
and lung function in
Llansamlet

particulate acid are remarkably low for an urban area. Whilst some correlation between peaks of sulphur dioxide pollution and thermal inversions can be seen, the evidence thus far accumulated does not indicate, with present sources of pollution, that there is a serious problem. It is felt, however, that this impression may not be entirely representative since the pollution gauges were not situated in the lowest parts of the valley, and, since surface inversions and accumulation of polluted atmosphere are often shallow phenomena, may not record the worst conditions. Ill-planned layouts of factories or residential areas could easily complicate still further the already complex pattern of air movement and fume dispersal which is characteristic of the valley. Too often in similar situations where development has taken place it has been a matter of being wise after the event. The devastating damage attributed to the fumes of the nineteenth-century copper industry arose partly from the contemporary technique of production and the highly concentrated distribution of the industry but was also aggravated by the local climate. It is unlikely that any future use will cause conditions of such severity, but here there is a reminder to the planner to keep in front of him the fact that meteorologically the valley has a potential pollution problem.

A full and final evaluation of the local climatic factors in either the plant habitat or the human environment of the Lower Swansea Valley must await the establishment of an intensive recording network and its operation over several years. The present inquiry must be considered as an interim statement but it is still adequate to indicate considerations which will have to be taken into account when planning for the future.

11 Atmospheric pollution in the Lower Swansea Valley

P. D. Gadgil, M.Sc., Ph.D.

The long history of atmospheric pollution in the Lower Swansea Valley has already been considered in Chapter 2. The pollutants chiefly were (1) sulphur dioxide produced during the roasting of ores to be smelted and (2) fumes containing poisonous heavy metals (e.g. zinc and lead) lost up the stack during the distillation process due to inefficient condensation of the volatilized metal. Past pollution has apparently resulted in the destruction of vegetation on the eastern slopes of the valley. This destruction of vegetation has been followed by extensive soil erosion and gully formation. Since the First World War, however, the extent of pollution has gradually abated due to the closure of most of the spelter and other works and improvements made in the smelting processes. Utilization of sulphur dioxide for the manufacture of sulphuric acid and use of more efficient distillation processes meant that the quantities of pollutants emitted to the atmosphere have been greatly reduced. There is evidence at present that vegetation is gradually coming back on the eroded, bare areas. This investigation was undertaken to measure the extent to which atmospheric pollution exists at present, and to determine the effect of pollution, if any, on the vegetation.

Measurement of sulphur dioxide

Two instruments of the design approved by the Department of Scientific and Industrial Research for daily volumetric determination of sulphur dioxide for use in the National

Survey of Air Pollution have been in operation in the Valley (Morriston, since June 1959; Llansamlet, since November 1962) and an additional instrument (Llansamlet Police Station) was placed in operation on 1 January 1964. (For their location see Fig. A.1.) These instruments are of very simple construction and consist of a Drechsol bottle containing dilute hydrogen peroxide through which air is bubbled. The sulphur dioxide in the air is converted to sulphuric acid and the amount of acid is determined daily by titration with a standard alkali solution. (For details of the instrument see National Survey of Air Pollution, *The use of the daily instrument measuring smoke and sulphur dioxide*; Department of Scientific and Industrial Research, Warren Spring Laboratory.) In addition to these standard gauges a Nash Interval Recorder (Nash, 1961) was in operation from 14 October to 7 December 1964. The interval recorder is an instrument which makes a continuous record of the sulphur dioxide concentration in the atmosphere. Peaks of pollution of short duration can thus be detected.

Table A.5 Average monthly concentrations of sulphur dioxide ($\mu g/m^3$) at six different sites in the British Isles

Adapted from the Investigation of Atmospheric Pollution. Tables of Observations for the year ended 31 March 1962. Warren Spring Laboratory.

Site name	Swansea (Morriston)	Welwyn Garden City	Cardiff	Bradford	Stoke-on-Trent
Site classification	A2	D2	A2	A2	X
Average concentration of SO_2 for:					
April 1961	116	37	85	269	252
May 1961	71	33	75	181	209
June 1961	57	40	36	156	178
July 1961	70	33	43	121	137
August 1961	55	27	41	131	114
September 1961	47	38	57	230	158
October 1961	65	66	130	308	235
November 1961	82	87	133	360	352
December 1961	—	—	—	679	552
January 1962	91	—	122	480	414
February 1962	75	138	120	238	—
March 1962	94	158	106	342	—

Site classification:
A2: Residential area with high-density housing or with medium-density housing in multiple occupation, in either case surrounded by other built-up areas. Interspersed with some industrial undertakings.
D2: Small town centre; limited commercial area mixed with old residential housing and possibly minor industry.
X: Unclassified site, or mixed area.
(—): Indicates that records are not available.

The general level of sulphur dioxide concentration measured by the gauge sited in the Lower Swansea Valley was found to be similar to those encountered in the less industrialized towns and to be lower than the levels of sulphur dioxide found in the atmosphere of highly industrialized areas. Table A.5, compiled from the tables published by the Warren Spring Laboratory, shows that the monthly average concentration of sulphur dioxide in the Lower Swansea Valley is much lower than that of Bradford or Stoke-on-Trent and on average slightly higher than Welwyn Garden City. Table A.6, compiled from the data obtained from the instruments operated in the valley from 1 January 1963, gives the number of days on which the average daily concentration of sulphur dioxide exceeded 100 $\mu g/m^3$ and the highest and lowest concentrations recorded in any one month. It should be appreciated that the Morriston pollution gauge is situated to the south of the main built-up area with only a thinly built-over area between it and Plasmarl farther south. Unless winds are blowing down the valley or stagnant air fills it up to the level of the gauge site, which would be a rare occurrence, one would not expect this gauge to register high sulphur dioxide levels in absolute terms under present conditions of pollution emission although, as Table A.6 shows, in terms of the local situation the pollution level recorded by the Morriston gauge was the highest of the three. The two Llansamlet gauges would be expected to record low values since they are some distance from the present limited source of pollution, although more nearly downwind from the most prevalent winds. The data show that there is a considerable rise in the sulphur dioxide concentration during the winter months when inversions are more common and meteorological conditions are less favourable for the

Table A.6 Number of days on which the daily sulphur dioxide concentration exceeded 100 $\mu g/m^3$ in each month and the highest and lowest daily concentrations ($\mu g/m^3$) observed in that month

1963	Morriston Clinic			Llansamlet Clinic			Llansamlet Police Station		
	Days	H	L	Days	H	L	Days	H	L
January	11	188	39	2	108	42	—	—	—
February	19	394	31	12	168	34	—	—	—
March	10	170	36	1	168	45	—	—	—
April	3	122	26	0	85	25	—	—	—
May	3	156	12	0	79	12	—	—	—
June	0	70	15	4	119	16	—	—	—
July	3	104	33	2	119	21	—	—	—
August	2	111	33	4	211	32	—	—	—
September	5	120	15	10	318	15	—	—	—
October	10	207	24	4	137	48	—	—	—
November	4	188	48	3	220	38	—	—	—
December	16	289	58	13	272	40	—	—	—
1964									
January	10	272	58	4	168	25	4	199	52
February	1	232	57	0	70	17	0	72	25
March	3	201	70	1	117	41	1	121	37
April	3	222	56	0	98	22	1	100	35
May	1	148	51	1	148	12	1	136	24
June	1	367	24	0	38	15	1	115	41
July	1	258	49	0	44	13	0	71	37
August	1	126	64	0	89	9	1	150	38
September	3	236	28	1	165	8	1	122	19
October	2	383	61	0	60	24	0	68	29
November	8	615	45	0	63	18	0	67	19
December	7	520	38	0	80	14	3	202	11
1965									
January	6	265	11	1	109	4	0	96	28
February	7	258	64	0	76	13	2	103	16

H: Highest daily concentration.
L: Lowest daily concentration.
(—): Indicates that no records are available.

diffusion of pollutants. The difference between the summer and winter levels and higher concentrations in the densely populated area also point to the fact that pollution is due to domestic fires rather than industrial pollution which would tend to be constant throughout the year. In the form in which the diurnal data are available, there may be a number of occasions when short-period high levels of pollution at night would not be apparent when averaged with the conditions prevailing over the rest of the twenty-four hours.

Table A.7   Readings of sulphur dioxide concentration above the general level (20–30 $\mu g/m^3$) obtained by the Nash Interval Recorder for the period 14 October to 7 December 1964

Date	Time	Sulphur dioxide concentration ($\mu g/m^3$)
27 October 1964	12.15	275
7 November 1964	12.00	1,200
8 November 1964	10.30	700
8 November 1964	11.00	850

The Nash interval recorder showed that during the period it was in operation the general concentration of sulphur dioxide was maintained at about 20–30 $\mu g/m^3$. Peaks of pollution far above this general level were observed on four occasions (Table A.7). These high concentrations persisted for less than half an hour.

Measurement of particulate acid

Particulate acid has been regularly observed in urban air. It is recognized that large concentrations are noticed only during periods of fog. Particulate acid measurements were made from 23 November 1964 up to 15 March 1965 using the method of Commins (1963). This involves collecting particulate matter by filtration and determining the amount of acid by immersing the collected sample in a known excess of 0·01 N sodium tetraborate at pH 7 and titrating back to pH 7 with 0·01 N sulphuric acid. Only very low concentrations of particulate acid were found (Table A.8).

Table A.8   Particulate acid concentration ($\mu g/m^3$) per week found in the atmosphere

Date	Concentration	Date	Concentration
23 Nov.–30 Nov. 1964	0·21	18 Jan.–25 Jan. 1965	0·62
30 Nov.–7 Dec. 1964	0·25	25 Jan.–1 Feb. 1965	0·57
7 Dec.–14 Dec. 1964	0·55	1 Feb.–8 Feb. 1965	0·76
14 Dec.–21 Dec. 1964	0·32	8 Feb.–15 Feb. 1965	0·48
21 Dec.–28 Dec. 1964	0·46	15 Feb.–22 Feb. 1965	0·61
28 Dec.–4 Jan. 1965	0·38	22 Feb.–1 Mar. 1965	0·66
4 Jan.–11 Jan. 1965	0·49	1 Mar.–8 Mar. 1965	0·51
11 Jan.–18 Jan. 1965	0·51	8 Mar.–15 Mar. 1965	0·58

Note: Typical daily concentrations of particulate acid in the City of London (Commins, 1963): summer, 7 $\mu g/m^3$; winter, 18 $\mu g/m^3$.

Effect of atmospheric pollution on vegetation

In order to see if any damage occurs to plants through atmospheric pollution, plants sensitive to pollution (Thomas, 1965) were grown at five sites in the valley during the summer of 1964. The plants selected were oats (*Avena sativa*), barley (*Hordeum vulgare*), lucerne (*Medicago sativa*), gladiolus (*Gladiolus sp.*), tobacco (*Nicotiana tabacum*) and tomato (*Lycopersicum esculentum*). All plants, with the exception of gladiolus, were grown in the greenhouse and transplanted into tubs of John Innes Compost. Gladiolus corms were planted directly in the tubs. The tubs containing the seedlings were then taken out to their sites in the valley. One batch of plants was kept in the University College Botanic Garden to serve as a control. These test plants showed no visible signs of injury due to atmospheric pollution throughout the growing season. As the inversion and pollution records show, the most frequent and marked cases of pollution occur outside the growing season.

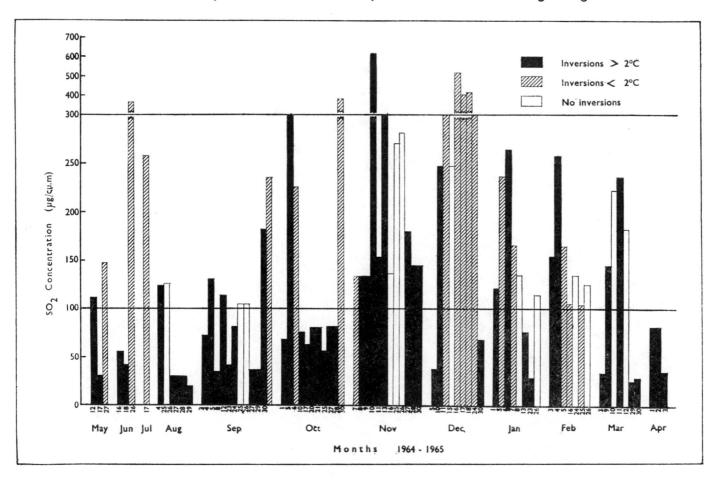

Figure A.3 Sulphur dioxide concentrations (μg/cu.m.) for all days (May 1964–April 1965) on which (i) the concentration exceeded 100μg/cu.m. and/or (ii) a temperature inversion exceeding or equalling 2° C existed. Hatched bars show days on which the SO_2 concentration exceeded 100μg/cu.m. and an inversion of below 2° C occurred

Climate and pollution

The climatic data show the frequent occurrence of temperature inversions in the valley. Under these conditions, where the lower cool air is shut in by a layer of warmer air above, it is to be expected that pollutants would accumulate in the valley atmosphere. A comparison of the sulphur dioxide concentration readings and the intensity of temperature inversions (Figure A.3 and Table A.9) shows that when an inversion of exceptionally long duration and magnitude (8–11 November 1964) occurred high concentrations of sulphur dioxide were obtained. But apart from this and two other occasions (5 October and 13 November 1964) there is no clear relationship between duration of inversions and high accumulation of sulphur dioxide. It would not be anticipated, however, that pollution would only occur with inversions of temperature nor that inversions must inevitably be associated with marked pollution. The final answer would only be arrived at after making a large number of simultaneous comparisons between pollution levels and inversion conditions. Until data are available in this particular form the link between air pollution and local climate must remain an open question, but with a strong likelihood that there is such a connection.

Table A.9 Record of inversions and levels of sulphur dioxide concentrations (μg/m³) at Morriston in the Lower Swansea Valley

Date		Temperature difference °C	Duration hours	Sulphur dioxide concentration*
1964				
May	12	4·6	8	112
	17	2·3	8	31
	27	0·9	8	148
June	16	2·1	7	56
	18	2·6	11	42
	26	0·6	9	367
July	17	1·3	11	258
August	4	2·1	9	124
	25	—	—	126
	26	4·2	4	31
	27	3·8	19	31
	28	2·6	14	31
	29	4·6	5	20
September	3	2·6	12	73
	4	2·8	14	131
	5	2·7	12	35
	8	3·0	9	114
	12	3·0	11	42
	23	3·8	12	81
	24	—	—	105
	25	—	—	105
	26	3·4	11	37
	27	3·1	14	37
	29	3·0	12	182
	30	1·8	8	236
October	1	2·4	6	68
	5	2·7	11	301
	6	0·9	7	226
	10	3·1	15	76
	17	2·2	10	63
	20	2·5	9	81
	21	2·6	13	81
	25	3·2	2	57

Table A.9—*contd.*

Date 1964		Temperature difference °C	Duration hours	Sulphur dioxide concentration*
October	27	2·8	16	82
	28	3·2	16	82
	30	0·3	5	383
November	7	0·8	4	134
	8	3·2	4	134
	9	4·6 ⎫		134
	10	3·9 ⎬ 50–2 hr break–further 36 hours		615
	11	3·0 ⎭		150
	13	2·7	8	305
	16	—	—	137
	25	—	—	271
	26	—	—	282
	27	2·0	13	180
	28	4·2	19	145
	30	2·2	18	145
December	5	2·5	2	38
	10	3·7	16	248
	11	1·7	12	305
	15	—	—	248
	16	1·7	17	520
	17	0·6	10	406
	18	1·4	20	418
	24	1·6	11	305
	30	2·6	5	68
1965 January	1	3·1	12	121
	5	1·9	18	237
	6	3·1	21	265
	7	0·9	4	166
	8	—	—	135
	13	2·3	6	76
	23	2·6	20	28
	26	—	—	117
February	3	2·2	19	155
	4	2·0	2	258
	5	1·2	12	165
	16	0·8	2	106
	24	—	—	135
	25	0·6	1	105
	26	—	—	123
March	3	5·8	2	34
	9	3·8	8	145
	10	—	—	222
	11	2·7	5	236
	12	—	—	182
	29	4·1	20	17
	30	4·1	13	29
April	1	2·7	10	82
	2	4·2	21	82
	3	2·8	22	36

* Morriston gauge readings

(—) Indicates that there was no temperature inversion on that date.

The table gives all days when SO_2 concentration exceeded 100 $\mu g/m^3$ and all days when inversions over 2° C occurred.

Analyses of smoke samples

Smoke samples for the period 23 November 1964 to 15 March 1965 were collected on Whatman No. 1 filter paper held in a 12·5 cm clamp. The filter papers were changed weekly. Polarographic analysis of these samples was undertaken by the M.R.C. Air Pollution Research Unit. Comparison of these data with those available (Table A.10) shows that the levels of zinc and lead in the valley atmosphere are similar to those obtained in semi-rural areas.

Table A.10 Average amounts of lead and zinc (μg/1,000 m^3) present in the atmosphere in the Lower Swansea Valley, semi-rural areas, industrial towns and the Merseyside conurbation

	Lower Swansea Valley	Semi-rural* areas‡	Industrial† towns‡	Merseyside conurbation‡
Lead	130	290	980	735
Zinc	100	114	369	339

* Conway Valley, Ruthin, Wetherby, Hoylake
† Salford, Leeds, St Helens, Warrington
‡ Data from Stocks et al. (1961)

Conclusions

A low level of sulphur dioxide concentration is normally characteristic of the pollution gauge sites located on the margins of the valley, although short periods of sulphur dioxide emission or accumulation causing high atmospheric concentrations are noticed. A longer period of continuous recording might well reveal short-term peaks of pollution at levels which could be more critical to health, associated with temperature inversions or exceptional but brief increases in emission.

There is no conclusive evidence that the vegetation of the valley suffers from the present level of atmospheric pollution, or that it is a factor in preventing colonization of tip areas. The relationship between health and pollution is more difficult to resolve, although the survey of respiratory symptoms in Llansamlet, which forms part of this appendix, suggests that this area at least is relatively more adversely affected by conditions conducive to such chest troubles. Any addition to the present limited sources of atmospheric pollution, whether from new residential areas or industrial processes, either in or on the margins of the valley, must introduce unfavourable modifications in the environment.

References

B. T. Commins (1963), 'Determination of particulate acid in town air', *Analyst*, **88**, 364–7.

T. Nash (1961), 'Low-velocity gas-liquid impinger for the continuous estimation of sulphur dioxide and other atmospheric pollutants', *J. Scientific Instruments*, 480–3.

P. Stocks, B. T. Commins and K. V. Aubrey (1961), 'A study of polycyclic hydrocarbons and trace elements in smoke at Merseyside and other Northern localities', *Int. J. Air and Water Poll.*, **4**, 141–53.

M. D. Thomas (1965), 'The effects of air pollution on plants and animals', *Ecology and the Industrial Society*, Brit. ecol. Soc. Symp. 5 (Goodman et al., eds.) 11–33, Blackwell.

III A physiological survey of respiratory symptoms and lung function in Llansamlet

M. McDermott, B.Sc., A.R.C.S., Medical Research Council, Pneumoconiosis Research Unit, Llandough Hospital, Penarth, Glam.

In 1964, as part of the general study of air pollution in the Lower Swansea Valley, a survey of respiratory symptoms and lung function in women was carried out in Llansamlet in order to investigate the physiological effects, if any, of air pollution in part of the area. It was decided to concentrate the survey on the female population of an area adjacent to a large zinc smelter at Llansamlet, which before the smelting process changed in about 1961, emitted considerable quantities of SO_2 and particulate acid. The female population of the survey area was chosen in preference to the male population because it was considered that it was less liable to be influenced by pollution influences extraneous to the neighbourhood such as those of occupation.

Plan of the survey

Using the zinc smelter as a focus, three zones were studied at distances of $0-\frac{1}{4}$ mile (Zone 1), $\frac{1}{4}-\frac{1}{2}$ mile (Zone 2), and $\frac{1}{2}-\frac{3}{4}$ mile (Zone 3), extending 45° either side of the axis of the valley in the N.E. direction (see base map). With a prevailing up-valley wind this was the direction in which the fumes would be carried, but it should be noted that smoke or fumes are not dispersed around a source such as a high chimney in decreasing concentration radially from the source. Maximum pollution will occur at some distance from the source where the descending fumes come to ground level. A chimney 165 ft high might produce most marked pollution at 2,000 ft from itself when the atmosphere is unstable but at 4,000 ft under average weather conditions. Zone 3 might, therefore, expect higher pollution levels than Zone 2. This zonal approach may therefore represent an over-simplification of the pattern of deposition of pollutants under the complicated wind conditions which occur in the valley, but it seemed to represent as a preliminary approach a simple way of comparing respiratory symptoms in groups of people with similar housing and occupations but possibly different exposures to particulate acid and SO_2.

A house-to-house census was made by health visitors and before the sample was chosen all women who had not lived at least one year in the zone, or who had ever lived in one of the other zones, were excluded. There were insufficient women in Zone 1 to use it at all, and a random sample of twenty women wherever possible in each of the four age groups 20–34, 35–44, 45–54 and 55–64 years was chosen for Zone 2 and Zone 3. The total sample numbered 158, seventy-nine from each zone.

Each person in the sample was visited in her home by a survey team of three. The tests of lung function which were made were the one-second forced expiratory volume (F.E.V.$_{.1.0}$) and the vital capacity (V.C.). The F.E.V.$_{.1.0}$ is the volume of air a subject can expire in one second with maximum effort starting from full inspiration; the V.C. is the total amount of air a subject can expire starting from full inspiration. Both measurements, but particularly the F.E.V.$_{.1.0}$, are of great value as indices of respiratory function especially in studies of pulmonary disability associated with dusty occupations, for example, coal mining (Higgins et al, 1961), cotton mills (Schilling et al., 1955) and the effect of cigarette smoking

(Higgins, 1959). The instrument (Figure A.4) used for the measurements was specially developed for such work (Collins *et al.*, 1964) and is easily portable. It consists of a folded rectangular polythene bellows into which the subject blows, and this drives a circular calibrated scale on which the F.E.V.$_{1.0}$ and V.C. are recorded by fixed pointers, the F.E.V.$_{1.0}$ pointer being held for one second by a mechanical catch operated by a transistor timer.

In addition to the lung function tests, the sitting height and standing height were measured, and a modified form of a Medical Research Council Questionnaire on respiratory symptoms (M.R.C., 1960) was asked. This included details of occupation and residence, smoking habits, and the following questions about symptoms:

Phlegm: Do you usually bring up phlegm from your chest on most days (or at night) for as much as three months each year?

Breathlessness: Do you get short of breath when walking with other people at an ordinary pace on the level?

Weather: Does the weather affect your chest?

Chest illnesses: During the past three years have you had any chest illness which has kept you off work, indoors, at home or in bed?

Asthma and hay fever Have you ever had asthma (hay fever)?

'Chronic bronchitis' has been defined as a positive answer to both the questions on phlegm and chest illness. This is the definition used by Higgins (1957) in a study of respiratory symptoms in women living in the Vale of Glamorgan.

The samples in the two zones were very similar in respect of the mean stem height, standing height and mean age of the four age groups. The number of years the women had lived in the zones was fairly comparable except in the 35–44 age group. The reason for this difference was found to be the completion of a new council housing estate in Zone 3 about ten years ago. This was used to rehouse families with young children, and has resulted in a large proportion of the women aged 35–44 having lived in Zone 3, eight, nine or ten years, whereas in Zone 2 the women had lived there on an average nineteen years.

Results

The age distribution for the women aged 15–64 in Llansamlet which was obtained from the original census data showed a proportionately greater number of women in the 35–44 and 45–54 age groups than would be expected from the approximately rectangular distribution for England and Wales as a whole (the Registrar-General's *Statistical Review*, 1962). Also the distribution differed between Zone 2 and Zone 3, in that Zone 3 had less than half the number of women aged 25–34 of Zone 2. These differences in age distribution suggest that the two zones are not similar in respect of movement in and out of the area, and they may therefore differ socially and economically.

Of the women in the sample, 92 per cent answered the questionnaire and 87 per cent technically satisfactory results were obtained for the F.E.V.$_{1.0}$. Some women refused to do the breathing test, some were ill, and a few found it too difficult.

Figure A.5 compares the incidence of symptoms and the number of smokers in the two zones, and there is a slightly higher prevalence of symptoms in Zone 3 than Zone 2.

Figure A.6 compares the F.E.V.$_{1.0}$ and V.C. in the two zones with the subjects divided into the four age groups.

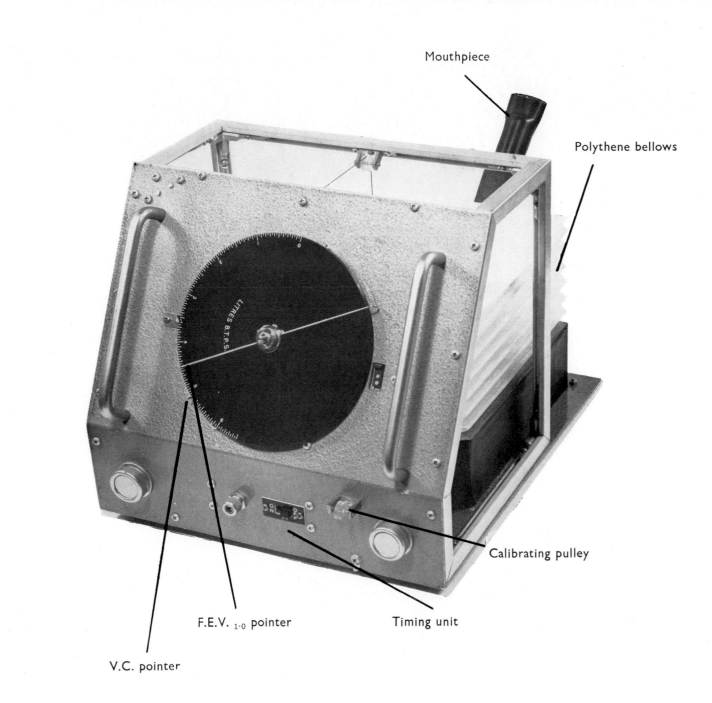

Mouthpiece

Polythene bellows

Calibrating pulley

F.E.V. $_{1\cdot0}$ pointer

Timing unit

V.C. pointer

Figure A.4.   McDermott Dry Spirometer

A physiological survey
of respiratory symptoms
and lung function in
Llansamlet

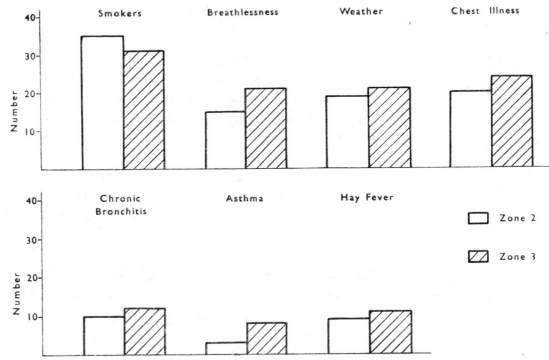

Figure A5 Comparison of respiratory symptoms in Zones 2 and 3

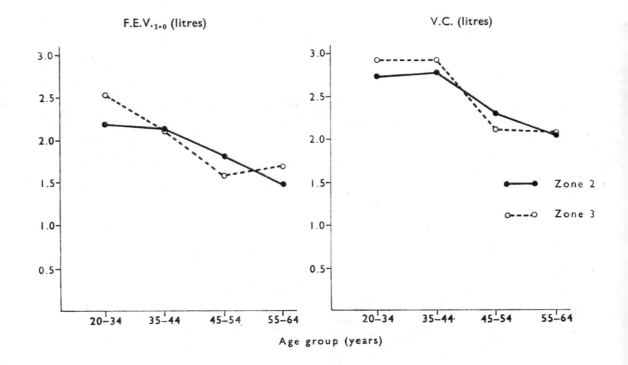

Figure A6 Comparison of the F.E.V.$_{1.0}$ and V.C. in Zones 2 and 3

In normal adults both the F.E.V.$_{1.0}$ and V.C. decrease with increasing age, for reasons that are not yet completely understood, but one cause is a change in the elastic properties of the tissues of the lung. The F.E.V.$_{1.0}$ and V.C. also depend on body size; with increasing height people have larger lungs and larger values for the F.E.V.$_{1.0}$ and V.C. Because of these effects of age and height on tests of ventilatory function it is not always possible to compare directly the F.E.V.$_{1.0}$ and V.C. in different groups of people. However, as already discussed, the ages and heights are comparable in the two zones, and from Figure A.5 it appears that as with the symptoms there is no difference between the mean F.E.V.$_{1.0}$ and V.C. in the two zones.

These results suggest that either (i) the inhalation of fumes produces no increase in respiratory symptoms or decrease in ventilatory capacity; or (ii) our original assumption that we have two similar groups of women exposed to different amounts of atmospheric pollution was incorrect.

Another possible approach to the problem was to study the effect of years of residence in either zone of Llansamlet on the F.E.V.$_{1.0}$ and V.C. This was done on 130 women out of the original sample of 158 by multiple regression analysis using an Elliott 803 computer.

The women were divided into twelve groups according to zone, 'bronchitic' or 'non-bronchitic', and whether they were non-smokers, light smokers (less than 15 cigarettes a day), or heavy smokers (15 or more cigarettes a day). The regression lines connecting the F.E.V.$_{1.0}$ and V.C. with age, standing height and years of residence were computed separately for the twelve groups, tested and found to be parallel and then combined to give one linear regression equation for the whole sample. The regression coefficients for years of residence were not significant for either the F.E.V.$_{1.0}$ or V.C.

The relationships with age and standing height were:

$$\text{F.E.V.}_{1.0} - 1{\cdot}932 = -0{\cdot}024\,(A - \overline{A}) + 0{\cdot}066\,(H - \overline{H})$$
$$\text{V.C.} \quad\;\; - 2{\cdot}512 = -0{\cdot}026\,(A - \overline{A}) + 0{\cdot}079\,(H - \overline{H})$$

where A is the age in years and $\overline{A}$ the mean age $= 44{\cdot}23$ years, and H is the standing height in inches and $\overline{H} = 61{\cdot}68$ inches. There are no figures obtained in this country which can be used for comparison, but Ferris et al. (1965) on a group of women without any respiratory disease in New Hampshire, U.S.A., found a year of age to be equivalent to a decrease of 22 ml in the F.E.V.$_{1.0}$ and an inch of height to an increase of 64 ml. Our figures of 24 and 66 ml respectively are very close to these, although in the New Hampshire study the F.E.V.$_{1.0}$ was for all ages about 400 ml higher than in our group. Such a direct comparison, however, is not necessarily satisfactory as our group, unlike that in New Hampshire, included women with respiratory symptoms.

Table A.11   The effect of smoking on the F.E.V.$_{1.0}$ (corrected for age and height) in Zones 2 and 3

		Non-smokers	Light smokers	Heavy smokers	Total
	Non-bronchitics	1·99 l. (26)	1·93 l. (20)	2·22 l. (7)	2·00 l. (53)
Zone 2	Bronchitics	1·56 l. (4)	1·89 l. (3)	1·30 l. (3)	1·58 l. (10)
	Total	1·93 l. (30)	1·92 l. (23)	1·94 l. (10)	1·93 l. (63)
	Non-bronchitics	2·06 l. (34)	1·84 l. (12)	1·83 l. (9)	1·97 l. (55)
Zone 3	Bronchitics	1·90 l. (5)	1·46 l. (5)	2·07 l. (2)	1·74 l. (12)
	Total	2·04 l. (39)	1·73 l. (17)	1·87 l. (11)	1·93 l. (67)

Table A.11 summarizes the computer analysis of the F.E.V.$_{1.0}$ data for all twelve groups after the regression equations have been used to obtain corrected values of the F.E.V.$_{1.0}$ allowing for age and height. With one exception only, that of the heavy smokers in Zone 3, the mean F.E.V.$_{1.0}$ of the bronchitics is lower than that of the non-bronchitics. This agreement between the physiological measurements and the results of the questionnaire suggests that the questionnaire was satisfactorily applied.

Effect of smoking

Of the 130 women for whom the results were analysed by computer, only sixty-one were smokers which is a considerably lower proportion than is usually found in men. The proportion of smokers is very similar to that published by the Tobacco Manufacturers for the United Kingdom as a whole. In their report the overall percentage for women from sixteen years upwards is given as 44 per cent in 1961, whereas our figure is 47 per cent. Despite this agreement, the survey team felt that the women tended not to admit to being smokers and also to underestimate their actual cigarette consumption. Table A.11 shows that for Zone 2 the F.E.V.$_{1.0}$ is no lower in the smokers than in non-smokers, but in Zone 3 there is a slight difference. The number of heavy smokers, however, is very small, which makes the validity of correcting the F.E.V.$_{1.0}$ results for age and height doubtful, and in Table A.12 the F.E.V.$_{1.0}$ values are shown uncorrected, and there is no apparent effect of smoking at all.

Table A.12 The effect of smoking on the F.E.V.$_{1.0}$ (uncorrected for age and height) in Zones 2 and 3 combined

	Non-smokers		Light smokers		Heavy smokers	
	F.E.V.$_{1.0}$ (I)	Age (years)	F.E.V.$_{1.0}$ (I)	Age (years)	F.E.V.$_{1.0}$ (I)	Age (years)
Non-bronchitics	1·98 (60)	44·9	1·89 (32)	43·6	2·05 (16)	42·9
Bronchitics	1·71 (9)	48·2	1·78 (8)	41·6	1·75 (5)	40·8

Cotes *et al.* (1966) have also found in men that when all those subjects with symptoms are excluded there is no apparent effect of smoking on the F.E.V.$_{1.0}$. Higgins and Cochrane (1961), in a study of 173 women aged 55–64 living in the Vale of Glamorgan, found a higher F.E.V.$_{1.0}$ in smokers than in non-smokers, but only twenty-nine of their sample smoked at all.

The results suggest that:

1 There is no relationship between the F.E.V.$_{1.0}$, or the V.C., or the incidence of respiratory symptoms and the distance the women lived from the source of pollution.

2 There is no relationship between either the F.E.V.$_{1.0}$ or the V.C. and the number of years the women have lived in Llansamlet.

3 The relationships between the F.E.V.$_{1.0}$ and age, and between the F.E.V.$_{1.0}$ and height, were similar to those found in other groups.

Discussion

There have been numerous epidemiological investigations of the association of bronchitis with air pollution. Fairbairn and Reid (1958), using civil servants' medical records, showed that for the whole country there was a relation between illness, retirements and deaths from bronchitis and the frequency of fogs in the winters of 1937 and 1938. Burn and Pemberton (1963) compared episodes of sickness reported to the Ministry of Pensions and National Insurance in three groups of wards in Salford, divided on the basis of a limited number of air sampling stations into high, medium and low pollution regions. The mortality from bronchitis and the number of periods of sickness due to bronchitis was greatest in the area of highest pollution. Almost all the studies have shown a similar picture, but differences of occupation, differences in smoking habits and absence of adequate measurements of air pollution make the evaluation of the relative importance of air pollution compared with other factors difficult.

As discussed elsewhere in the report, air pollution in Llansamlet was considerable until 1961, and the two approaches discussed so far in this paper used to study the problem might have been expected to show a relation between air pollution and the incidence of chronic bronchitis and other respiratory symptoms. The zonal method might have failed because the zones chosen did not correspond to differences in air pollution in the past in the valley. The weakness of the analysis in terms of the number of years a person has lived in Llansamlet is that the population could be a self-selected group of people unaffected by the air pollution who were willing to live in the area. This objection also applies to the analysis in terms of zones. The only other possible approach to the problem is to compare the women living in Llansamlet with groups of women living elsewhere.

Comparison with other areas

Higgins (1957) studied the prevalence of respiratory symptoms and 'chronic bronchitis' in 300 women aged 25–64 living in the Vale of Glamorgan, and for all symptoms there was a considerably higher prevalence in Llansamlet than in the Vale.

Table A.13   Comparison of chest illness and chronic bronchitis in Llansamlet and the Vale of Glamorgan

Age group	20–34*		35–44		45–54		55–64	
	Vale	Llan.	Vale	Llan.	Vale	Llan.	Vale	Llan.
Chest illness	10·6	27·8	17·0	15·4	4·2	30·8	12·0	50·0
Chronic bronchitis	6·4	16·7	4·3	10·3	2·1	15·4	4·3	18·8

* 25–34 in the Vale of Glamorgan

Table A.13 shows the comparison of the per cent incidence of chest illness and 'chronic bronchitis' in the two areas. It is only in the age group 35–44 that the incidence of symptoms is somewhat similar, and this is the age group in which there was a large influx of people from outside Llansamlet into Zone 3 about ten years ago.

The objection to this comparison is that it is possible for different techniques of the observers to influence the answers to the respiratory questionnaire. Measurements such as the F.E.V.$_{1·0}$ and V.C. are less subject to such errors, but these were not recorded in the Vale study.

It appeared that, despite the low levels of the daily averages of present pollution and the failure of the analyses by zone and years of residence to show any correlation between

A physiological survey
of respiratory symptoms
and lung function in
Llansamlet

respiratory symptoms and exposure to fumes in the past, there was a high incidence of 'chronic bronchitis' and chest illness in Llansamlet.

The study in Llansamlet was made in the summer of 1964, and it was decided to do a similar survey in the summer of 1965 using the same observers but in a different area of Swansea. On the recommendations of the Sociology Department at Swansea University and the Department of the Medical Officer of Health in Swansea, Waunarlwydd on the west side of Swansea was chosen as having similar social and economic circumstances. The area contained the same type of old houses and a council housing estate. An age group analysis based on the Enumeration Districts of the 1961 Census of Population showed that the age distribution of the women in Llansamlet and Waunarlwydd should be similar. Waunarlwydd, although an industrial area, did not lie at the bottom of a valley, and air pollution in the past had not been as high as in Llansamlet.

The preliminary census was done, and a random sample of 160 women aged 20–64 picked as before.

Results

As was expected from the preliminary analysis of the 1961 Census of Population, the age distributions are similar for Waunarlwydd and Llansamlet, both having a proportionately greater number of women aged 35–54 than would be expected from the national distribution.

In Waunarlwydd 94 per cent of the sample answered the questionnaire and 87 per cent technically satisfactory $F.E.V._{1.0}$ measurements were obtained. The mean age of the groups, the mean stem height, and the proportion of smokers in all the age groups was very similar to that in Llansamlet, but the mean standing height in Waunarlwydd was from 0·3 to 1·5 inches more than in Llansamlet. This is a very odd occurrence and raises the problem of whether the $F.E.V._{1.0}$ and V.C. should be corrected for differences in stem height or differences in standing height. A full analysis of the distributions of stem and standing height in the two areas has not been completed, but probably very little error will be introduced by comparing the uncorrected $F.E.V._{1.0}$ and V.C. results.

The incidence of all the symptoms (Figure A.7) is higher in Llansamlet than in Waunarlwydd, and the percentages for hay fever are 13·7 per cent in Llansamlet and 7·9 per cent in Waunarlwydd, for asthma 7·5 per cent and 4 per cent respectively, for the effect of weather 27·4 per cent and 16·6 per cent and for chest illness 30·1 per cent and 25·8 per cent. The differences are greater for 'chronic bronchitis' with an incidence of 15·1 per cent in Llansamlet and 6·6 per cent in Waunarlwydd. The figure for Waunarlwydd is not very different from that obtained in the Vale of Glamorgan (Table A.13) where the incidence of 'chronic bronchitis' is approximately 4 per cent.

The $F.E.V._{1.0}$ and V.C. (Figure A.8) are slightly higher in Waunarlwydd than in Llansamlet in all but the oldest age group. It is common in comparisons between groups for the older people to differ less, and is presumably because the fittest people live longest. For the age group 35–44, the incidence of respiratory symptoms and the mean values of $F.E.V._{1.0}$ and V.C. are more alike than in the 20–34 and 45–54 age groups. The standing heights in the 35–44 age group differ by only 0·3 inch and these facts support the previous tentative finding that this group in Llansamlet is different from the rest of the population.

Index

This index includes references to the scientific and common names of the plants found in the **Project Area**. The small number of animals occurring are only indexed under their common names. Reference is made to the commercial firms who have occupied sites in the area. It may be taken that an unqualified reference refers to that item occurring or happening in the Project Area. In order to keep the index within limits only the more important facts concerning places outside the area are indexed and the index should be used together with the Contents to be found on p. vii.

A page number printed in *italic type* indicates that on that page the full bibliographic reference of the author's work quoted in the text is given.

320